Cambridge
International AS and A Level Mathematics

Statistics

Sophie Goldie
Series Editor: Roger Porkess

HODDER
EDUCATION
AN HACHETTE UK COMPANY

Questions from the Cambridge International Examinations AS and A Level Mathematics papers are reproduced by permission of University of Cambridge International Examinations.

Questions from the MEI AS and A Level Mathematics papers are reproduced by permission of OCR.

We are grateful to the following companies, institutions and individuals who have given permission to reproduce photographs in this book.

Photo credits: page 3 © Artur Shevel / Fotolia; page 77 © Luminis / Fotolia; page 105 © Ivan Kuzmin / Alamy; page 123 © S. Ferguson; page 134 © Peter Küng / Fotolia; page 141 © Mathematics in Education and Industry; p.192 © Claudia Paulussen / Fotolia.com; page 202 © Ingram Publishing Limited; page 210 © Peter Titmuss / Alamy; page 216 © Monkey Business / Fotolia; page 233 © StockHouse / Fotolia; page 236 © Ingram Publishing Limited / Ingram Image Library 500-Animals; page 256 © Kevin Peterson / Photodisc / Getty Images; page 277 © Charlie Edwards / Getty Images; page 285 © Stuart Miles / Fotolia.com

Hachette UK's policy is to use papers that are natural, renewable and recyclable products and made from wood grown in sustainable forests. The logging and manufacturing processes are expected to conform to the environmental regulations of the country of origin.

Orders: please contact Bookpoint Ltd, 130 Milton Park, Abingdon, Oxon OX14 4SB. Telephone: (44) 01235 827720. Fax: (44) 01235 400454. Lines are open 9.00–5.00, Monday to Saturday, with a 24-hour message answering service. Visit our website at www.hoddereducation.co.uk

Much of the material in this book was published originally as part of the MEI Structured Mathematics series. It has been carefully adapted for the Cambridge International AS and A Level Mathematics syllabus.

The original MEI author team for Statistics comprised Michael Davies, Ray Dunnett, Anthony Eccles, Bob Francis, Bill Gibson, Gerald Goddall, Alan Graham, Nigel Green and Roger Porkess.

First published in 2012 by
Hodder Education, an Hachette UK company,
Carmelite House, 50 Victoria Embankment,
London EC4Y 0DZ

Impression number   5
Year   2017

Cover photo © Kaz Chiba/Photodisc/Getty Images/Natural Patterns BS13
Illustrations by Pantek Media, Maidstone, Kent
Typeset in 10.5pt Minion by Pantek Media, Maidstone, Kent
Printed in India

A catalogue record for this title is available from the British Library

ISBN 978 1444 14650 9

Contents

Key to symbols in this book

? This symbol means that you may want to discuss a point with your teacher. If you are working on your own there are answers in the back of the book. It is important, however, that you have a go at answering the questions before looking up the answers if you are to understand the mathematics fully.

⚠ This is a warning sign. It is used where a common mistake, misunderstanding or tricky point is being described.

▢ This is the ICT icon. It indicates where you could use a graphic calculator or a computer. Graphic calculators and computers are not permitted in any of the examinations for the Cambridge International AS and A Level Mathematics 9709 syllabus, however, so these activities are optional.

e This symbol and a dotted line down the right-hand side of the page indicate material which is beyond the syllabus for the unit but which is included for completeness.

Introduction

This is part of a series of books for the University of Cambridge International Examinations syllabus for Cambridge International AS and A Level Mathematics 9709. There are thirteen chapters in this book; the first seven cover Statistics 1 and the remaining six Statistics 2. The series also includes two books for pure mathematics and one for mechanics.

These books are based on the highly successful series for the Mathematics in Education and Industry (MEI) syllabus in the UK but they have been redesigned for Cambridge international students; where appropriate, new material has been written and the exercises contain many past Cambridge examination questions. An overview of the units making up the Cambridge international syllabus is given in the diagram on the next page.

Throughout the series the emphasis is on understanding the mathematics as well as routine calculations. The various exercises provide plenty of scope for practising basic techniques; they also contain many typical examination questions.

An important feature of this series is the electronic support. There is an accompanying disc containing two types of Personal Tutor presentation: examination-style questions, in which the solutions are written out, step by step, with an accompanying verbal explanation, and test-yourself questions; these are multiple-choice with explanations of the mistakes that lead to the wrong answers as well as full solutions for the correct ones. In addition, extensive online support is available via the MEI website, www.mei.org.uk.

The books are written on the assumption that students have covered and understood the work in the Cambridge IGCSE® syllabus. However, some of the early material is designed to provide an overlap and this is designated 'Background'. There are also places where the books show how the ideas can be taken further or where fundamental underpinning work is explored and such work is marked as 'Extension'.

The original MEI author team would like to thank Sophie Goldie who has carried out the extensive task of presenting their work in a suitable form for Cambridge international students and for her original contributions. They would also like to thank University of Cambridge International Examinations for their detailed advice in preparing the books and for permission to use many past examination questions.

Roger Porkess
Series Editor

The Cambridge International AS and A Level Mathematics syllabus

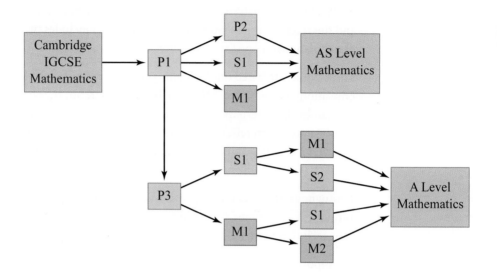

Statistics 1

1

Exploring data

A judicious man looks at statistics, not to get knowledge but to save himself from having ignorance foisted on him.

Carlyle

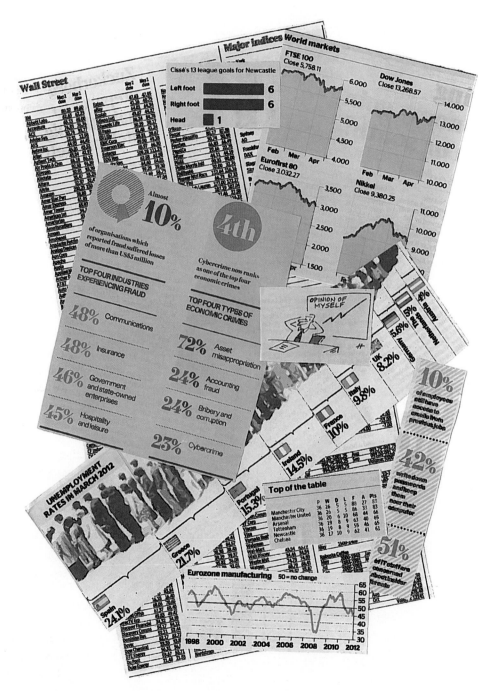

Source: The Times 2012

The cuttings on page 2 all appeared in one newspaper on one day. Some of them give data as figures, others display them as diagrams.

How do you interpret this information? Which data do you take seriously and which do you dismiss as being insignificant or even misleading?

To answer these questions fully you need to understand how data are collected and analysed before they are presented to you, and how you should evaluate what you are given to read (or see on the television). This is an important part of the subject of statistics.

In this book, many of the examples are set as stories from fictional websites. Some of them are written as articles or blogs; others are presented from the journalists' viewpoint as they sort through data trying to write an interesting story. As you work through the book, look too at the ways you are given such information in your everyday life.

bikingtoday.com

Another cyclist seriously hurt. *Will you be next?*

On her way back home from school on Wednesday afternoon, little Rita Roy was knocked off her bicycle and taken to hospital with suspected concussion.

Rita was struck by a Ford Transit van, only 50 metres from her own house.

Rita is the fourth child from the Nelson Mandela estate to be involved in a serious cycling accident this year.

The busy road where Rita Roy was knocked off her bicycle yesterday.

After reading the blog, the editor of a local newspaper commissioned one of the paper's reporters to investigate the situation and write a leading article for the paper on it. She explained to the reporter that there was growing concern locally about cycling accidents involving children. She emphasised the need to collect good quality data to support presentations to the paper's readers.

Is the aim of the investigation clear?
Is the investigation worth carrying out?
What makes good quality data?

The reporter started by collecting data from two sources. He went through back numbers of the newspaper for the previous two years, finding all the reports of cycling accidents. He also asked an assistant to carry out a survey of the ages of local cyclists; he wanted to know whether most cyclists were children, young adults or whatever.

? Are the reporter's data sources appropriate?

Before starting to write his article, the reporter needed to make sense of the data for himself. He then had to decide how he was going to present the information to his readers. These are the sorts of data he had to work with.

Name	Age	Distance from home	Cause	Injuries	Treatment
Rahim Khan	45	3 km	skid	Concussion	Hospital outpatient
Debbie Lane	5	75 km	hit kerb	Broken arm	Hospital outpatient
Arvinder Sethi	12	1200 m	lorry	Multiple fractures	Hospital 3 weeks
Husna Mahar	8	300 m	hit each other	Bruising	Hospital outpatient
David Huker	8	50 m		Concussion	Hospital outpatient

There were 92 accidents listed in the reporter's table.

Ages of cyclists (from survey)

66	6	62	19	20		15	21	8	21	63		44	10	44	34	18
35	26	61	13	61		28	21	7	10	52		13	52	20	17	26
64	11	39	22	9		13	9	17	64	32		8	9	31	19	22
37	18	138	16	67		45	10	55	14	66		67	14	62	28	36
9	23	12	9	37		7	36	9	88	46		12	59	61	22	49
18	20	11	25	7		42	29	6	60	60		16	50	16	34	14
18	15														

This information is described as *raw data*, which means that no attempt has yet been made to organise it in order to look for any patterns.

Looking at the data

At the moment the arrangement of the ages of the 92 cyclists tells you very little at all. Clearly these data must be organised so as to reveal the underlying shape, the *distribution*. The figures need to be ranked according to size and preferably grouped as well. The reporter had asked an assistant to collect the information and this was the order in which she presented it.

Tally

Tallying is a quick, straightforward way of grouping data into suitable intervals. You have probably met it already.

Stated age (years)	Tally	Frequency
0–9	ЖЖ ЖЖ |||	13
10–19	ЖЖ ЖЖ ЖЖ ЖЖ ЖЖ		26
20–29	ЖЖ ЖЖ ЖЖ		16
30–39	ЖЖ ЖЖ	10
40–49	ЖЖ		6
50–59	ЖЖ	5
60–69	ЖЖ ЖЖ ||||	14
70–79		0
80–89			1
⋮		
130–139			1
Total		92

Extreme values

A tally immediately shows up any extreme values, that is values which are far away from the rest. In this case there are two extreme values, usually referred to as *outliers*: 88 and 138. Before doing anything else you must investigate these.

In this case the 88 is genuine, the age of Millie Smith, who is a familiar sight cycling to the shops.

The 138 needless to say is not genuine. It was the written response of a man who was insulted at being asked his age. Since no other information about him is available, this figure is best ignored and the sample size reduced from 92 to 91. You should always try to understand an outlier before deciding to ignore it; it may be giving you important information.

Practical statisticians are frequently faced with the problem of *outlying observations*, observations that depart in some way from the general pattern of a data set. What they, and you, have to decide is whether any such observations belong to the data set or not. In the above example the data value 88 is a genuine member of the data set and is retained. The data value 138 is not a member of the data set and is therefore rejected.

Describing the shape of a distribution

An obvious benefit of using a tally is that it shows the overall shape of the distribution.

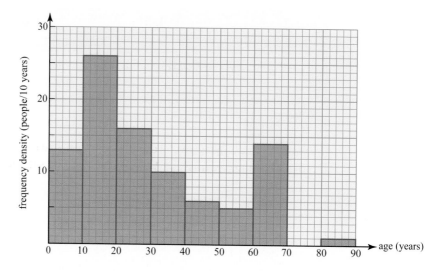

Figure 1.1 Histogram to show the ages of people involved in cycling accidents

You can now see that a large proportion (more than a quarter) of the sample are in the 10 to 19 year age range. This is the *modal* group as it is the one with the most members. The single value with the most members is called the *mode*, in this case age 9.

You will also see that there is a second peak among those in their sixties; so this distribution is called *bimodal*, even though the frequency in the interval 10–19 is greater than the frequency in the interval 60–69.

Different types of distribution are described in terms of the position of their modes or modal groups, see figure 1.2.

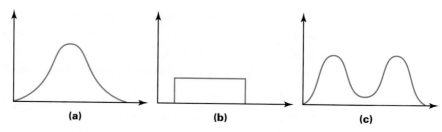

Figure 1.2 Distribution shapes: **(a)** unimodal and symmetrical **(b)** uniform (no mode but symmetrical) **(c)** bimodal

When the mode is off to one side the distribution is said to be *skewed*. If the mode is to the left with a long tail to the right the distribution has positive (or right) skewness; if the long tail is to the left the distribution has negative (or left) skewness. These two cases are shown in figure 1.3.

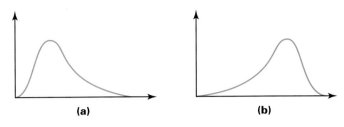

Figure 1.3 Skewness: **(a)** positive **(b)** negative

Stem-and-leaf diagrams

The quick and easy view of the distribution from the tally has been achieved at the cost of losing information. You can no longer see the original figures which went into the various groups and so cannot, for example, tell from looking at the tally whether Millie Smith is 80, 81, 82, or any age up to 89. This problem of the loss of information can be solved by using a *stem-and-leaf diagram* (or *stemplot*).

This is a quick way of grouping the data so that you can see their distribution and still have access to the original figures. The one below shows the ages of the 91 cyclists surveyed.

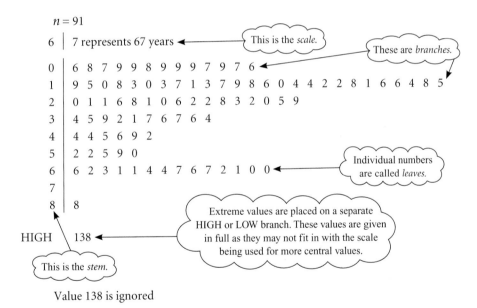

Figure 1.4 Stem-and-leaf diagram showing the ages of a sample of 91 cyclists (unsorted)

? Do all the branches have leaves?

The column of figures on the left (going from 0 to 8) corresponds to the tens digits of the ages. This is called the *stem* and in this example it consists of 9 branches. On each branch on the stem are the *leaves* and these represent the units digits of the data values.

In figure 1.4, the leaves for a particular branch have been placed in the order in which the numbers appeared in the original raw data. This is fine for showing the general shape of the distribution, but it is usually worthwhile sorting the leaves, as shown in figure 1.5.

$n = 91$

6 | 7 represents 67 years

```
0 | 6 6 7 7 7 8 8 9 9 9 9 9 9
1 | 0 0 0 1 1 2 2 3 3 3 4 4 4 5 5 6 6 6 7 7 8 8 8 8 9 9
2 | 0 0 0 1 1 1 2 2 2 3 5 6 6 8 8 9
3 | 1 2 4 4 5 6 6 7 7 9
4 | 2 4 4 5 6 9
5 | 0 2 2 5 9
6 | 0 0 1 1 1 2 2 3 4 4 6 6 7 7
7 |
8 | 8
```

Note that the value 138 is left out as it has been identified as not belonging to this set of data.

Figure 1.5 Stem-and-leaf diagram showing the ages of a sample of 91 cyclists (sorted)

The stem-and-leaf diagram gives you a lot of information at a glance:

- The youngest cyclist is 6 and the oldest is 88 years of age

- More people are in the 10–19 year age range than in any other 10 year age range

- There are three 61 year olds

- The modal age (i.e. the age with the most people) is 9

- The 17th oldest cyclist in the survey is 55 years of age.

If the values on the basic stem-and-leaf diagram are too cramped, that is, if there are so many leaves on a line that the diagram is not clear, you may *stretch* it. To do this you put values 0, 1, 2, 3, 4 on one line and 5, 6, 7, 8, 9 on another. Doing this to the example results in the diagram shown in figure 1.6.

When stretched, this stem-and-leaf diagram reveals the skewed nature of the distribution.

n = 91

6 | 7 represents 67 years

```
0  |
0  | 6 6 7 7 7 8 8 9 9 9 9 9 9
1* | 0 0 0 1 1 2 2 3 3 3 4 4 4
1  | 5 5 6 6 6 7 7 8 8 8 8 9 9
2* | 0 0 0 1 1 1 2 2 2 3
2  | 5 6 6 8 8 9
3* | 1 2 4 4
3  | 5 6 6 7 7 9
4* | 2 4 4
4  | 5 6 9
5* | 0 2 2
5  | 5 9
6* | 0 0 1 1 1 2 2 3 4 4
6  | 6 6 7 7
7* |
7  |
8* |
8  | 8
```

Figure 1.6 Stem-and-leaf diagram showing the ages of a sample of 91 cyclists (sorted)

❓ How would you squeeze a stem-and-leaf diagram? What would you do if the data have more significant figures than can be shown on a stem-and-leaf diagram?

Stem-and-leaf diagrams are particularly useful for comparing data sets. With two data sets a back-to-back stem-and-leaf diagram can be used, as shown in figure 1.7.

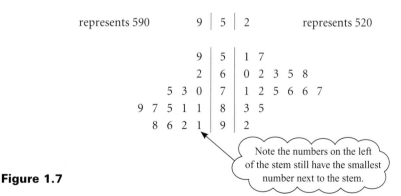

represents 590   9 | 5 | 2   represents 520

```
              9 | 5 | 1 7
              2 | 6 | 0 2 3 5 8
          5 3 0 | 7 | 1 2 5 6 6 7
      9 7 5 1 1 | 8 | 3 5
      8 6 2 1 | 9 | 2
```

Note the numbers on the left of the stem still have the smallest number next to the stem.

Figure 1.7

❓ How would you represent positive and negative data on a stem-and-leaf diagram?

1 Write down the numbers which are represented by this stem-and-leaf diagram.

$n = 15$

32 | 1   represents 3.21 cm

32	7
33	2 6
34	3 5 9
35	0 2 6 6 8
36	1 1 4
37	2

2 Write down the numbers which are represented by this stem-and-leaf diagram.

$n = 19$

8 | 9   represents 0.089 mm

8	3 6 7
9	0 1 4 8
10	2 3 5 8 9 9
11	0 1 4
12	3 5
13	1

3 Show the following numbers on a sorted stem-and-leaf diagram with six branches, remembering to include the appropriate scale.

| 0.212 | 0.223 | 0.226 | 0.230 | 0.233 | 0.237 | 0.241 |
| 0.242 | 0.248 | 0.253 | 0.253 | 0.259 | 0.262 | |

4 Show the following numbers on a sorted stem-and-leaf diagram with five branches, remembering to include the appropriate scale.

| 81.07 | 82.00 | 78.01 | 80.08 | 82.05 |
| 81.09 | 79.04 | 81.03 | 79.06 | 80.04 |

5 Write down the numbers which are represented by this stem-and-leaf diagram.

$n = 21$

34 | 5   represents 3.45 m

LOW   0.013, 0.089, 1.79

34	3
35	1 7 9
36	0 4 6 8
37	1 1 3 8 9
38	0 5
39	4

HIGH   7.45, 10.87

6 Forty motorists entered for a driving competition. The organisers were anxious to know if the contestants had enjoyed the event and also to know their ages, so that they could plan and promote future events effectively. They therefore asked entrants to fill in a form on which they commented on the various tests and gave their ages.

The information was copied from the forms and the ages listed as:

28	52	44	28	38	46	62	59	37	60
19	55	34	35	66	37	22	26	45	5
61	38	26	29	63	38	29	36	45	33
37	41	39	81	35	35	32	36	39	33

(i) Plot these data as a sorted stem-and-leaf diagram.

(ii) Describe the shape of the distribution.

7 The unsorted stem-and-leaf diagram below gives the ages of males whose marriages were reported in a local newspaper one week.

```
n = 42
1 | 9   represents 19

0 |
1 | 9 6 9 8
2 | 5 6 8 9 1 1 0 3 6 8 4 1 2 7
3 | 0 0 5 2 3 9 1 2 0
4 | 8 4 7 9 6 5 3 3 5 6
5 | 2 2 1 7
6 |
7 |
8 | 3
```

(i) What was the age of the oldest person whose marriage is included?

(ii) Redraw the stem-and-leaf diagram with the leaves sorted.

(iii) Stretch the stem-and-leaf diagram by using steps of five years between the levels rather than ten.

(iv) Describe and comment on the distribution.

8 On 1 January the average daily temperature was recorded for 30 cities around the world. The temperatures, in °C, were as follows.

21	3	18	−4	10	27	14	7	19	−14
32	2	−9	29	11	26	−7	−11	15	4
35	14	23	19	−15	8	8	−2	3	1

(i) Illustrate the distribution of temperatures on a stem-and-leaf diagram.

(ii) Describe the shape of the distribution.

9 The following marks were obtained on an A Level mathematics paper by the candidates at one centre.

26 54 50	37 54	34 34 66 44 76	45 71	51 75 30
29 52 43	66 59	22 74 51 49 39	32 37	57 37 18
54 17 26	40 69	80 90 95 96 95	70 68	97 87 68
77 76 30	100 98	44 60 46 97 75	52 82	92 51 44
73 87 49	90 53	45 40 61 66 94	62 39	100 91 66
35 56 36	74 25	70 69 67 48 65	55 64	

Draw a sorted stem-and-leaf diagram to illustrate these marks and comment on their distribution.

10 The ages of a sample of 40 hang-gliders (in years) are given below.

28 19 24 20 28	26 22 19 37 40	19 25 65 34 66
35 69 65 26 17	22 26 45 58 30	31 58 26 29 23
72 23 21 30 28	65 21 67 23 57	

(i) Using intervals of ten years, draw a sorted stem-and-leaf diagram to illustrate these figures.

(ii) Comment on and give a possible explanation for the shape of the distribution.

11 An experimental fertiliser called GRO was applied to 50 lime trees, chosen at random, in a plantation. Another 50 trees were left untreated. The yields in kilograms were as follows.

Treated

59 25 52 19 32	26 33 24 35 30	23 54 33 31 25
23 61 35 38 44	27 24 30 62 23	47 42 41 53 31
20 21 41 33 35	38 61 63 44 18	53 38 33 49 54
50 44 25 42 18		

Untreated

8 11 22 22 20	5 31 40 14 45	10 16 14 20 51
55 30 30 25 29	12 48 17 12 52	58 61 14 32 5
29 40 61 53 22	33 41 62 51 56	10 48 50 14 8
63 43 61 12 42		

Draw a sorted back-to-back stem-and-leaf diagrams to compare the two sets of data and comment on the effects of GRO.

12 A group of 25 people were asked to estimate the length of a line which they were told was between 1 and 2 metres long. Here are their estimates, in metres.

1.15 1.33 1.42 1.26 1.29	1.30 1.30 1.46 1.18 1.24
1.21 1.30 1.32 1.33 1.29	1.30 1.40 1.26 1.32 1.30
1.41 1.28 1.65 1.54 1.14	

(i) Represent these data in a sorted stem-and-leaf diagram.

(ii) From the stem-and-leaf diagram which you drew, read off the third highest and third lowest length estimates.

(iii) Find the middle of the 25 estimates.

(iv) On the evidence that you have, could you make an estimate of the length of the line? Justify your answer.

Categorical or qualitative data

Chapter 2 will deal in more detail with ways of displaying data. The remainder of this chapter looks at types of data and the basic analysis of numerical data.

Some data come to you in classes or categories. Such data, like these for the sizes of sweatshirts, are called categorical or qualitative.

XL, S, S, L, M, S, M, M, XL, L, XS

XS = extra small; S = small; M = Medium; L = Large; XL = extra large

Most of the data you encounter, however, will be numerical data (also called quantitative data).

Numerical or quantitative data

Variables

The score you get when you throw an ordinary die is one of the values 1, 2, 3, 4, 5 or 6. Rather than repeatedly using the phrase 'The score you get when you throw an ordinary die', statisticians find it convenient to use a capital letter, X, say. They let X stand for 'The score you get when you throw an ordinary die' and because this varies, X is referred to as a *variable*.

Similarly, if you are collecting data and this involves, for example, noting the temperature in classrooms at noon, then you could let T stand for 'the temperature in a classroom at noon'. So T is another example of a variable.

Values of the variable X are denoted by the lower case letter x, e.g. $x = 1, 2, 3, 4, 5$ or 6.

Values of the variable T are denoted by the lower case letter t, e.g. $t = 18, 21, 20, 19, 23, ...$.

Discrete and continuous variables

The scores on a die, 1, 2, 3, 4, 5 and 6, the number of goals a football team scores, 0, 1, 2, 3, ... and amounts of money, $0.01, $0.02, ... are all examples of *discrete variables*. What they have in common is that all possible values can be listed.

Distance, mass, temperature and speed are all examples of *continuous variables.* Continuous variables, if measured accurately enough, can take any appropriate value. You cannot list all possible values.

You have already seen the example of age. This is rather a special case. It is nearly always given rounded down (i.e. truncated). Although your age changes continuously every moment of your life, you actually state it in steps of one year, in completed years, and not to the nearest whole year. So a man who is a few days short of his 20th birthday will still say he is 19.

In practice, data for a continuous variable are always given in a rounded form.

- A person's height, h, given as 168 cm, measured to the nearest centimetre; $167.5 \leqslant h < 168.5$

- A temperature, t, given as 21.8 °C, measured to the nearest tenth of a degree; $21.75 \leqslant t < 21.85$

- The depth of an ocean, d, given as 9200 m, measured to the nearest 100 m; $9150 \leqslant d < 9250$

Notice the rounding convention here: if a figure is on the borderline it is rounded up. There are other rounding conventions.

Measures of central tendency

When describing a typical value to represent a data set most people think of a value at the centre and use the word *average.* When using the word average they are often referring to the *arithmetic mean,* which is usually just called the *mean* and when asked to explain how to get the mean most people respond by saying 'add up the data values and divide by the total number of data values'.

There are actually several different averages and so, in statistics, it is important for you to be more precise about the *average* to which you are referring. Before looking at the different types of average or *measure of central tendency,* you need to be familiar with some notation.

Σ notation and the mean, $\bar{x}$

A sample of size n taken from a population can be identified as follows.

The first item can be called x_1, the second item x_2 and so on up to x_n.

The sum of these n items of data is given by $x_1 + x_2 + x_3 + \ldots + x_n$.

A shorthand for this is $\sum_{i=1}^{i=n} x_i$ or $\sum_{i=1}^{n} x_i$. This is read as 'the sum of all the terms x_i when i equals 1 to n'.

So $\sum_{i=1}^{n} x_i = x_1 + x_2 + x_3 + \cdots + x_n.$ Σ is the Greek capital letter, sigma.

If there is no ambiguity about the number of items of data, the subscripts i can be dropped and $\sum_{i=1}^{n} x_i$ becomes $\sum x$.

$\sum x$ is read as 'sigma x' meaning 'the sum of all the x items'.

The mean of these n items of data is written as $\bar{x} = \dfrac{x_1 + x_2 + x_3 + \cdots + x_n}{n}$

where $\bar{x}$ is the symbol for the mean, referred to as 'x-bar'.

It is usual to write $\bar{x} = \dfrac{\sum x}{n}$ or $\dfrac{1}{n}\sum x$.

This is a formal way of writing 'To get the mean you add up all the data values and divide by the total number of data values'.

The mean from a frequency table

Often data is presented in a frequency table. The notation for the mean is slightly different in such cases.

Alex is a member of the local bird-watching group. The group are concerned about the effect of pollution and climatic change on the well-being of birds. One spring Alex surveyed the nests of a type of owl. Healthy owls usually lay up to 6 eggs. Alex collected data from 50 nests. His data are shown in the following frequency table.

Number of eggs, x	Frequency, f
1	4
2	12
3	9
4	18
5	7
6	0
Total	$\sum f = 50$

This represents 'the sum of the separate frequencies is 50'. That is, $4 + 12 + 9 + 18 + 7 = 50$

It would be possible to write out the data set in full as 1, 1, 1, … , 5, 5 and then calculate the mean as before. However, it would not be sensible and in practice the mean is calculated as follows:

$$\bar{x} = \frac{1 \times 4 + 2 \times 12 + 3 \times 9 + 4 \times 18 + 5 \times 7}{50}$$

$$= \frac{162}{50}$$

$$= 3.24$$

This represents the sum of each of the x terms multiplied by its frequency

In general, this is written as $\bar{x} = \dfrac{\sum xf}{n}$

$n = \sum f$

⚠ In the survey at the beginning of this chapter the mean of the cyclists' ages,

$$\bar{x} = \frac{2717}{91} = 29.9\,\text{years}$$

However, a mean of the ages needs to be adjusted because age is always rounded down. For example, Rahim Khan gave his age as 45. He could be exactly 45 years old or possibly his 46th birthday may be one day away. So, each of the people in the sample could be from 0 to almost a year older than their quoted age. To adjust for this discrepancy you need to add 0.5 years on to the average of 29.9 to give 30.4 years.

Note

The mean is the most commonly used average in statistics. The mean described here is correctly called the *arithmetic mean*; there are other forms, for example, the geometric mean, harmonic mean and weighted mean, all of which have particular applications.

The mean is used when the total quantity is also of interest. For example, the staff at the water treatment works for a city would be interested in the mean amount of water used per household ($\bar{x}$) but would also need to know the total amount of water used in the city (Σx). The mean can give a misleading result if exceptionally large or exceptionally small values occur in the data set.

There are two other commonly used statistical measures of a typical (or representative) value of a data set. These are the median and the mode.

Median

The median is the value of the middle item when all the data items are ranked in order. If there are n items of data then the median is the value of the $\frac{n+1}{2}$th item.

If n is odd then there is a middle value and this is the median. In the survey of the cyclists we have

> The 46th item of data is 22 years.

$$6, 6, 7, 7, 7, 8, \ldots, 20, 21, 21, 21, 22, 22, 22, \ldots$$

So for the ages of the 91 cyclists, the median is the age of the $\frac{91+1}{2} = 46$th person and this is 22 years.

If n is even and the two middle values are a and b then the median is $\frac{a+b}{2}$.

For example, if the reporter had not noticed that 138 was invalid there would have been 92 items of data. Then the median age for the cyclists would be found as follows.

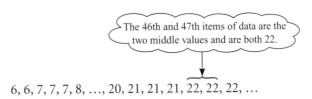

The 46th and 47th items of data are the two middle values and are both 22.

6, 6, 7, 7, 7, 8, …, 20, 21, 21, 21, 22, 22, 22, …

So the median age for the cyclists is given as the mean of the 46th and 47th items of data. That is, $\dfrac{22 + 22}{2} = 22$.

It is a coincidence that the median turns out to be the same. However, what is important to notice is that an extreme value has little or no effect on the value of the median. The median is said to be resistant to outliers.

The *median* is easy to work out if the data are already ranked, otherwise it can be tedious. However, with the increased availability of computers, it is easier to sort data and so the use of the median is increasing. Illustrating data on a stem-and-leaf diagram orders the data and makes it easy to identify the median. The median usually provides a good representative value and, as seen above, it is not affected by extreme values. It is particularly useful if some values are missing; for example, if 50 people took part in a marathon then the median is halfway between the 25th and 26th values. If some people failed to complete the course the mean would be impossible to calculate, but the median is easy to find.

In finding an *average* salary the median is often a more appropriate measure than the mean since a few people earning very large salaries may have a big effect on the mean but not on the median.

Mode

The *mode* is the value which occurs most frequently. If two non-adjacent values occur more frequently than the rest, the distribution is said to be *bimodal*, even if the frequencies are not the same for both modes.

Bimodal data usually indicates that the sample has been taken from two populations. For example, a sample of students' heights (male and female) would probably be bimodal reflecting the different average heights of males and females.

For the cyclists' ages, the mode is 9 years (the frequency is 6).

For a small set of discrete data the mode can often be misleading, especially if there are many values the data can take. Several items of data can happen to fall on a particular value. The mode is used when the most probable or most frequently occurring value is of interest. For example, a dress shop manager who is considering stocking a new style would first buy dresses of the new style in the modal size, as she would be most likely to sell those ones.

Which average you use will depend on the particular data you have and on what you are trying to find out.

The measures for the cyclists' ages are summarised below.

Mean   29.9 years   (adjusted = 30.4 years)
Mode   9 years
Median   22 years

❓ Which do you think is most representative?

EXAMPLE 1.1

These are the times, in minutes, that a group of people took to answer a Sudoku puzzle.

5, 4, 11, 8, 4, 43, 10, 7, 12

Calculate an appropriate measure of central tendency to summarise these times. Explain why the other measures are not suitable.

SOLUTION

First order the data.

4, 4, 5, 7, 8, 10, 11, 12, 43

One person took much longer to solve the puzzle than the others, so the mean is not appropriate to use as it is affected by outliers.

The mode is 4 which is the lowest data value and is not representative of the data set.

So the most appropriate measure to use is the median.

There are nine data values; the median is the $\left(\dfrac{9+1}{2}\right)$th value, which is 8 minutes.

EXERCISE 1B

1 Find the mode, mean and median of these figures.

(i)   23 46 45 45 29   51 36 41 37 47   45 44 41 31 33

(ii) 110 111 116 119 129   126 132 116 122 130
      116 132 118 122 127   132 126 138 117 111

(iii) 5 7 7 9 1   2 3 5 6 6   8 6 5 7 9   2 2 5 6 6
      6 4 7 7 6   1 3 3 5 7   8 2 8 7 6   5 4 3 6 7

2 For each of these sets of data

(a) find the mode, mean and median

(b) state, with reasons, which you consider to be the most appropriate form of average to describe the distribution.

(i) The ages of students in a class in years and months.

14.1	14.11	14.5	14.6	14.0	14.7	14.7	14.9	14.1	14.2
14.6	14.5	14.8	14.2	14.0	14.9	14.2	14.8	14.11	14.8
15.0	14.7	14.8	14.9	14.3	14.5	14.4	14.3	14.6	14.1

(ii) Students' marks on an examination paper.

55	78	45	54	0	62	43	56	71	65	0	67	75	51	100
39	45	66	71	52	71	0	0	59	61	56	59	64	57	63

(iii) The scores of a cricketer during a season's matches.

10	23	65	0	1	24	47	2	21	53	5	4	23	169	21
17	34	33	21	0	10	78	1	56	3	2	0	128	12	19

(iv) Scores when a die is thrown 40 times.

2	4	5	5	1	3	4	6	2	5	2	4	6	1	2	5	4	4	1	1
3	4	6	5	5	2	3	3	1	6	5	4	2	1	3	3	2	1	6	6

3 The lengths of time in minutes to swim a certain distance by the members of a class of twelve 9-year-olds and by the members of a class of eight 16-year-olds are shown below.

9-year-olds: 13.0 16.1 16.0 14.4 15.9 15.1 14.2 13.7 16.7 16.4 15.0 13.2

16-year-olds: 14.8 13.0 11.4 11.7 16.5 13.7 12.8 12.9

(i) Draw a back-to-back stem-and-leaf diagram to represent the information above.

(ii) A new pupil joined the 16-year-old class and swam the distance. The mean time for the class of nine pupils was now 13.6 minutes. Find the new pupil's time to swim the distance.

[Cambridge International AS and A Level Mathematics 9709, Paper 6 Q4 June 2007]

Frequency distributions

You will often have to deal with data that are presented in a frequency table. Frequency tables summarise the data and also allow you to get an idea of the shape of the distribution.

EXAMPLE 1.2

Claire runs a fairground stall. She has designed a game where customers pay $1 and are given 10 marbles which they have to try to get into a container 4 metres away. If they get more than 8 in the container they win $5. Before introducing the game to the customers she tries it out on a sample of 50 people. The number of successes scored by each person is noted.

5	7	8	7	5	4	0	9	10	6
4	8	8	9	5	6	3	2	4	4
6	5	5	7	6	7	5	6	9	2
7	7	6	3	5	5	6	9	8	7
5	2	1	6	8	5	4	4	3	3

The data are discrete. They have not been organised in any way, so they are referred to as raw data.

Calculate the mode, median and mean scores. Comment on your results.

SOLUTION

The *frequency distribution* of these data can be illustrated in a table. The number of 0s, 1s, 2s, etc. is counted to give the frequency of each mark.

Score	Frequency
0	1
1	1
2	3
3	4
4	6
5	10
6	8
7	7
8	5
9	4
10	1
Total	**50**

With the data presented in this form it is easier to find or calculate the different averages.

The mode is 5 (frequency 10).

As the number of items of data is even, the distribution has two middle values, the 25th and 26th scores. From the distribution, by adding up the frequencies, it can be seen that the 25th score is 5 and the 26th score is 6. Consequently the median score is $\frac{1}{2}(5 + 6) = 5.5$.

Representing a score by x and its frequency by f, the calculation of the mean is shown in this table.

Score, x	Frequency, f	$x \times f$
0	1	$0 \times 1 = 0$
1	1	$1 \times 1 = 1$
2	3	$2 \times 3 = 6$
3	4	12
4	6	24
5	10	50
6	8	48
7	7	49
8	5	40
9	4	36
10	1	10
Totals	50	276

So $\quad \bar{x} = \dfrac{\sum xf}{n} \qquad \left(n = \Sigma f \right)$

$$= \frac{276}{50} = 5.52$$

The values of the mode (5), the median (5.5) and the mean (5.52) are close. This is because the distribution of scores does not have any extreme values and is reasonably symmetrical.

EXAMPLE 1.3

The table shows the number of mobile phones owned by h households.

Number of mobile phones	0	1	2	3	4	5
Frequency	3	5	b	10	13	7

The mean number of mobile phones is 3. Find the values of b and h.

SOLUTION

The total number of households, $h = 3 + 5 + b + 10 + 13 + 7$.

So $\quad h = b + 38$

The total number of mobile phones $= 0 \times 3 + 1 \times 5 + 2 \times b + 3 \times 10 + 4 \times 13 + 5 \times 7$

$$= 2b + 122$$

$$\text{Mean} = \frac{\text{total number of mobile phones}}{\text{total frequency}} = 3$$

So $h = b + 38$

So, $\dfrac{2b + 122}{b + 38} = 3$

$2b + 122 = 3(b + 38)$

$2b + 122 = 3b + 114$

So $b = 8$ and $h = 8 + 38 = 46$.

EXERCISE 1C

1 A bag contained six counters numbered 1, 2, 3, 4, 5 and 6. A counter was drawn from the bag, its number was noted and then it was returned to the bag. This was repeated 100 times. The results were recorded in a table giving the frequency distribution shown.

(i)   State the mode.

(ii) Find the median.

(iii) Calculate the mean.

Number, x	Frequency, f
1	15
2	25
3	16
4	20
5	13
6	11

2 A sample of 50 boxes of matches with stated contents 40 matches was taken. The actual number of matches in each box was recorded. The resulting frequency distribution is shown in the table.

Number of matches, x	Frequency, f
37	5
38	5
39	10
40	8
41	7
42	6
43	5
44	4

(i)   State the mode.

(ii) Find the median.

(iii) Calculate the mean.

(iv) State, with reasons, which you think is the most appropriate form of average to describe the distribution.

3 A survey of the number of students in 80 classrooms in Avonford College was carried out. The data were recorded in a table as follows.

  (i) State the mode.

  (ii) Find the median.

  (iii) Calculate the mean.

  (iv) State, with reasons, which you think is the most appropriate form of average to describe the distribution.

Number of students, x	Frequency, f
5	1
11	1
15	6
16	9
17	12
18	16
19	18
20	13
21	3
22	1
Total	**80**

4 The tally below gives the scores of the football teams in the matches of the 1982 World Cup finals.

Score	Tally
0	⟊⟊ ⟊⟊ ⟊⟊ ⟊⟊ ⟊⟊ ⟊⟊ |
1	⟊⟊ ⟊⟊ ⟊⟊ ⟊⟊ ⟊⟊ ⟊⟊ ⟊⟊ |||
2	⟊⟊ ⟊⟊ ⟊⟊ |
3	⟊⟊ |||
4	⟊⟊ |
5	||
6	
7	
8	
9	
10	|

  (i) Find the mode, mean and median of these data.

  (ii) State which of these you think is the most representative measure.

  (For football enthusiasts: find out which team conceded 10 goals and why.)

5 The vertical line chart below shows the number of times the various members of a school year had to take their driving test before passing it.

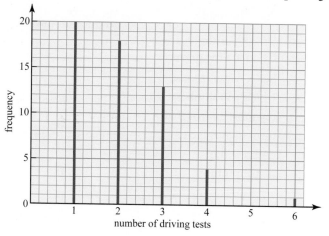

(i)   Find the mode, mean and median of these data.

(ii) State which of these you think is the most representative measure.

Grouped data

Grouping means putting the data into a number of classes. The number of data items falling into any class is called the *frequency* for that class.

When numerical data are grouped, each item of data falls within a *class interval* lying between *class boundaries*.

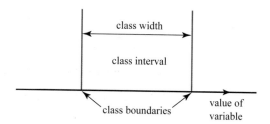

Figure 1.8

You must always be careful about the choice of class boundaries because it must be absolutely clear to which class any item belongs. A form with the following wording:

How old are you? Please tick one box.

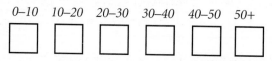

would cause problems. A ten-year-old could tick either of the first two boxes.

A better form of wording would be:

How old are you (in completed years)? Please tick one box.

0–9   *10–19*   *20–29*   *30–39*   *40–49*   *50+*

☐   ☐   ☐   ☐   ☐   ☐

Notice that this says 'in completed years'. Otherwise a $9\frac{1}{2}$-year-old might not know which of the first two boxes to tick.

Another way of writing this is:

$$0 \leqslant A < 10 \qquad 10 \leqslant A < 20 \qquad 20 \leqslant A < 30$$
$$30 \leqslant A < 40 \qquad 40 \leqslant A < 50 \qquad 50 \leqslant A$$

Even somebody aged 9 years and 364 days would clearly still come in the first group.

Another way of writing these classes, which you will sometimes see, is

0–, 10–, 20–, ... , 50–.

What is the disadvantage of this way?

Working with grouped data

There is often a good reason for grouping raw data.

● There may be a lot of data.

● The data may be spread over a wide range.

● Most of the values collected may be different.

Whatever the reason, grouping data should make it easier to analyse and present a summary of findings, whether in a table or in a diagram.

For some *discrete data* it may not be necessary or desirable to group them. For example, a survey of the number of passengers in cars using a busy road is unlikely to produce many integer values outside the range 0 to 4 (not counting the driver). However, there are cases when grouping the data (or perhaps constructing a stem-and-leaf diagram) is an advantage.

Discrete data

At various times during one week the number of cars passing a survey point was noted. Each item of data relates to the number of cars passing during a five-minute period. A hundred such periods were surveyed. The data is summarised in the following frequency table.

Number of cars, x	Frequency, f
0–9	5
10–19	8
20–29	13
30–39	20
40–49	22
50–59	21
60–70	11
Total	100

From the frequency table you can see there is a slight negative (or left) skew.

Estimating the mean

When data are grouped the individual values are lost. This is not often a serious problem; as long as the data are reasonably distributed throughout each interval it is possible to *estimate* statistics such as the mean, knowing that your answers will be reasonably accurate.

To estimate the mean you first assume that all the values in an interval are equally spaced about a mid-point. The mid-points are taken as representative values of the intervals.

The mid-value for the interval 0–9 is $\dfrac{0+9}{2} = 4.5$.

The mid-value for the interval 10–19 is $\dfrac{10+19}{2} = 14.5$, and so on.

The $x \times f$ column can now be added to the frequency distribution table and an estimate for the mean found.

Number of cars, x (mid-values)	Frequency, f	$x \times f$
4.5	5	$4.5 \times 5 = 22.5$
14.5	8	$14.5 \times 8 = 116.0$
24.5	13	318.5
34.5	20	690.0
44.5	22	979.0
54.5	21	1144.5
65.0	11	715.0
Totals	100	3985.5

The mean is given by

$$\bar{x} = \frac{\sum xf}{\sum f}$$

$$= \frac{3985.5}{100} = 39.855$$

The original raw data, summarised in the frequency table on the previous page, are shown below.

10	18	68	67	25	62	49	11	12	8
9	46	53	57	30	63	34	21	68	31
20	16	29	13	31	56	9	34	45	55
35	40	45	48	54	50	34	32	47	60
70	52	21	25	53	41	29	63	43	50
40	48	45	38	51	25	52	55	47	46
46	50	8	25	56	18	20	36	36	9
38	39	53	45	42	42	61	55	30	38
62	47	58	54	59	25	24	53	42	61
18	30	32	45	49	28	31	27	54	38

In this form it is impossible to get an overview of the number of cars, nor would listing every possible value in a frequency table (0 to 70) be helpful.

However, grouping the data and estimating the mean was not the only option. Constructing a stem-and-leaf diagram and using it to find the median would have been another possibility.

? Is it possible to find estimates for the other measures of centre?
Find the mean of the original data and compare it to the estimate.

The data the reporter collected when researching his article on cycling accidents included the distance from home, in metres, of those involved in cycling accidents. In full these were as follows.

3000	75	1200	300	50	10	150	1500	250	25
200	4500	35	60	120	400	2400	140	45	5
1250	3500	30	75	250	1200	250	50	250	450
15	4000								

It is clear that there is considerable spread in the data. It is continuous data and the reporter is aware that they appear to have been rounded but he does not know to what level of precision. Consequently there is no way of reflecting the level of precision in setting the interval boundaries.

The reporter wants to estimate the mean and decides on the following grouping.

Location relative to home	Distance, d, in metres	Distance mid-value, x	Frequency (number of accidents), f	$x \times f$
Very close	$0 \leqslant d < 100$	50	12	600
Close	$100 \leqslant d < 500$	300	11	3 300
Not far	$500 \leqslant d < 1500$	1000	3	3 000
Quite far	$1500 \leqslant d < 5000$	3250	6	19 500
Totals			32	26 400

$$\bar{x} = \frac{26\,400}{32} = 825\,\text{m}$$

A summary of the measures of centre for the original and grouped accident data is given below.

	Raw data	**Grouped data**
Mean	$25\,785 \div 32 = 806\,\text{m}$	$825\,\text{m}$
Mode	$250\,\text{m}$	Modal group $0 \leqslant d < 100\,\text{m}$
Median	$\frac{1}{2}(200 + 250) = 225\,\text{m}$	

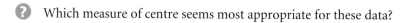

? Which measure of centre seems most appropriate for these data?

The reporter's article

The reporter decided that he had enough information and wrote the article below.

A town council that does not care

The level of civilisation of any society can be measured by how much it cares for its most vulnerable members.

On that basis our town council rates somewhere between savages and barbarians. Every day they sit back complacently while those least able to defend themselves, the very old and the very young, run the gauntlet of our treacherous streets.

I refer of course to the lack of adequate safety measures for our cyclists, 60% of whom are children or senior citizens. Statistics show that they only have to put one wheel outside their front doors to be in mortal danger. 80% of cycling accidents happen within 1500 metres of home.

Last week Rita Roy became the latest unwitting addition to these statistics. Luckily she is now on the road to recovery but that is no thanks to the members of our unfeeling town council who set people on the road to death and injury without a second thought.

What, this paper asks our councillors, are you doing about providing safe cycle tracks from our housing estates to our schools and shopping centres? And what are you doing to promote safety awareness among our cyclists, young and old?

Answer: Nothing.

? Is it a fair article? Is it justified, based on the available evidence?

Continuous data

For a statistics project Robert, a student at Avonford College, collected the heights of 50 female students.

He constructed a frequency table for his project and included the calculations to find an estimate for the mean of his data.

Height, h	Mid-value, x	Frequency, f	xf
$157 < h \leqslant 159$	158	4	632
$159 < h \leqslant 161$	160	11	1760
$161 < h \leqslant 163$	162	19	3078
$163 < h \leqslant 165$	164	8	1312
$165 < h \leqslant 167$	166	5	830
$167 < h \leqslant 169$	168	3	504
Totals		50	8116

$$\bar{x} = \frac{8116}{50}$$

$$= 162.32$$

Note: Class boundaries

His teacher was concerned about the class boundaries and asked Robert 'To what degree of accuracy have you recorded your data? 'Robert told him 'I rounded all my data to the nearest centimetre'. Robert showed his teacher his raw data.

163	160	167	168	166	164	166	162	163	163
165	163	163	159	159	158	162	163	163	166
164	162	164	160	161	162	162	160	169	162
163	160	167	162	158	161	162	163	165	165
163	163	168	165	165	161	160	161	161	161

Robert's teacher said that the class boundaries should have been

$157.5 \leqslant h < 159.5$

$159.5 \leqslant h < 161.5$, and so on.

He explained that a height recorded to the nearest centimetre as 158 cm has a value in the interval 158 ± 0.5 cm (this can be written as $157.5 \leqslant h < 158.5$). Similarly the actual values of those recorded as 159 cm lie in the interval $158.5 \leqslant h < 159.5$. So, the interval $157.5 \leqslant h < 159.5$ covers the *actual* values of the data items 158 and 159. The interval $159.5 \leqslant h < 161.5$ covers the actual values of 160 and 161 and so on.

? What adjustment does Robert need to make to his estimated mean in the light of his teacher's comments?

Find the mean of the raw data. What do you notice when you compare it with your estimate?

You are not always told the level of precision of summarised data and the class widths are not always equal, as the reporter for the local newspaper discovered. Also, there are different ways of representing class boundaries, as the following example illustrates.

EXAMPLE 1.4

The frequency distribution shows the lengths of telephone calls made by Emily during August. Choose suitable mid-class values and estimate Emily's mean call time for August.

SOLUTION

Time (seconds)	Mid-value, x	Frequency, f	xf
0–	30	39	1170
60–	90	15	1350
120–	150	12	1800
180–	240	8	1920
300–	400	4	1600
500–1000	750	1	750
Totals		79	8590

$$\bar{x} = \frac{8590}{79}$$

$$= 108.7 \text{ seconds}$$

Emily's mean call time is 109 seconds, to 3 significant figures.

Notes

1 The interval '0–' can be written as $0 \leqslant x < 60$, the interval '60–' can be written as $60 \leqslant x < 120$, and so on, up to '500–1000' which can be written as $500 \leqslant x \leqslant 1000$.

2 There is no indication of the level of precision of the recorded data. They may have been recorded to the nearest second.

3 The class widths vary.

EXERCISE 1D

1 A college nurse keeps a record of the heights, measured to the nearest centimetre, of a group of students she treats.

Her data are summarised in the following grouped frequency table.

Height (cm)	Number of students
110–119	1
120–129	3
130–139	10
140–149	28
150–159	65
160–169	98
170–179	55
180–189	15

Choose suitable mid-class values and calculate an estimate for the mean height.

2 A junior school teacher noted the time to the nearest minute a group of children spent reading during a particular day.

The data are summarised as follows.

Time (nearest minute)	Number of children
20–29	12
30–39	21
40–49	36
50–59	24
60–69	12
70–89	9
90–119	2

(i) Choose suitable mid-class values and calculate an estimate for the mean time spent reading by the pupils.

(ii) Some time later, the teacher collected similar data from a group of 25 children from a neigbouring school. She calculated the mean to be 75.5 minutes. Compare the estimate you obtained in part (i) with this value.

What assumptions must you make for the comparison to be meaningful?

3 The stated ages of the 91 cyclists considered earlier are summarised by the following grouped frequency distribution.

Stated age (years)	Frequency
0–9	13
10–19	26
20–29	16
30–39	10
40–49	6
50–59	5
60–69	14
70–79	0
80–89	1
Total	91

(i) Choose suitable mid-interval values and calculate an estimate of the mean stated age.

(ii) Make a suitable error adjustment to your answer to part (i) to give an estimate of the mean age of the cyclists.

(iii) The adjusted mean of the actual data was 30.4 years. Compare this with your answer to part (ii) and comment.

4 In an agricultural experiment, 320 plants were grown on a plot. The lengths of the stems were measured, to the nearest centimetre, 10 weeks after planting. The lengths were found to be distributed as in the following table.

Length, x (cm)	Frequency (number of plants)
$20.5 \leqslant x < 32.5$	30
$32.5 \leqslant x < 38.5$	80
$38.5 \leqslant x < 44.5$	90
$44.5 \leqslant x < 50.5$	60
$50.5 \leqslant x < 68.5$	60

Calculate an estimate of the mean of the stem lengths from this experiment.

5 The reporter for the local newspaper considered choosing different classes for the data dealing with the cyclists who were involved in accidents.

He summarised the distances from home of 32 cyclists as follows.

Distance, d (metres)	Frequency
$0 \leqslant d < 50$	7
$50 \leqslant d < 100$	5
$100 \leqslant d < 150$	2
$150 \leqslant d < 200$	1
$200 \leqslant d < 300$	5
$300 \leqslant d < 500$	3
$500 \leqslant d < 1000$	0
$1000 \leqslant d < 5000$	9
Total	32

(i) Choose suitable mid-class values and estimate the mean.

(ii) The mean of the raw data is 806 m and his previous grouping gave an estimate for the mean of 825 m. Compare your answer to this value and comment.

6 A crate containing 270 oranges was opened and each orange was weighed. The masses, given to the nearest gram, were grouped and the resulting distribution is as follows.

Mass, x (grams)	Frequency (number of oranges)
60–99	20
100–119	60
120–139	80
140–159	50
160–220	60

(i) State the class boundaries for the interval 60–99.

(ii) Calculate an estimate for the mean mass of the oranges from the crate.

Measures of spread (variation)

In the last section you saw how an estimate for the mean can be found from grouped data. The mean is just one example of a *typical value* of a data set. You also saw how the mode and the median can be found from small data sets. The next chapter considers the use of the median as a *typical value* when dealing with grouped data and also the *interquartile range* as a *measure of spread*. In this chapter we will consider the range, the mean absolute deviation, the variance and the standard deviation as measures of spread.

Range

The simplest measure of spread is the *range*. This is just the difference between the largest value in the data set (the upper extreme) and the smallest value (the lower extreme).

- Range = largest − smallest

The figures below are the prices, in cents, of a 100 g jar of *Nesko* coffee in ten different shops.

$$161 \quad 161 \quad 163 \quad 163 \quad 167 \qquad 168 \quad 170 \quad 172 \quad 172 \quad 172$$

The range for this data is

Range = 172 − 161 = 11 cents.

EXAMPLE 1.5

Ruth is investigating the amount of money, in dollars, students at Avonford College earn from part-time work on one particular weekend. She collects and orders data from two classes and this is shown below.

Class 1	Class 2
10 10 10 10 10 10 12 15 15 15	10 10 10 10 10 10 12 12 12 12
16 16 16 16 18 18 20 25 38 90	15 15 15 15 16 17 18 19 20 20
	25 35 35

She calculates the mean amount earned for each class. Her results are

$$\text{Class 1:} \qquad \bar{x}_1 = \$19.50$$
$$\text{Class 2:} \qquad \bar{x}_2 = \$16.22$$

She concludes that the students in Class 1 each earn about $3 more, on average, than do the students in Class 2.

Her teacher suggests she look at the spread of the data. What further information does this reveal?

SOLUTION

Ruth calculates the range for each class:
Range (Class 1) = $80
Range (Class 2) = $25

She concludes that the part-time earnings in Class 1 are much more spread out.

However, when Ruth looks again at the raw data she notices that one student in Class 1 earned $90, considerably more than anybody else. If that item of data is ignored then the spread of data for the two classes is similar.

⚠ One of the problems with the range is that it is prone to the effect of extreme values.

❓ Calculate the mean earnings of Class 1 with the item $90 removed.

What can you conclude about the effect of extreme values on the mean?

The range does not use all of the available information; only the extreme values are used. In quality control this can be an advantage as it is very sensitive to something going wrong on a production line. Also the range is easy to calculate. However, usually we want a measure of spread that uses all the available data and that relates to a central value.

e   The mean absolute deviation

Kim and Joe play as strikers for two local football teams. They are being considered for the state team. The team manager is considering their scoring records.

Kim's scoring record over ten matches looks like this:

    0   1   0   3   0   2   0   0   0   4

Joe's record looks like this:

    1   1   1   0   0   2   1   1   2   2

The mean scores are, for Kim, $\bar{x}_1 = 1$ and, for Joe, $\bar{x}_2 = 1.1$.

Looking first at Kim's data consider the differences, or *deviations*, of his scores from the mean.

Number of goals scored, x	0	1	0	3	0	2	0	0	0	4
Deviations $(x - \bar{x})$	−1	0	−1	2	−1	1	−1	−1	−1	3

To find a summary measure you need to combine the deviations in some way. If you just add them together they total zero.

❓ Why does the sum of the deviations always total zero?

The mean absolute deviation ignores the signs and adds together the *absolute deviations*. The symbol $|d|$ tells you to take the positive, or absolute, value of d.

For example $|-2| = 2$ and $|2| = 2$.

It is now possible to sum the deviations:

$$1 + 0 + 1 + 2 + 1 + 1 + 1 + 1 + 1 + 3 = 12,$$

the *total of the absolute deviations.*

It is important that any measure of spread is not linked to the sample size so you have to average out this total by dividing by the sample size.

In this case the sample size is 10. The *mean absolute deviation* = $\frac{12}{10} = 1.2$.

- The mean absolute deviation from the mean = $\frac{1}{n}\sum|x - \bar{x}|$

> Remember
> $n = \Sigma f.$

For Joe's data the mean absolute deviation is

$$\tfrac{1}{10}(0.1 + 0.1 + 0.1 + 1.1 + 1.1 + 0.9 + 0.1 + 0.1 + 0.9 + 0.9) = 0.54$$

The average numbers of goals scored by Kim and Joe are similar (1.0 and 1.1) but Joe is less variable (or more consistent) in his goal scoring (0.54 compared to 1.2).

The mean absolute deviation is an acceptable measure of spread but is not widely used because it is difficult to work with. The *standard deviation* is more important mathematically and is more extensively used.

The variance and standard deviation

An alternative to ignoring the signs is to square the differences or deviations. This gives rise to a measure of spread called the *variance*, which when square-rooted gives the *standard deviation*.

Though not as easy to calculate as the absolute mean deviation, the standard deviation has an important role in the study of more advanced statistics.

To find the variance of a data set:

- Square the deviations $\quad (x - \bar{x})^2$
- Sum the squared deviations $\quad \sum(x - \bar{x})^2$

- Find their mean $\quad \dfrac{\sum(x - \bar{x})^2}{n}$

This is known as the variance.

- Variance = $\dfrac{\sum(x - \bar{x})^2}{n}$

The square root of the variance is called the *standard deviation*.

- $sd = \sqrt{\dfrac{\sum(x - \bar{x})^2}{n}}$

For Kim's data this is:

$(0 - 1)^2, (1 - 1)^2, (0 - 1)^2,$ etc.

$1 + 0 + 1 + 4 + 1 + 1 + 1 +$
$1 + 9 = 20$

$\dfrac{20}{10} = 2$

> So, for Kim's data the variance is 2, but what are the units? In calculating the variance the data are squared. In order to get a measure of spread that has the same units as the original data it is necessary to take the square root of the variance. The resulting statistical measure is known as the *standard deviation*.

In other books or on the internet, you may see this calculation carried out using $n-1$ rather than n as the divisor. In this case the answer is denoted by s.

$$s = \sqrt{\frac{\sum(x-\bar{x})^2}{n-1}}$$

In Statistics 1, you should always use n as the divisor. You will meet s if you go on to study Statistics 2.

So for Kim's data the variance is 2, sd is $\sqrt{2} = 1.41$ (to 3 s.f.).

This example, using Joe's data, shows how the variance and standard deviation are calculated when the data are given in a frequency table. We've already calculated the mean; $\bar{x} = 1.1$.

Number of goals scored, x	Frequency, f	Deviation $(x-\bar{x})$	Deviation^2 $(x-\bar{x})^2$	Deviation$^2 \times f$ $[(x-\bar{x})^2 f]$
0	2	$0 - 1.1 = -1.1$	1.21	$1.21 \times 2 = 2.42$
1	5	$1 - 1.1 = -0.1$	0.01	$0.01 \times 5 = 0.05$
2	3	$2 - 1.1 = 0.9$	0.81	$0.81 \times 3 = 2.43$
Totals	10			4.90

For data presented in this way,

$$\text{standard deviation} = \sqrt{\frac{\sum(x-\bar{x})^2 f}{n}} = \sqrt{\frac{\sum(x-\bar{x})^2 f}{\sum f}} \quad \left(\Sigma f = n\right)$$

The standard deviation for Joe's data is $sd = \sqrt{\frac{4.90}{10}} = 0.7\,\text{goals}$.

Comparing this to the standard deviation of Kim's data (1.41), we see that Joe's goal scoring is more consistent (or less variable) than Kim's. This confirms what was found when the mean absolute deviation was calculated for each data set. Joe was found to be a more consistent scorer (mean absolute deviation = 0.54) than Kim (mean absolute deviation = 1.2).

An alternative form for the standard deviation

The arithmetic involved in calculating $\sum(x-\bar{x})^2 f$ can often be very messy.

An alternative formula for calculating the standard deviation is given by

- $\text{standard deviation} = \sqrt{\frac{\sum x^2 f}{n} - \bar{x}^2}$ or $\sqrt{\frac{\sum x^2 f}{\sum f} - \bar{x}^2}$

Consider Joe's data one more time.

Number of goals scored, x	Frequency, f	xf	x^2f
0	2	0	0
1	5	5	5
2	3	6	12
Total	10	11	17

$$\bar{x} = \frac{11}{10} = 1.1 \quad \text{standard deviation} = \sqrt{\frac{17}{10} - 1.1^2}$$

$$= \sqrt{1.7 - 1.21}$$

$$= \sqrt{0.49}$$

$$= 0.7$$

This gives the same result as using $\sqrt{\dfrac{\sum(x - \bar{x})^2 f}{\sum f}}$. The derivation of this alternative form for the standard deviation is given in Appendix 1 on the CD.

 In practice you will make extensive use of your calculator's statistical functions to find the mean and standard deviation of sets of data.

Care should be taken as the notations S, s, sd, σ and $\hat{\sigma}$ are used differently by different calculator manufacturers, authors and users. You will meet σ in Chapter 4.

The following examples involve finding or using the sample variance.

EXAMPLE 1.6

Find the mean and the standard deviation of a sample with

$$\sum x = 960, \sum x^2 = 18\,000, n = 60.$$

SOLUTION

$$\bar{x} = \frac{\sum x}{n} = \frac{960}{60} = 16$$

$$\text{variance} = \frac{\sum x^2}{n} - \bar{x}^2 = \frac{18\,000}{60} - 16^2 = 44$$

$$\text{standard deviation} = \sqrt{44} = 6.63 \,(\text{to 3 s.f.})$$

EXAMPLE 1.7

Find the mean and the standard deviation of a sample with

$$\sum(x-\bar{x})^2 = 2000, \sum x = 960, \sum f = 60.$$

SOLUTION

$$\bar{x} = \frac{960}{60} = 16$$

Remember:

$$\sum f = n$$

$$\text{variance} = \frac{\sum(x-\bar{x})^2}{\sum f} = \frac{2000}{60} = 33.3...$$

$$\text{standard deviation} = \sqrt{33.3...} = 5.77 \text{ (to 3 s.f.).}$$

EXAMPLE 1.8

As part of her job as quality controller, Stella collected data relating to the life expectancy of a sample of 60 light bulbs produced by her company. The mean life was 650 hours and the standard deviation was 8 hours. A second sample of 80 bulbs was taken by Sol and resulted in a mean life of 660 hours and standard deviation 7 hours.

Find the overall mean and standard deviation.

SOLUTION

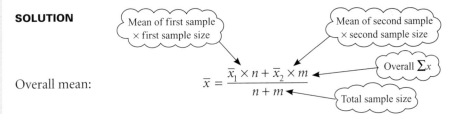

Overall mean:

$$\bar{x} = \frac{\bar{x}_1 \times n + \bar{x}_2 \times m}{n + m}$$

Mean of first sample × first sample size

Mean of second sample × second sample size

Overall $\sum x$

Total sample size

$$\bar{x} = \frac{650 \times 60 + 660 \times 80}{60 + 80} = \frac{91\,800}{140} = 655.71... = 656 \text{ hours (to 3 s.f.)}$$

For Stella's sample the variance is 8^2. Therefore $8^2 = \dfrac{\sum x_1^2}{60} - 650^2$.

For Sol's sample the variance is 7^2. Therefore $7^2 = \dfrac{\sum x_2^2}{80} - 660^2$.

From the above Stella found that

$$\sum x_1^2 = (8^2 + 650^2) \times 60 = 25\,353\,840 \text{ and } \sum x_2^2 = 34\,851\,920.$$

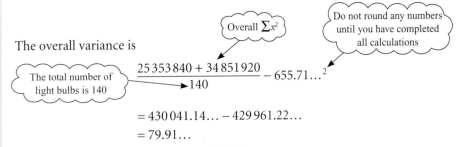

The overall variance is

Overall $\sum x^2$

Do not round any numbers until you have completed all calculations

The total number of light bulbs is 140

$$\frac{25\,353\,840 + 34\,851\,920}{140} - 655.71...^2$$

$$= 430\,041.14... - 429\,961.22...$$

$$= 79.91...$$

The overall standard deviation is $\sqrt{79.91...} = 8.94$ hours (to 3 s.f.).

Carry out the calculation in Example 1.8 using rounded numbers. That is, use 656 for the overall mean rather than 655.71…. What do you notice?

The standard deviation and outliers

Data sets may contain extreme values and when this occurs you are faced with the problem of how to deal with them.

Many data sets are samples drawn from parent populations which are normally distributed. You will learn more about the normal distribution in Chapter 7. In these cases approximately:

- 68% of the values lie within 1 standard deviation of the mean

- 95% lie within 2 standard deviations of the mean

- 99.75% lie within 3 standard deviations of the mean.

If a particular value is *more than two standard deviations from the mean* it should be investigated as possibly not belonging to the data set. If it is as much as three standard deviations or more from the mean then the case to investigate it is even stronger.

⚠ The 2-standard-deviation test should not be seen as a way of defining outliers. It is only a way of identifying those values which it might be worth looking at more closely.

In an A level Spanish class the examination marks at the end of the year are shown below.

$$35 \quad 52 \quad 55 \quad 61 \quad 96 \quad 63 \quad 50 \quad 58 \quad 58 \quad 49 \quad 61$$

The value 96 was thought to be significantly greater than the other values. The mean and standard deviation of the data are $\bar{x} = 58$ and $sd = 14.16…$. The value 96 is more than two standard deviations above the mean:

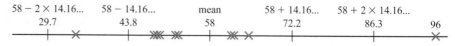

| $58 - 2 \times 14.16…$ | $58 - 14.16…$ | mean | $58 + 14.16…$ | $58 + 2 \times 14.16…$ | |
| 29.7 | 43.8 | 58 | 72.2 | 86.3 | 96 |

Figure 1.9

When investigated further it turned out that the mark of 96 was achieved by a Spanish boy who had taken A level Spanish because he wanted to study Spanish at university. It might be appropriate to omit this value from the data set.

? Calculate the mean and standard deviation of the data with the value 96 left out. Investigate the value using your new mean and standard deviation.

The times taken, in minutes, for some train journeys between Kolkata and Majilpur were recorded as shown.

56 61 57 55 58 57 5 60 61 59

It is unnecessary here to calculate the mean and standard deviation. The value 5 minutes is obviously a mistake and should be omitted unless it is possible to correct it by referring to the original source of data.

EXERCISE 1E

1 (i) Find the mean of the following data.

0 0 0 1 1 1 1 1 2 2 2 2 2 2 3 3 3 3 4 4 4 4 4 5 5

(ii) Find the standard deviation using both forms of the formula.

2 Find the mean and standard deviation of the following data.

x	3	4	5	6	7	8	9
f	2	5	8	14	9	4	3

3 Mahmood and Raheem are football players. In the 30 games played so far this season their scoring records are as follows.

Goals scored	0	1	2	3	4
Frequency (Mahmood)	12	8	8	1	1
Frequency (Raheem)	4	21	5	0	0

(i) Find the mean and the standard deviation of the number of goals each player scored.

(ii) Comment on the players' goal scoring records.

4 For a set of 20 items of data $\sum x = 22$ and $\sum x^2 = 55$. Find the mean and the standard deviation of the data.

5 For a data set of 50 items of data $\sum (x - \bar{x})^2 f = 8$ and $\sum xf = 20$. Find the mean and the standard deviation of the data.

6 Two thermostats were used under identical conditions. The water temperatures, in °C, are given below.

Thermostat A:	24	25	27	23	26
Thermostat B:	26	26	23	22	28

(i) Calculate the mean and standard deviaton for each set of water temperatures.

(ii) Which is the better thermostat? Give a reason.

A second sample of data was collected using thermostat A.

25   24   24   25   26   25   24   24

(iii) Find the overall mean and the overall standard deviation for the two sets of data for thermostat A.

7 Ditshele has a choice of routes to work. She timed her journey along each route on several occasions and the times in minutes are given below.

Town route:	15	16	20	28	21
Country route:	19	21	20	22	18

(i) Calculate the mean and standard deviation of each set of jourmey times.
(ii) Which route would you recommend? Give a reason.

8 In a certain district, the mean annual rainfall is 80 cm, with standard deviation 4 cm.

(i) One year it was 90 cm. Was this an exceptional year?
(ii) The next year had a total of 78 cm. Was that exceptional?

Jake, a local amateur meteorologist, kept a record of the weekly rainfall in his garden. His first data set, comprising 20 weeks of figures, resulted in a mean weekly rainfall of 1.5 cm. The standard deviation was 0.1 cm. His second set of data, over 32 weeks, resulted in a mean of 1.7 cm and a standard deviation of 0.09 cm.

(iii) Calculate the overall mean and the overall standard deviation for the whole year.
(iv) Estimate the annual rainfall in Jake's garden.

9 A farmer expects to harvest a crop of 3.8 tonnes, on average, from each hectare of his land, with standard deviation 0.2 tonnes.

One year there was much more rain than usual and he harvested 4.1 tonnes per hectare.

(i) Was this exceptional?
(ii) Do you think the crop was affected by the unusual weather or was the higher yield part of the variability which always occurs?

10 A machine is supposed to produce ball bearings with a mean diameter of 2.0 mm. A sample of eight ball bearings was taken from the production line and the diameters measured. The results, in millimetres, were as follows:

$$2.0 \quad 2.1 \quad 2.0 \quad 1.8 \quad 2.4 \quad 2.3 \quad 1.9 \quad 2.1$$

(i) Calculate the mean and standard deviation of the diameters.

(ii) Do you think the machine is correctly set?

11 On page 29 you saw the example about Robert, the student at Avonford College, who collected data relating to the heights of female students. This is his corrected frequency table and his calculations so far.

Height, h	Mid-value, x	Frequency, f	xf
$157.5 < h \leqslant 159.5$	158.5	4	634.0
$159.5 < h \leqslant 161.5$	160.5	11	1765.5
$161.5 < h \leqslant 163.5$	162.5	19	3087.5
$163.5 < h \leqslant 165.5$	164.5	8	1316.0
$165.5 < h \leqslant 167.5$	166.5	5	832.5
$167.5 < h \leqslant 169.5$	168.5	3	505.5
Totals		50	8141.0

$$\bar{x} = \frac{8141.0}{50} = 162.82$$

(i) Calculate the standard deviation.

Robert's friend Asha collected a sample of heights from 50 male PE students. She calculated the mean and standard deviation to be 170.4 cm and 2.50 cm. Later on they realised they had excluded two measurements. It was not clear to which of the two data sets, Robert's or Asha's, the two items of data belonged. The values were 171 cm and 166 cm. Robert felt confident about one of the values but not the other.

(ii) Investigate and comment.

12 As part of a biology experiment Thabo caught and weighed 120 minnows. He used his calculator to find the mean and standard deviation of their weights.

> Mean   26.231 g
> Standard deviation   4.023 g

(i) Find the total weight, $\sum x$, of Thabo's 120 minnows.

(ii) Use the formula standard deviation $= \sqrt{\dfrac{\sum x^2}{n} - \bar{x}^2}$ to find $\sum x^2$ for Thabo's minnows.

Another member of the class, Sharon, did the same experiment with minnows caught from a different stream. Her results are summarised by:

$$n = 80 \quad \bar{x} = 25.214 \quad \text{standard deviation} = 3.841$$

Their teacher says they should combine their results into a single set but they have both thrown away their measurements.

(iii) Find n, $\sum x$ and $\sum x^2$ for the combined data set.

(iv) Find the mean and standard deviation for the combined data set.

13 A frequency diagram for a set of data is shown below. No scale is given on the frequency axis, but summary statistics are given for the distribution.

$$\sum f = 50, \quad \sum fx = 100, \quad \sum fx^2 = 344$$

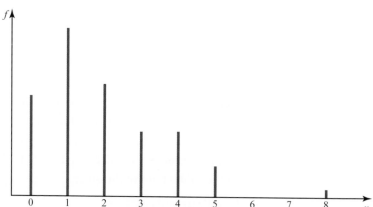

(i) State the mode of the data.

(ii) Identify two features of the distribution.

(iii) Calculate the mean and standard deviation of the data and explain why the value 8, which occurs just once, may be regarded as an outlier.

(iv) Explain how you would treat the outlier if the diagram represents

    (a) the difference of the scores obtained when throwing a pair of ordinary dice

    (b) the number of children per household in a neighbourhood survey.

(v) Calculate new values for the mean and standard deviation if the single outlier is removed.

[MEI, *adapted*]

14 A group of 10 married couples and 3 single men found that the mean age $\bar{x}_w$ of the 10 women was 41.2 years and the standard deviation of the women's ages was 15.1 years. For the 13 men, the mean age $\bar{x}_m$ was 46.3 years and the standard deviation was 12.7 years.

   (i) Find the mean age of the whole group of 23 people.

   (ii) The individual women's ages are denoted by x_w and the individual men's ages by x_m. By first finding $\sum x_w^2$ and $\sum x_m^2$, find the standard deviation for the whole group.

[Cambridge International AS and A Level Mathematics 9709, Paper 6 Q4 November 2005]

15 The numbers of rides taken by two students, Fei and Graeme, at a fairground are shown in the following table.

Student	Roller coaster	Water slide	Revolving drum
Fei	4	2	0
Graeme	1	3	6

   (i) The mean cost of Fei's rides is $2.50 and the standard deviation of the costs of Fei's rides is $0. Explain how you can tell that the roller coaster and the water slide each cost $2.50 per ride.

   (ii) The mean cost of Graeme's rides is $3.76. Find the standard deviation of the costs of Graeme's rides.

[Cambridge International AS and A Level Mathematics 9709, Paper 61 Q4 June 2010]

Working with an assumed mean

Human computer has it figured   mathman.com

Schoolboy, Simon Newton, astounded his classmates and their parents at a school open evening when he calculated the average of a set of numbers in seconds while everyone else struggled with their adding up.

Mr Truscott, a parent of one of the other children, said, 'I was still looking for my calculator when Simon wrote the answer on the board'.

Simon modestly said when asked about his skill 'It's simply a matter of choosing a good assumed mean'.

Mathman.com wants to know 'What is the secret method, Simon?'

Without a calculator, see if you can match Simon's performance. The data is repeated below. Send your result and how you did it into Mathman.com. Don't forget – no calculators!

Number	Frequency
3510	6
3512	4
3514	3
3516	1
3518	2
3520	4

Simon gave a big clue about how he calculated the mean so quickly. He said 'It's simply a matter of choosing a good assumed mean'. Simon noticed that subtracting 3510 from each value simplified the data significantly. This is how he did his calculations.

Number, x	Number – 3510, y	Frequency, f	$x \times f$
3510	0	6	$0 \times 6 = 0$
3512	2	4	$2 \times 4 = 8$
3514	4	3	$4 \times 3 = 12$
3516	6	1	$6 \times 1 = 6$
3518	8	2	$8 \times 2 = 16$
3520	10	4	$10 \times 4 = 40$
Totals		20	82

Average (mean) $= \dfrac{82}{20} = 4.1$

(3510 is now added back) $3510 + 4.1 = 3514.1$

Simon was using an *assumed mean* to ease his arithmetic.

Sometimes it is easier to work with an assumed mean in order to find the standard deviation.

EXAMPLE 1.9

Using an assumed mean of 7, find the true mean and the standard deviation of the data set 5, 7, 9, 4, 3, 8.

> It doesn't matter if the assumed mean is not very close to the correct value for the mean but the closer it is, the simpler the working will be.

SOLUTION

Let d represent the variation from the mean. So $d = x - 7$.

x	$d = x - 7$	$d^2 = (x - 7)^2$
5	$5 - 7 = -2$	4
7	$7 - 7 = 0$	0
9	$9 - 7 = 2$	4
4	$4 - 7 = -3$	9
3	$3 - 7 = -4$	16
8	$8 - 7 = 1$	1
Totals	$\sum d = \sum (x - 7) = -6$	$\sum d^2 = \sum (x - 7)^2 = 34$

The mean of d is given by

$$\bar{d} = \frac{\sum d}{n} = \frac{-6}{6} = -1$$

The standard deviation of d is given by

$$sd_d = \sqrt{\frac{\sum d^2}{n} - \left(\frac{\sum d}{n}\right)^2} = \sqrt{\frac{34}{6} - \left(\frac{-6}{6}\right)^2} \longleftarrow \quad \overline{d^2}$$

$$= 2.16 \text{ to } 3 \text{ s.f.}$$

So the true mean is $7 - 1 = 6$.

The true standard deviation is 216 to 3 s.f.

> 7 is the assumed mean.

In general,

- $\bar{x} = a + \bar{d}$ where a is the assumed mean.
- the standard deviation of x is the standard deviation of d.

The following example uses summary statistics, rather than the raw data values.

EXAMPLE 1.10

For a set of 10 data items, $\sum(x-9) = 7$ and $\sum(x-9)^2 = 17$.

Find their mean and standard deviation.

SOLUTION

Let $x - 9 = d$

$$\sum(x-9) = 7 \implies \sum d = 7$$

$$\implies \bar{d} = \frac{7}{10} = 0.7$$

$$\implies \bar{x} = 9 + 0.7 = 9.7$$

The mean of x is 9.7.

> The assumed mean is 9.

The standard deviation of $d = \sqrt{\dfrac{\sum d^2}{n} - \left(\dfrac{\sum d}{n}\right)^2}$ where $d = x - 9$

$$= \sqrt{\frac{17}{10} - \left(\frac{7}{10}\right)^2}$$

$$= \sqrt{1.7 - 0.49}$$

$$= \sqrt{1.21}$$

$$= 1.1$$

Since the standard deviation of x is equal to the standard deviation of d, it follows that the standard deviation of x is 1.1.

The next example shows you how to use an assumed mean with grouped data.

EXAMPLE 1.11

Using 162.5 as an assumed mean, find the mean and standard deviation of the data in this table. (These are Robert's figures for the heights of female students.)

Height, x (cm) mid-points	Frequency, f
158.5	4
160.5	11
162.5	19
164.5	8
166.5	5
168.5	3
Total	50

SOLUTION

The working is summarised in the table below.

Height, x (cm) mid-points	$d = x - 162.5$	Frequency, f	df	d^2f
158.5	−4	4	−16	64
160.5	−2	11	−22	44
162.5	0	19	0	0
164.5	2	8	16	32
166.5	4	5	20	80
168.5	6	3	18	108
Totals		50	16	328

$$\bar{d} = \frac{16}{50} = 0.32$$

$$(sd_d)^2 = \frac{328}{50} - 0.32^2 = 6.4576$$

$$sd_d = 2.54 \text{ to 3 s.f.}$$

So the mean and standard deviation of the original data are

$$\bar{x} = 162.5 + 0.32 = 162.82$$

$$sd_x = 2.54 \text{ to 3 s.f.}$$

1 Calculate the mean and standard deviation of the following masses, measured to the nearest gram, using a suitable assumed mean.

Mass (g)	241–244	245–248	249–252	253–256	257–260	261–264
Frequency	4	7	14	15	7	3

2 A production line produces steel bolts which have a nominal length of 95 mm. A sample of 50 bolts is taken and measured to the nearest 0.1 mm. Their deviations from 95 mm are recorded in tenths of a millimetre and summarised as $\sum x = -85$, $\sum x^2 = 734$. (For example, a bolt of length 94.2 mm would be recorded as −8.)

(i) Find the mean and standard deviation of the x values.

(ii) Find the mean and standard deviation of the lengths of the bolts in millimetres.

(iii) One of the figures recorded is −18. Suggest why this can be regarded as an outlier.

(iv) The figure of −18 is thought to be a mistake in the recording. Calculate the new mean and standard deviation of the lengths in *millimetres*, with the −18 value removed.

3 A system is used at a college to predict a student's A level grade in a particular subject using their GCSE results. The GCSE score is g and the A level score is a and for Maths in 2011 the equation of the line of best fit relating them was $a = 2.6g - 9.42$.

This year there are 66 second-year students and their GCSE scores are summarised as $\sum g = 408.6$, $\sum g^2 = 2545.06$.

(i) Find the mean and standard deviation of the GCSE scores.

(ii) Find the mean of the predicted A level scores using the 2011 line of best fit.

4 (i) Find the mode, mean and median of:

    2 8 6 5 4   5 6 3 6 4   9 1 5 6 5

Hence write down, without further working, the mode, mean and median of:

(ii) 20 80 60 50 40   50 60 30 60 40   90 10 50 60 50

(iii) 12 18 16 15 14   15 16 13 16 14   19 11 15 16 15

(iv) 4 16 12 10 8   10 12 6 12 8   18 2 10 12 10

5 A manufacturer produces electrical cable which is sold on reels. The reels are supposed to hold 100 metres of cable. In the quality control department the length of cable on randomly chosen reels is measured. These measurements are recorded as deviations, in centimetres, from 100 m. (So, for example, a length of 99.84 m is recorded as −16.)

For a sample of 20 reels the recorded values, x, are summarised by

$$\sum x = -86 \qquad \sum x^2 = 4281$$

(i) Calculate the mean and standard deviation of the values of x.

(ii) Later it is noticed that one of the values of x is -47, and it is thought that so large a value is likely to be an error. Give a reason to support this view.

(iii) Find the new mean and standard deviation of the values of x when the value -47 is discarded.

6 On her summer holiday, Felicity recorded the temperatures at noon each day for use in a statistics project. The values recorded, f degrees Fahrenheit, were as follows, correct to the nearest degree.

47   59   68   62   49   67   66   73   70   68   74   84   80   72

(i) Represent Felicity's data on a stem-and-leaf diagram. Comment on the shape of the distribution.

(ii) Using a suitable assumed mean, find the mean and standard deviation of Felicity's data.

7 For a set of ten data items, $\sum(x - 20) = -140$ and $\sum(x - 20)^2 = 2050$. Find their mean and standard deviation.

8 For a set of 20 data items, $\sum(x + 3) = 140$ and $\sum(x + 3)^2 = 1796$. Find their mean and standard deviation.

9 For a set of 15 data items, $\sum(x + a) = 156$ and $\sum(x + a)^2 = 1854$. The mean of these values is 5.4.
Find the value of a and the standard deviation.

10 For a set of 10 data items, $\sum(x - a) = -11$ and $\sum(x - a)^2 = 75$. The mean of these values is 5.9.
Find the value of a and the standard deviation.

11 The length of time, t minutes, taken to do the crossword in a certain newspaper was observed on 12 occasions. The results are summarised below.

$$\sum(t - 35) = -15 \qquad \sum(t - 35)^2 = 82.23$$

Calculate the mean and standard deviation of these times taken to do the crossword.

[Cambridge International AS and A Level Mathematics 9709, Paper 6 Q1 June 2007]

12 A summary of 24 observations of x gave the following information:

$$\sum(x - a) = -73.2 \quad \text{and} \quad \sum(x - a)^2 = 2115.$$

The mean of these values of x is 8.95.

(i) Find the value of the constant a.

(ii) Find the standard deviation of these values of x.

[Cambridge International AS and A Level Mathematics 9709, Paper 6 Q1 November 2007]

1 An item of data x may be identifed as an outlier if

$$|x - \bar{x}| > 2 \times \text{standard deviation}.$$

That is, if x is more than two standard deviations above or below the sample mean.

2 Categorical data are non-numerical; discrete data can be listed; continuous data can be measured to any degree of accuracy and it is not possbile to list all values.

3 Stem-and-leaf diagrams (or stemplots) are suitable for discrete or continuous data. All data values are retained as well as indicating properties of the distribution.

4 The mean, median and the mode or modal class are measures of central tendency.

5 The mean, $\bar{x} = \dfrac{\sum x}{n}$. For grouped data $\bar{x} = \dfrac{\sum xf}{\sum f}$.

6 The median is the mid-value when the data are presented in rank order; it is the value of the $\dfrac{n+1}{2}$th item of n data items.

7 The mode is the most common item of data. The modal class is the class containing the most data, when the classes are of equal width.

8 The range, variance and standard deviation are measures of spread or variation or dispersion.

9 Range = maximum data value − minimum data value.

10 The standard deviation $= \sqrt{\dfrac{\sum(x - \bar{x})^2 f}{n}}$ or $\sqrt{\dfrac{\sum(x - \bar{x})^2 f}{\sum f}}$

11 An alternative form is

$$\text{standard deviation} = \sqrt{\dfrac{\sum x^2 f}{n} - \bar{x}^2} \text{ or } \sqrt{\dfrac{\sum x^2 f}{\sum f} - \bar{x}^2}$$

12 Working with an assumed mean a,

$$\bar{x} = a + \bar{d}$$

where a is the assumed mean and d is the deviation from the assumed mean and the standard deviation of x is the standard deviation of d.

2 Representing and interpreting data

A picture is worth a thousand numbers.

Anon

Latest news from Alpha High

The Psychology department at Alpha High have found that girls have more on-line friends than boys. Mr Rama, the head of department, said 'The results are quite marked, girls in all age groups with the exception of the youngest age group had significantly more on-line friends. We have several hypotheses to explain this, but want to do more research before we draw any conclusions.' The group of student psychologists have won first prize in a competition run by *Psychology Now* for their research.

The Psychology department are now intending to compare these results with the number of friends that students have 'real-life' contact with.

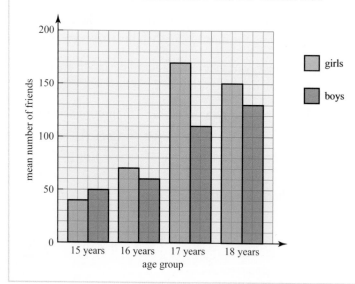

What is the mean number of friends for 17-year-old girls?

220 students aged 17 were surveyed from Alpha High. 120 of these students were girls. What is the overall mean number of friends for the 17-year-olds?

Most raw data need to be *summarised* to make it easier to see any patterns that may be present. You will often want to draw a diagram too. The Psychology department used the following table to construct the diagram for their article.

Age group	15 years	16 years	17 years	18 years
Sample size	200	170	220	310
Mean number of friends – girls	40	70	170	150
Mean number of friends – boys	50	60	110	130

You will often want to use a diagram to communicate statistical findings. People find diagrams to be a very useful and easy way of presenting and understanding statistical information.

Histograms

Histograms are used to illustrate continuous data. The columns in a histogram may have different widths and the area of each column is proportional to the frequency. Unlike bar charts, there are no gaps between the columns because where one class ends, the next begins.

Continuous data with equal class widths

A sample of 60 components is taken from a production line and their diameters, d mm, recorded. The resulting data are summarised in the following frequency table.

Diameter (mm)	Frequency
$25 \leqslant d < 30$	1
$30 \leqslant d < 35$	3
$35 \leqslant d < 40$	7
$40 \leqslant d < 45$	15
$45 \leqslant d < 50$	17
$50 \leqslant d < 55$	10
$55 \leqslant d < 60$	5
$60 \leqslant d < 65$	2

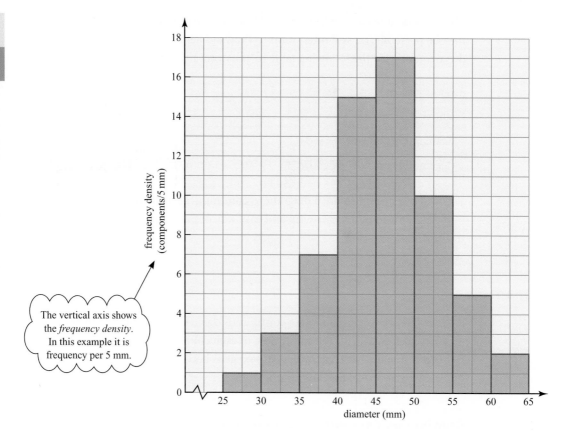

The vertical axis shows the *frequency density*. In this example it is frequency per 5 mm.

Figure 2.1 Histogram to show the distribution of component diameters

The class boundaries are 25, 30, 35, 40, 45, 50, 55, 60 and 65. The width of each class is 5.

The area of each column is proportional to the class frequency. In this example the class widths are equal so the height of each column is also proportional to the class frequency.

The column representing $45 \leqslant d < 50$ is the highest and this tells you that this is the modal class, that is, the class with highest frequency per 5 mm.

 How would you identify the modal class if the intervals were not of equal width?

Labelling the frequency axis

The vertical axis tells you the frequency *density*. Figure 2.3 looks the same as figure 2.2 but it is not a histogram. This type of diagram is, however, often incorrectly referred to as a histogram. It is more correctly called a frequency chart. A histogram shows the frequency density on the vertical axis.

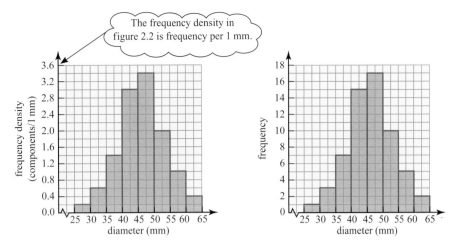

Figure 2.2   Figure 2.3

Comparing Figures 2.1 and 2.2, you will see that the shape of the distribution remains the same but the values on the vertical axes are different. This is because different units have been used for the frequency density.

Continuous data with unequal class widths

The heights of 80 broad bean plants were measured, correct to the nearest centimetre, ten weeks after planting. The data are summarised in the following frequency table.

Height (cm)	Frequency	Class width (cm)	Frequency density
$7.5 \leqslant x < 11.5$	1	4	0.25
$11.5 \leqslant x < 13.5$	3	2	1.5
$13.5 \leqslant x < 15.5$	7	2	3.5
$15.5 \leqslant x < 17.5$	11	2	5.5
$17.5 \leqslant x < 19.5$	19	2	9.5
$19.5 \leqslant x < 21.5$	14	2	7
$21.5 \leqslant x < 23.5$	13	2	6.5
$23.5 \leqslant x < 25.5$	9	2	4.5
$25.5 \leqslant x < 28.5$	3	3	1

When the class widths are unequal you can use

$$\text{frequency density} = \frac{\text{frequency}}{\text{class width}}$$

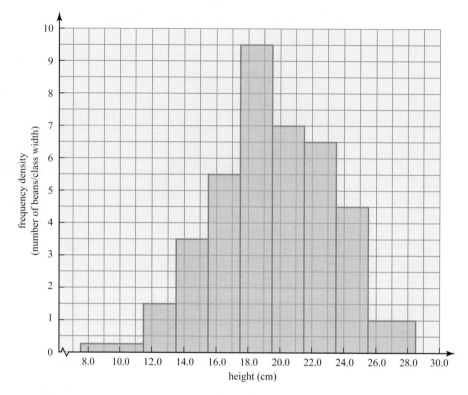

Figure 2.4

Discrete data

 Histograms are occasionally used for grouped *discrete* data. However, you should always first consider the alternatives.

A test was given to 100 students. The maximum mark was 70. The raw data are shown below.

10	18	68	67	25	62	49	11	12	8
9	46	53	57	30	63	34	21	68	31
20	16	29	13	31	56	9	34	45	55
35	40	45	48	54	50	34	32	47	60
70	52	21	25	53	41	29	63	43	50
40	48	45	38	51	25	52	55	47	46
46	50	8	25	56	18	20	36	36	9
38	39	53	45	42	42	61	55	30	38
62	47	58	54	59	25	24	53	42	61
18	30	32	45	49	28	31	27	54	38

Illustrating this data using a vertical line graph results in figure 2.5.

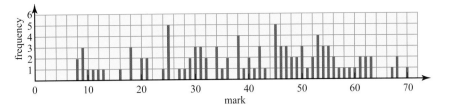

Figure 2.5

This diagram fails to give a clear picture of the overall distribution of marks.
In this case you could consider a bar chart or, as the individual marks are known,
a stem-and-leaf diagram, as follows.

$n = 100$

2 | 5 represents 25 marks

0	8 8 9 9 9
1	0 1 2 3 6 8 8 8
2	0 0 1 1 4 5 5 5 5 5 7 8 9 9
3	0 0 0 1 1 1 2 2 4 4 4 5 6 6 8 8 8 8 9
4	0 0 1 2 2 2 3 5 5 5 5 5 6 6 6 7 7 7 8 8 9 9
5	0 0 0 1 2 2 3 3 3 3 4 4 4 5 5 5 6 6 7 8 9
6	0 1 1 2 2 3 3 7 8 8
7	0

Figure 2.6

If the data have been grouped and the original data have been lost, or are
otherwise unknown, then a histogram may be considered. A grouped frequency
table and histogram illustrating the marks are shown below.

Marks, x	Frequency, f
0–9	5
10–19	8
20–29	14
30–39	19
40–49	22
50–59	21
60–70	11

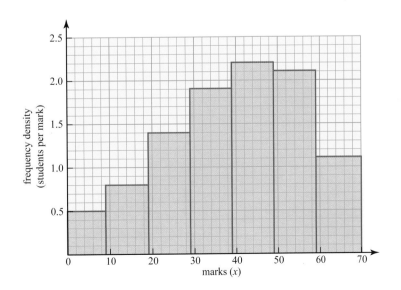

Figure 2.7

? Look at the intervals for the first and last classes. How do they differ from the others? Why is this the case?

Grouped discrete data are illustrated well by a histogram if the distribution is particularly skewed as is the case in the next example.

The first 50 positive integers squared are:

1	4	9	16	25	36	49	64
81	100	121	144	169	196	225	256
289	324	361	400	441	484	529	576
625	676	729	784	841	900	961	1024
1089	1156	1225	1296	1369	1444	1521	1600
1681	1764	1849	1936	2025	2116	2209	2304
2401	2500						

Number, n	Frequency, f
$0 < n \leqslant 250$	15
$250 < n \leqslant 500$	7
$500 < n \leqslant 750$	5
$750 < n \leqslant 1000$	4
$1000 < n \leqslant 1250$	4
$1250 < n \leqslant 1500$	3
$1500 < n \leqslant 1750$	3
$1750 < n \leqslant 2000$	3
$2000 < n \leqslant 2250$	3
$2250 < n \leqslant 2500$	3

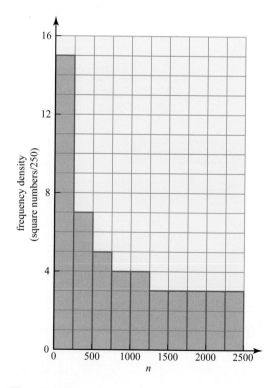

Figure 2.8

The main points to remember when drawing a histogram are:

- Histograms are usually used for illustrating continuous data. For discrete data it is better to draw a stem-and-leaf diagram, line graph or bar chart.

- Since the data are continuous, or treated as if they were continuous, adjacent columns of the histogram should touch (unlike a bar chart where the columns should be drawn with gaps between them).

- It is the areas and not the heights of the columns that are proportional to the frequency of each class.

- The vertical axis should be marked with the appropriate frequency density (*frequency per 5 mm* for example), rather than frequency.

EXERCISE 2A

1 A number of trees in two woods were measured. Their diameters, correct to the nearest centimetre, are summarised in the table below.

Diameter (cm)	1–10	11–15	16–20	21–30	31–50	Total
Mensah's Wood	10	5	3	11	1	30
Ashanti Forest	6	8	20	5	1	40

(Trees less than $\frac{1}{2}$ cm in diameter are not included.)

(i) Write down the actual class boundaries.

(ii) Draw two separate histograms to illustrate this information.

(iii) State the modal class for each wood.

(iv) Describe the main features of the distributions for the two woods.

2 Listed below are the prime numbers, p, from 1 up to 1000. (1 itself is not usually defined as a prime.)

Primes up to 1000

2	3	5	7	11	13	17	19	23	29	31	37	41	43
47	53	59	61	67	71	73	79	83	89	97	101	103	107
109	113	127	131	137	139	149	151	157	163	167	173	179	181
191	193	197	199	211	223	227	229	233	239	241	251	257	263
269	271	277	281	283	293	307	311	313	317	331	337	347	349
353	359	367	373	379	383	389	397	401	409	419	421	431	433
439	443	449	457	461	463	467	479	487	491	499	503	509	521
523	541	547	557	563	569	571	577	587	593	599	601	607	613
617	619	631	641	643	647	653	659	661	673	677	683	691	701
709	719	727	733	739	743	751	757	761	769	773	787	797	809
811	821	823	827	829	839	853	857	859	863	877	881	883	887
907	911	919	929	937	941	947	953	967	971	977	983	991	997

(i) Draw a histogram to illustrate these data with the following class intervals:

$$1 \leqslant p < 20 \qquad 20 \leqslant p < 50 \qquad 50 \leqslant p < 100 \qquad 100 \leqslant p < 200$$
$$200 \leqslant p < 300 \qquad 300 \leqslant p < 500 \text{ and } 500 \leqslant p < 1000.$$

(ii) Comment on the shape of the distribution.

3 A crate containing 270 oranges was opened and each orange was weighed to the nearest gram. The masses were found to be distributed as in this table.

Mass (grams)	Number of oranges
60–99	20
100–119	60
120–139	80
140–159	50
160–219	60

(i) Draw a histogram to illustrate the data.

(ii) From the table, calculate an estimate of the mean mass of an orange from this crate.

4 In an agricultural experiment, 320 plants were grown on a plot, and the lengths of the stems were measured to the nearest centimetre ten weeks after planting. The lengths were found to be distributed as in this table.

Length (cm)	Number of plants
20–31	30
32–37	80
38–43	90
44–49	60
50–67	60

(i) Draw a histogram to illustrate the data.

(ii) From the table, calculate an estimate of the mean length of stem of a plant from this experiment.

5 The lengths of time of sixty songs recorded by a certain group of singers are summarised in the table below.

Song length in seconds (x)	Number of songs
$0 < x < 120$	1
$120 \leqslant x < 180$	9
$180 \leqslant x < 240$	15
$240 \leqslant x < 300$	17
$300 \leqslant x < 360$	13
$360 \leqslant x < 600$	5

(i) Display the data on a histogram.

(ii) Determine the mean song length.

6 A random sample of 200 batteries, of nominal potential 6 V, was taken from a very large batch of batteries. The potential difference between the terminals of each battery was measured, resulting in the table of data below.

Potential difference in volts (mid-interval value)	Number of batteries
5.80	1
5.85	4
5.90	22
5.95	42
6.00	60
6.05	44
6.10	24
6.15	2
6.20	1

Calculate the mean and standard deviation of these voltages and illustrate the data on a histogram. Mark clearly on the histogram the mean voltage and the voltages which are two standard deviations either side of the mean.

[MEI]

7 After completing a long assignment, a student was told by his tutor that it was more like a book than an essay. He decided to investigate how many pages there are in a typical book and started by writing down the numbers of pages in the books on one of his shelves, as follows.

256	128	160	128	192	64	356	96	64	160
464	128	96	96	556	148	64	192	96	512
940	676	128	196	640	44	64	144	256	72

(i) Look carefully at the data and state, giving your reasons, whether they are continuous or discrete. Give an explanation for your answer.

(ii) Decide on the most helpful method of displaying the data and draw the appropriate diagram.

8 As part of a data collection exercise, members of a certain school year group were asked how long they spent on their Mathematics homework during one particular week. The times are given to the nearest 0.1 hour. The results are displayed in the following table.

Time spent (t hours)	$0.1 \leqslant t \leqslant 0.5$	$0.6 \leqslant t \leqslant 1.0$	$1.1 \leqslant t \leqslant 2.0$	$2.1 \leqslant t \leqslant 3.0$	$3.1 \leqslant t \leqslant 4.5$
Frequency	11	15	18	30	21

(i) Draw, on graph paper, a histogram to illustrate this information.

(ii) Calculate an estimate of the mean time spent on their Mathematics homework by members of this year group.

[Cambridge International AS and A Level Mathematics 9709, Paper 6 Q5 June 2008]

Measures of central tendency and of spread using quartiles

You saw in Chapter 1 how to find the median of a set of discrete data. As a reminder, the median is the value of the middle item when all the data items have been ranked in order.

The median is the value of the $\frac{n+1}{2}$th item and is half-way through the data set.

The values one-quarter of the way through the data set and three-quarters of the way through the data set are called the *lower quartile* and the *upper quartile* respectively. The lower quartile, median and upper quartile are usually denoted using Q_1, Q_2 and Q_3.

Quartiles are used mainly with large data sets and their values found by looking at the $\frac{1}{4}$, $\frac{1}{2}$ and $\frac{3}{4}$ points. So, for a data set of 1000, you would take Q_1 to be the value of the 250th data item, Q_2 to be the value of the 500th data item and Q_3 to be the value of the 750th data item.

Quartiles for small data sets

For small data sets, where each data item is known (raw data), calculation of the middle quartile Q_2, the median, is straightforward. However, there are no standard formulae for the calculation of the lower and upper quartiles, Q_1 and Q_3, and you may meet different ones. The one we will use is consistent with the output from some calculators which display the quartiles of a data set and depends on whether the number of items, n, is even or odd.

If n is *even* then there will be an equal number of items in the lower half and upper half of the data set. To calculate the lower quartile, Q_1, find the median of the lower half of the data set. To calculate the upper quartile, Q_3, find the median of the upper half of the data set.

For example, for the data set $\{1, 3, 6, 10, 15, 21, 28, 36, 45, 55\}$ the median, Q_2, is $\frac{15 + 21}{2} = 18$. The lower quartile, Q_1, is the median of $\{1, 3, 6, 10, 15\}$, i.e. 6. The upper quartile, Q_3, is the median of $\{21, 28, 36, 45, 55\}$, i.e. 36.

If n is *odd* then define the 'lower half' to be all data items *below* the median. Similarly define the 'upper half' to be all data items *above* the median. Then proceed as if n were even.

For example, for the data set $\{1, 3, 6, 10, 15, 21, 28, 36, 45\}$ the median, Q_2, is 15. The lower quartile, Q_1, is the median of $\{1, 3, 6, 10\}$, i.e. $\frac{3+6}{2} = 4.5$. The upper quartile, Q_3, is the median of $\{21, 28, 36, 45\}$, i.e. $\frac{28+36}{2} = 32$.

The definition of quartiles on a spreadsheet may be different from that described above. Values of Q_1 and Q_3 in the even case shown above are given as 7 and 34 respectively on an *Excel* spreadsheet. Similarly, values of Q_1 and Q_3 in the odd case shown above are given as 6 and 28 respectively.

ACTIVITY 2.1

Use a spreadsheet to find the median and quartiles of a small data set. Find out the method the spreadsheet uses to determine the position of the lower and upper quartiles.

EXAMPLE 2.1

Catherine is a junior reporter. As part of an investigation into consumer affairs she purchases 0.5 kg of chicken from 12 shops and supermarkets in the town. The resulting data, put into rank order, are as follows:

$1.39 $1.39 $1.46 $1.48 $1.48 $1.50 $1.52 $1.54 $1.60 $1.65 $1.68 $1.72

Find Q_1, Q_2 and Q_3.

SOLUTION

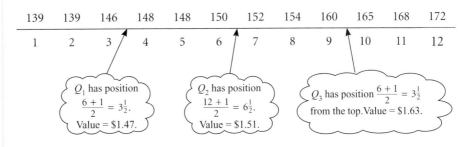

In fact, the upper quartile has a value of $1.625 but this has been rounded up to the nearest cent.

 You may encounter different formulae for finding the lower and upper quartiles. The ones given here are relatively easy to calculate and usually lead to values of Q_1 and Q_3 which are close to the true values.

? What are the true values?

Interquartile range or quartile spread

The difference between the lower and upper quartiles is known as the *interquartile range* or *quartile spread*.

- Interquartile range $(IQR) = Q_3 - Q_1$.

In Example 2.1 $IQR = 163 - 147 = 16$ cents.

The interquartile range covers the middle 50% of the data. It is relatively easy to calculate and is a useful measure of spread as it avoids extreme values. It is said to be resistant to outliers.

Box-and-whisker plots (boxplots)

The three quartiles and the two extreme values of a data set may be illustrated in a *box-and-whisker plot*. This is designed to give an easy-to-read representation of the location and spread of a distribution. Figure 2.9 shows a box-and-whisker plot for the data in Example 2.1.

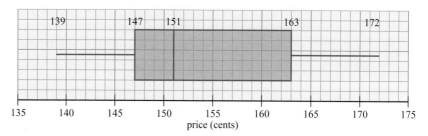

Figure 2.9

The box represents the middle 50% of the distribution and the whiskers stretch out to the extreme values.

Outliers

In Chapter 1 you met a definition of an outlier based on the mean and standard deviation. A different approach gives the definition of an outlier in terms of the median and interquartile range (IQR).

Data which are more than $1.5 \times IQR$ beyond the lower or upper quartiles are regarded as outliers.

The corresponding boundary values beyond which outliers may be found are

$$Q_1 - 1.5 \times (Q_3 - Q_1) \qquad \text{and} \qquad Q_3 + 1.5 \times (Q_3 - Q_1).$$

For the data relating to the ages of the cyclists involved in accidents discussed in Chapter 1, for all 92 data values $Q_1 = 13.5$ and $Q_3 = 45.5$.

Hence $Q_1 - 1.5 \times (Q_3 - Q_1) = 13.5 - 1.5 \times (45.5 - 13.5)$
$$= 13.5 - 1.5 \times 32$$
$$= -34.5$$

and $Q_3 + 1.5 \times (Q_3 - Q_1) = 45.5 + 1.5 \times (45.5 - 13.5)$
$$= 45.5 + 1.5 \times 32$$
$$= 93.5$$

From these boundary values you will see that there are no outliers at the lower end of the range, but the value of 138 is an outlier at the upper end of the range.

Figure 2.10 shows a box-and-whisker plot for the ages of the cyclists with the outlier removed. For the remaining 91 data items $Q_1 = 13$ and $Q_3 = 45$.

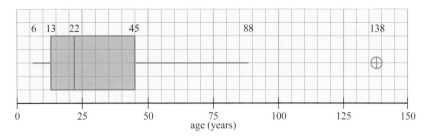

Figure 2.10

From the diagram you can see that the distribution has positive or right skewness. The ⊕ indicates an outlier and is above the upper quartile. Outliers are usually labelled as they are often of special interest. The whiskers are drawn to the most extreme data points which are not outliers.

Cumulative frequency curves

When working with large data sets or grouped data, percentiles and quartiles can be found from *cumulative frequency curves* as shown in the next section.

Sheuligirl

I am a student trying to live on a small allowance. I'm trying my best to allow myself a sensible monthly budget but my lecturers have given me a long list of textbooks to buy. If I buy just half of them I will have nothing left to live on this month. The majority of books on my list are over $16.

I want to do well at my studies but I won't do well without books and I won't do well if I am ill through not eating properly.

Please tell me what to do, and don't say 'go to the library' because the books I need are never there.

After reading this opening post a journalist wondered if there was a story in it. He decided to carry out a survey of the prices of textbooks in a large shop. The reporter took a large sample of 470 textbooks and the results are summarised in the table.

Cost, C ($)	Frequency (no. of books)
$0 \leqslant C < 10$	13
$10 \leqslant C < 15$	53
$15 \leqslant C < 20$	97
$20 \leqslant C < 25$	145
$25 \leqslant C < 30$	81
$30 \leqslant C < 35$	40
$35 \leqslant C < 40$	23
$40 \leqslant C < 45$	12
$45 \leqslant C < 50$	6

He decided to estimate the median and the upper and lower quartiles of the costs of the books. (Without the original data you cannot find the actual values so all calculations will be estimates.) The first step is to make a cumulative frequency table, then to plot a cumulative frequency curve.

Cost, C ($)	Frequency	Cost	Cumulative frequency
$0 \leqslant C < 10$	13	$C < 10$	13
$10 \leqslant C < 15$	53	$C < 15$	66
$15 \leqslant C < 20$	97	$C < 20$	163
$20 \leqslant C < 25$	145	$C < 25$	308
$25 \leqslant C < 30$	81	$C < 30$	389
$30 \leqslant C < 35$	40	$C < 35$	429
$35 \leqslant C < 40$	23	$C < 40$	452
$40 \leqslant C < 45$	12	$C < 45$	464
$45 \leqslant C < 50$	6	$C < 50$	470

← See note 1.

← See note 2.

Notes

1 Notice that the interval $C < 15$ means $0 \leqslant C < 15$ and so includes the 13 books in the interval $0 \leqslant C < 10$ and the 53 books in the interval $10 \leqslant C < 15$, giving 66 books in total.

2 Similarly, to find the total for the interval $C < 20$ you must add the number of books in the interval $15 \leqslant C < 20$ to your previous total, giving you $66 + 97 = 163$.

A cumulative frequency curve is obtained by plotting the *upper boundary* of each class against the cumulative frequency. The points are joined by a smooth curve, as shown in figure 2.11.

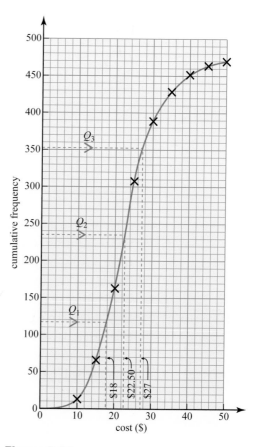

Figure 2.11

⚠ In this example the actual values are unknown and the median must therefore be an estimate. It is usual in such cases to find the *estimated* value of the $\frac{n}{2}$ th item. This gives a better estimate of the median than is obtained by using $\frac{n+1}{2}$, which is used for ungrouped data. Similarly, estimates of the lower and upper quartiles are found from the $\frac{n}{4}$ th and $\frac{3n}{4}$ th items.

The 235th $\left(\frac{470}{2}\right)$ item of data identifies the median which has a value of about $22.50. The 117.5th $\left(\frac{470}{4}\right)$ item of data identifies the lower quartile, which has a value of about $18 and the 352.5th $\left(\frac{3}{4} \times 470\right)$ item of data identifies the upper quartile, which has a value of about $27.

Notice the distinctive shape of the cumulative frequency curve. It is like a stretched out S-shape leaning forwards.

What about Sheuligirl's claim that the majority of textbooks cost more than $16? $Q_1 = \$18$. By definition 75% of books are more expensive than this, so Sheuligirl's claim seems to be well founded. We need to check exactly how many books are estimated to be more expensive than $16.

From the cumulative frequency curve 85 books cost $16 or less (figure 2.12). So 385 books or about 82% are more expensive.

⚠ You should be cautious about any conclusions you draw. This example deals with books, many of which have prices like $9.95 or $39.99. In using a cumulative frequency curve you are assuming an even spread of data throughout the intervals and this may not always be the case.

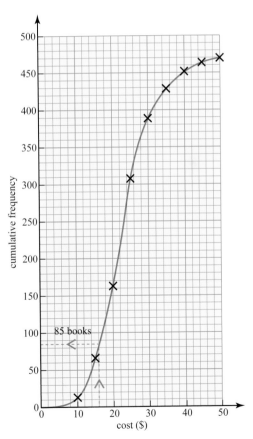

Figure 2.12

Box-and-whisker plots for grouped data

It is often helpful to draw a box-and-whisker plot. In cases when the extreme values are unknown the whiskers are drawn out to the 10th and 90th percentiles. Arrows indicate that the minimum and maximum values are further out.

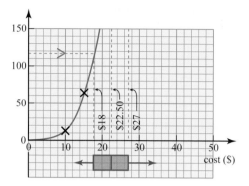

Figure 2.13

EXAMPLE 2.2

A random sample of people were asked how old they were when they first met their partner. The histogram represents this information.

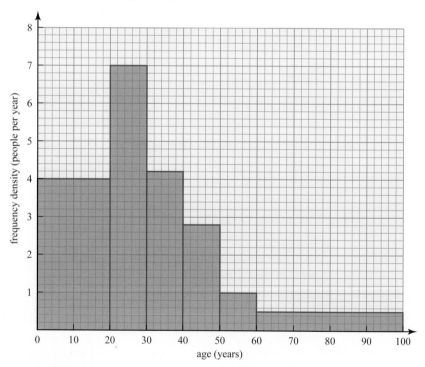

Figure 2.14

(i)   What is the modal age group?

(ii) How many people took part in the survey?

(iii) Find an estimate for the mean age that a person first met their partner.

(iv) Draw a cumulative frequency curve for the data and use the curve to provide an estimate for the median.

SOLUTION

(i)   The bar with the greatest frequency density represents the modal age group. So the modal age group is $20 \leqslant a < 30$.

(ii) Frequency density $= \dfrac{\text{frequency}}{\text{class width}}$

      So,

$$\text{Frequency} = \text{frequency density} \times \text{class width}$$

Age (years)	Frequency density	Class width	Frequency
$0 \leqslant a < 20$	4	20	$4 \times 20 = 80$
$20 \leqslant a < 30$	7	10	$7 \times 10 = 70$
$30 \leqslant a < 40$	4.2	10	$4.2 \times 10 = 42$
$40 \leqslant a < 50$	2.8	10	$2.8 \times 10 = 28$
$50 \leqslant a < 60$	1	10	$1 \times 10 = 10$
$60 \leqslant a < 100$	0.5	40	$0.5 \times 40 = 20$

The total number of people is $80 + 70 + 42 + 28 + 10 + 20 = 250$

 You will see that the class with the greatest frequency is $0 \leqslant a < 20$, with 80 people. However, this is not the modal class because its frequency density of 4 people per year is lower than the frequency density of 7 people per year for the $20 \leqslant a < 30$ class. The modal class is that with the highest frequency density. The class width for $0 \leqslant a < 20$ is twice that for $20 \leqslant a < 30$ and this is taken into account in working out the frequency density.

(iii) To find an estimate for the mean, work out the mid-point of each class multiplied by its frequency; then sum the results and divide the answer by the total frequency.

$$\text{Estimated mean} = \frac{80 \times 10 + 70 \times 25 + 42 \times 35 + 28 \times 45 + 10 \times 55 + 20 \times 80}{250}$$

$$= \frac{7430}{250}$$

$$= 29.7 \text{ years to 3 s.f.}$$

(iv)

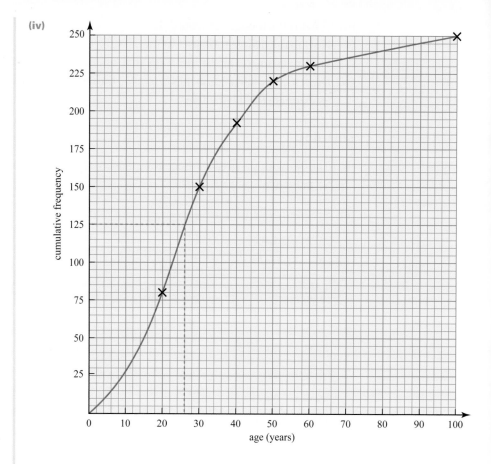

Figure 2.15

The median age is 26 years.

EXAMPLE 2.3 These are the times, in seconds, that 15 members of an athletics club took to run 800 metres.

139	148	151	140	162
182	154	171	157	142
145	178	132	148	166

(i)   Draw a stem-and-leaf diagram of the data.
(ii) Find the median, the upper and lower quartiles and the interquartile range.
(iii) Draw a box-and-whisker plot of the data.

SOLUTION

(i) $n = 15$

13 | 2 represents 132 seconds

```
13 | 2 9
14 | 0 2 5 8 8
15 | 1 4 7
16 | 2 6
17 | 1 8
18 | 2
```

(ii) There are 15 data values, so the median is the 8th data value.
So the median is 151 seconds.

The upper quartile is the median of the upper half of the data set.
So the upper quartile is 166 seconds.

The lower quartile is the median of the lower half of the data set.
So the lower quartile is 142 seconds.

Interquartile range = upper quartile − lower quartile
$$= 166 - 142$$
$$= 24 \text{ seconds}$$

(iii) Draw a box that starts at the lower quartile and ends at the upper quartile.
Add a line inside the box to show the position of the median.
Extend the whiskers to the greatest and least values in the data set.

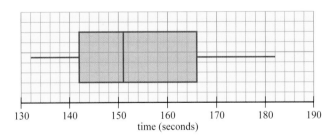

Figure 2.16

1 For each of the following data sets, find

(a) the range

(b) the median

(c) the lower and upper quartiles

(d) the interquartile range

(e) any outliers.

(i)   6   8   3   2   1   5   4   6   8   5   6   7   8   8   6   6

(ii) 12   5   17   11   4   10   12   19   12   5   9   15   11   16   8

      18   12   8   9   11   12   14   8   14   7

(iii) 25   28   33   14   37   19   23   27   25   28

(iv) 115   123   132   109   127   116   141   132   114   109

      125   121   117   118   117   116   123   105   125

2 (i) For the following data set, find the median and interquartile range.

   2   8   4   6   3   5   1   8   2   5   8   0   3   7   8   5

Use your answers to part **(i)** to deduce the median and interquartile range for each of the following data sets.

(ii) 32   38   34   36   33   35   31   38   32   35   38   30   33   37   38   35

(iii) 20   80   40   60   30   50   10   80   20   50   80   0   30   70   80   50

(iv) 50   110   70   90   60   80   40   110   50   80   110   30   60   100   110   80

3 Find

(i)   the median

(ii) the upper and lower quartiles

(iii) the interquartile range

for the scores of golfers in the first round of a competition.

Score	Tally
70	I
71	II
72	IIII
73	ЖІ III
74	ЖІ ЖІ II
75	ЖІ II
76	ЖІ
77	ЖІ I
78	
79	III
80	I
81	
82	I

(iv) Illustrate the data with a box-and-whisker plot.

(v) The scores for the second round are illustrated on the box-and-whisker plot below. Compare the two and say why you think the differences might have arisen.

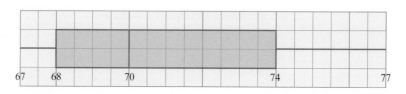

4 The numbers of goals scored by a hockey team in its matches one season are illustrated on the vertical line chart below.

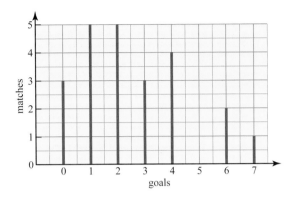

(i) Draw a box-and-whisker plot to illustrate the same data.

(ii) State, with reasons, which you think is the better method of display in this case.

5 One year the yields, y, of a number of walnut trees were recorded to the nearest kilogram as follows.

Yield, y (kg)	Frequency
$40 < y \leqslant 50$	1
$50 < y \leqslant 60$	5
$60 < y \leqslant 70$	7
$70 < y \leqslant 80$	4
$80 < y \leqslant 90$	2
$90 < y \leqslant 100$	1

(i) Construct the cumulative frequency table for these data.

(ii) Draw the cumulative frequency graph.

(iii) Use your graph to estimate the median and interquartile range of the yields.

(iv) Draw a box-and-whisker plot to illustrate the data.

The piece of paper where the actual figures had been recorded was then found, and these were:

        44 59 67 76 52   62 68 78 53 63
        85 93 56 65 74   69 82 53 65 70

(v) Use these data to find the median and interquartile range and compare your answers with those you obtained from the grouped data.

(vi) What are the advantages and disadvantages of grouping data?

6 The intervals of time, t seconds, between successive emissions from a weak radioactive source were measured for 200 consecutive intervals, with the following results.

Interval (t seconds)	$0 < t \leqslant 5$	$5 < t \leqslant 10$	$10 < t \leqslant 15$	$15 < t \leqslant 20$
Frequency	23	67	42	26
Interval (t seconds)	$20 < t \leqslant 25$	$25 < t \leqslant 30$	$30 < t \leqslant 35$	
Frequency	21	15	6	

(i) Draw a cumulative frequency graph for this distribution.

(ii) Use your graph to estimate

   (a) the median

   (b) the interquartile range.

(iii) Calculate an estimate of the mean of the distribution.

7 In a sample of 800 eggs from an egg farm each egg was weighed and classified according to its mass, m grams. The frequency distribution was as follows.

Mass in grams	$40 < m \leqslant 45$	$45 < m \leqslant 50$	$50 < m \leqslant 55$
Number of eggs	36	142	286
Mass in grams	$55 < m \leqslant 60$	$60 < m \leqslant 65$	$65 < m \leqslant 70$
Number of eggs	238	76	22

Draw a cumulative frequency graph of the data, using a scale of 2 cm to represent 5 grams on the horizontal axis (which should be labelled from 40 to 70 grams) and a scale of 2 cm to represent 100 eggs on the vertical axis. Use your graph to estimate for this sample

(i) the percentage of eggs which would be classified as large (over 62 grams)

(ii) the median mass of an egg

(iii) the interquartile range.

Indicate clearly on your diagram how you arrive at your results.

8 The table summarises the observed lifetimes, x, in seconds, of 50 fruit flies subjected to a new spray in a controlled experiment.

Interval	Mid-interval value	Frequency
$0.5 \leqslant x < 5.5$	3	3
$5.5 \leqslant x < 10.5$	8	22
$10.5 \leqslant x < 15.5$	13	12
$15.5 \leqslant x < 20.5$	18	9
$20.5 \leqslant x < 25.5$	23	2
$25.5 \leqslant x < 30.5$	28	1
$30.5 \leqslant x < 35.5$	33	1

(i) Making clear your methods and showing all your working, estimate the mean and standard deviation of these lifetimes. Give your answers correct to 3 significant figures and do not make any corrections for grouping.

(ii) Draw the cumulative frequency graph and use it to estimate the minimum lifetime below which 70% of all lifetimes lie.

9 During January the numbers of people entering a store during the first hour after opening were as follows.

Time after opening, x minutes	Frequency	Cumulative frequency
$0 < x \leqslant 10$	210	210
$10 < x \leqslant 20$	134	344
$20 < x \leqslant 30$	78	422
$30 < x \leqslant 40$	72	a
$40 < x \leqslant 60$	b	540

(i) Find the values of a and b.

(ii) Draw a cumulative frequency graph to represent this information. Take a scale of 2 cm for 10 minutes on the horizontal axis and 2 cm for 50 people on the vertical axis.

(iii) Use your graph to estimate the median time after opening that people entered the store.

(iv) Calculate estimates of the mean, m minutes, and standard deviation, s minutes, of the time after opening that people entered the store.

(v) Use your graph to estimate the number of people entering the store between $(m - \frac{1}{2}s)$ and $(m + \frac{1}{2}s)$ minutes after opening.

[Cambridge International AS and A Level Mathematics 9709, Paper 6 Q6 June 2009]

10 The numbers of people travelling on a certain bus at different times of the day are as follows.

$$17 \quad 5 \quad 2 \quad 23 \quad 16 \quad 31 \quad 8$$
$$22 \quad 14 \quad 25 \quad 35 \quad 17 \quad 27 \quad 12$$
$$6 \quad 23 \quad 19 \quad 21 \quad 23 \quad 8 \quad 26$$

(i) Draw a stem-and-leaf diagram to illustrate the information given above.

(ii) Find the median, the lower quartile, the upper quartile and the interquartile range.

(iii) State, in this case, which of the median and mode is preferable as a measure of central tendency, and why.

[Cambridge International AS and A Level Mathematics 9709, Paper 61 Q2 June 2010]

1 **Histograms:**

- commonly used to illustrate continuous data

- horizontal axis shows the variable being measured (cm, kg, etc.)

- vertical axis labelled frequency density where

$$\text{frequency density} = \frac{\text{frequency}}{\text{class width}}$$

- no gaps between columns

- the frequency is proportional to the area of each column.

2 For a small data set with n items,

- the median, Q_2, is the value of the $\frac{n+1}{2}$th item of data.

If n is even then

- the lower quartile, Q_1, is the median of the lower half of the data set

- the upper quartile, Q_3, is the median of the upper half of the data set.

If n is odd then exclude the median from either 'half' and proceed as if n were even.

3 Interquartile range $(IQR) = Q_3 - Q_1$.

4 When data are illustrated using a cumulative frequency curve the median and the lower and upper quartiles are estimated by identifying the data values with cumulative frequencies $\frac{1}{2}n$, $\frac{1}{4}n$ and $\frac{3}{4}n$.

5 An item of data x may be identified as an outlier if it is more than $1.5 \times IQR$ beyond the lower or upper quartile, i.e. if

$$x < Q_1 - 1.5 \times (Q_3 - Q_1) \quad \text{or} \quad x > Q_3 + 1.5 \times (Q_3 - Q_1).$$

6 A box-and-whisker plot is a useful way of summarising data and showing the median, upper and lower quartiles and any outliers.

3

Probability

If we knew Lady Luck better, Las Vegas would still be a roadstop in the desert.

Stephen Jay Gould

📖 📖 thelibrarian.com 📖 📖

A library without books

If you plan to pop into your local library and pick up the latest bestseller, then forget it. All the best books 'disappear' practically as soon as they are put on the shelves.

I talked about the problem with the local senior librarian, Gina Clarke.

'We have a real problem with unauthorised loans at the moment,' Gina told me. 'Out of our total stock of, say 80 000 books, something like 44 000 are out on loan at any one time. About 20 000 are on the shelves and I'm afraid the rest are unaccounted for.'

Librarian Gina Clarke is worried about the problem of 'disappearing books'

That means that the probability of finding the particular book you want is exactly $\frac{1}{4}$. With odds like that, don't bet on being lucky next time you visit your library.

How do you think the figure of $\frac{1}{4}$ at the end of the article was arrived at? Do you agree that the probability is *exactly* $\frac{1}{4}$?

The information about the different categories of book can be summarised as follows.

Category of book	Typical numbers
On the shelves	20 000
Out on loan	44 000
Unauthorised loan	16 000
Total stock	80 000

On the basis of these figures it is possible to estimate the probability of finding the book you want. Of the total stock of 80 000 books bought by the library, you might expect to find about 20 000 on the shelves at any one time. As a fraction, this is $\frac{20}{80}$ or $\frac{1}{4}$ of the total. So, as a rough estimate, the probability of your finding a particular book is 0.25 or 25%.

Similarly, 16 000 out of the total of 80 000 books are on unauthorised loan, a euphemism for *stolen*, and this is 20%, or $\frac{1}{5}$.

An important assumption underlying these calculations is that all the books are equally likely to be unavailable, which is not very realistic since popular books are more likely to be stolen. Also, the numbers given are only rough approximations, so it is definitely incorrect to say that the probability is *exactly* $\frac{1}{4}$.

Measuring probability

Probability (or chance) is a way of describing the likelihood of different possible *outcomes* occurring as a result of some *experiment*.

In the example of the library books, the experiment is looking in the library for a particular book. Let us assume that you already know that the book you want is on the library's stocks. The three possible outcomes are that the book is on the shelves, out on loan or missing.

It is important in probability to distinguish experiments from the outcomes which they may generate. Here are a few examples.

Experiment	Possible outcomes
Guessing the answer to a four-option multiple choice question	A B C D
Predicting the next vehicle to go past the corner of my road	car bus lorry bicycle van other
Tossing a coin	heads tails

Another word for experiment is *trial*. This is used in Chapter 6 of this book to describe the binomial situation where there are just two possible outcomes.

Another word you should know is *event*. This often describes several outcomes put together. For example, when rolling a die, an event could be 'the die shows an even number'. This event corresponds to three different outcomes from the trial, the die showing 2, 4 or 6. However, the term *event* is also often used to describe a single outcome.

Estimating probability

Probability is a number which measures likelihood. It may be estimated experimentally or theoretically.

Experimental estimation of probability

In many situations probabilities are estimated on the basis of data collected experimentally, as in the following example.

Of 30 drawing pins tossed in the air, 21 of them were found to have landed with their pins pointing up. From this you would estimate the probability that the next pin tossed in the air will land with its pin pointing up to be $\frac{21}{30}$ or 0.7.

You can describe this in more formal notation.

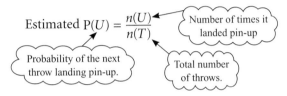

$$\text{Estimated } P(U) = \frac{n(U)}{n(T)}$$

Number of times it landed pin-up

Probability of the next throw landing pin-up.

Total number of throws.

Theoretical estimation of probability

There are, however, some situations where you do not need to collect data to make an estimate of probability.

For example, when tossing a coin, common sense tells you that there are only two realistic outcomes and, given the symmetry of the coin, you would expect them to be equally likely. So the probability, $P(H)$, that the next coin will produce the outcome heads can be written as follows:

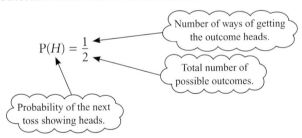

$$P(H) = \frac{1}{2}$$

Number of ways of getting the outcome heads.

Total number of possible outcomes.

Probability of the next toss showing heads.

EXAMPLE 3.1

Using the notation described above, write down the probability that the correct answer for the next four-option multiple choice question will be answer A. What assumptions are you making?

SOLUTION

Assuming that the test-setter has used each letter equally often, the probability, $P(A)$, that the next question will have answer A can be written as follows:

$$P(A) = \frac{1}{4}$$

Answer A.

Answers A, B, C and D.

Notice that we have assumed that the four options are equally likely. Equiprobability is an important assumption underlying most work on probability.

Expressed formally, the probability, P(A), of event A occurring is:

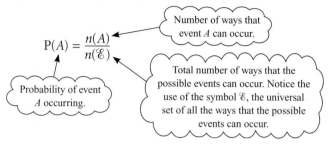

Probabilities of 0 and 1

The two extremes of probability are *certainty* at one end of the scale and impossibility at the other. Here are examples of certain and impossible events.

Experiment	Certain event	Impossible event
Rolling a single die	The result is in the range 1 to 6 inclusive	The result is a 7
Tossing a coin	Getting either heads or tails	Getting neither heads nor tails

Certainty

As you can see from the table above, for events that are certain, the number of ways that the event can occur, $n(A)$ in the formula, is equal to the total number of possible events, $n(\mathcal{E})$.

$$\frac{n(A)}{n(\mathcal{E})} = 1$$

So the probability of an event which is certain is one.

Impossibility

For impossible events, the number of ways that the event can occur, $n(A)$, is zero.

$$\frac{n(A)}{n(\mathcal{E})} = \frac{0}{n(\mathcal{E})} = 0$$

So the probability of an event which is impossible is zero.

Typical values of probabilities might be something like 0.3 or 0.9. If you arrive at probability values of, say, −0.4 or 1.7, you will know that you have made a mistake since these are meaningless.

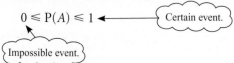

The complement of an event

The complement of an event A, denoted by A', is the event *not-A*, that is the event 'A does not happen'.

EXAMPLE 3.2

It was found that, out of a box of 50 matches, 45 lit but the others did not. What was the probability that a randomly selected match would not have lit?

SOLUTION

The probability that a randomly selected match lit was

$$P(A) = \frac{45}{50} = 0.9.$$

The probability that a randomly selected match did not light was

$$P(A') = \frac{50 - 45}{50} = \frac{5}{50} = 0.1.$$

From this example you can see that

$$P(A') = 1 - P(A)$$

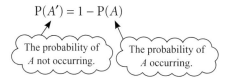

The probability of A not occurring.   The probability of A occurring.

This is illustrated in figure 3.1.

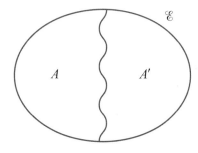

Figure 3.1 Venn diagram showing events A and *not-A* (A')

Expectation

Health services braced for flu epidemic

Local health services are poised for their biggest challenge in years. The virulent strain of flu, named Trengganu B from its origins in Malaysia, currently sweeping across the world is expected to hit any day.

With a chance of one in three of any individual contracting the disease, and 120 000 people within the Health Area, surgeries and hospitals are expecting to be swamped with patients.

Local doctor Aloke Ghosh says 'Immunisation seems to be ineffective against this strain'.

How many people can the health services expect to contract flu? The answer is easily seen to be $120\,000 \times \frac{1}{3} = 40\,000$. This is called the *expectation* or *expected frequency* and is given in this case by np, where n is the population size and p the probability.

Expectation is a technical term and need not be a whole number. Thus the expectation of the number of heads when a coin is tossed 5 times is $5 \times \frac{1}{2} = 2.5$. You would be wrong to go on to say 'That means either 2 or 3' or to qualify your answer as 'about $2\frac{1}{2}$'. The expectation is 2.5.

The idea of expectation of a discrete random variable is explored more thoroughly in Chapter 4. Applications of the binomial distribution are covered in Chapter 6.

The probability of either one event or another

So far we have looked at just one event at a time. However, it is often useful to bracket two or more of the events together and calculate their combined probability.

EXAMPLE 3.3

The table below is based on the data at the beginning of this chapter and shows the probability of the next book requested falling into each of the three categories listed, assuming that each book is equally likely to be requested.

Category of book	Typical numbers	Probability
On the shelves (S)	20 000	0.25
Out on loan (L)	44 000	0.55
Unauthorised loan (U)	16 000	0.20
Total ($S + L + U$)	80 000	1.00

What is the probability that a randomly requested book is *either* out on loan *or* on unauthorised loan (i.e. that it is not available)?

SOLUTION

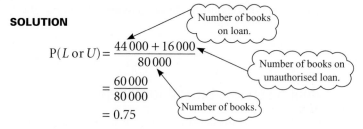

$$P(L \text{ or } U) = \frac{44\,000 + 16\,000}{80\,000}$$

Number of books on loan.

Number of books on unauthorised loan.

$$= \frac{60\,000}{80\,000}$$

Number of books.

$$= 0.75$$

This can be written in more formal notation as

$$P(L \cup U) = \frac{n(L \cup U)}{n(\mathcal{E})}$$

$$= \frac{n(L)}{n(\mathcal{E})} + \frac{n(U)}{n(\mathcal{E})}$$

$$P(L \cup U) = P(L) + P(U)$$

Notice the use of the *union* symbol, ∪, to mean *or*. This is illustrated in figure 3.2.

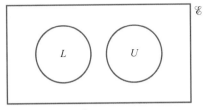

Key: *L* = out on loan
       U = out on unauthorised loan

Figure 3.2 Venn diagram showing events *L* and *U*. It is not possible for both to occur.

In this example you could add the probabilities of the two events to get the combined probability of *either one or the other* event occurring. However, you have to be very careful adding probabilities as you will see in the next example.

EXAMPLE 3.4

Below are further details of the categories of books in the library.

Category of book	Number of books
On the shelves	20 000
Out on loan	44 000
Adult fiction	22 000
Adult non-fiction	40 000
Junior	18 000
Unauthorised loan	16 000
Total stock	80 000

Asaph is trying to find the probability that the next book requested will be either out on loan or a book of adult non-fiction.

He writes

Assuming all the books in the library are equally likely to be requested,

$$P\text{(on loan)} + P\text{(adult non-fiction)} = \frac{44\,000}{80\,000} + \frac{40\,000}{80\,000}$$
$$= 0.55 + 0.5$$
$$= 1.05$$

Explain why Asaph's answer must be wrong. What is his mistake?

SOLUTION

This answer is clearly wrong as you cannot have a probability greater than 1.

The way this calculation was carried out involved some double counting. Some of the books classed as adult non-fiction were counted twice because they were also in the on-loan category, as you can see from figure 3.3.

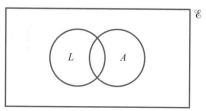

Key: L = out on loan
A = adult non-fiction

Figure 3.3 Venn diagram showing events L and A. It is possible for both to occur.

If you add all six of the book categories together, you find that they add up to 160 000, which represents twice the total number of books owned by the library.

A more useful representation of the data in the previous example is given in the two-way table below.

	Adult fiction	Adult non-fiction	Junior	Total
On the shelves	4 000	12 000	4 000	20 000
Out on loan	14 000	20 000	10 000	44 000
Unauthorised loan	4 000	8 000	4 000	16 000
Totals	22 000	40 000	18 000	80 000

If you simply add 44 000 and 40 000, you *double count* the 20 000 books which fall into both categories. So you need to subtract the 20 000 to ensure that it is counted only once. Thus:

Number either out on loan or adult non-fiction
$$= 44\,000 + 40\,000 - 20\,000$$
$$= 64\,000 \text{ books.}$$

So, the required probability $= \dfrac{64\,000}{80\,000} = 0.8$.

Mutually exclusive events

The problem of double counting does not occur when adding two rows in the table. Two rows cannot overlap, or *intersect*, which means that those categories are *mutually exclusive* (i.e. the one excludes the other). The same is true for two columns within the table.

Where two events, A and B, are mutually exclusive, the probability that either A or B occurs is equal to the sum of the separate probabilities of A and B occurring.

Where two events, A and B, are *not* mutually exclusive, the probability that either A or B occurs is equal to the sum of the separate probabilities of A and B occurring minus the probability of A and B occurring together.

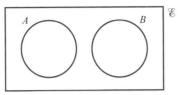

Figure 3.4 (a) Mutually exclusive events   **(b)** Not mutually exclusive events

$P(A \text{ or } B) = P(A) + P(B)$ $P(A \text{ or } B) = P(A) + P(B) - P(A \text{ and } B)$

$P(A \cup B) = P(A) + P(B)$ $P(A \cup B) = P(A) + P(B) - P(A \cap B)$

> Notice the use of the intersection sign, $\cap$, to mean *both ... and ...*

EXAMPLE 3.5

A fair die is thrown. What is the probability that it shows each of these?

(i) Event A: an even number

(ii) Event B: a number greater than 4

(iii) Either A or B (or both): a number which is either even or greater than 4

SOLUTION

(i) Event A:

Three out of the six numbers on a die are even, namely 2, 4 and 6.

So $P(A) = \frac{3}{6} = \frac{1}{2}$.

(ii) Event B:

Two out of the six numbers on a die are greater than 4, namely 5 and 6.

So $P(B) = \frac{2}{6} = \frac{1}{3}$.

(iii) Either A or B (or both):

Four of the numbers on a die are either even or greater than 4, namely 2, 4, 5 and 6.

So $P(A \cup B) = \frac{4}{6} = \frac{2}{3}$.

This could also be found using

$$P(A \cup B) = P(A) + P(B) - P(A \cap B)$$

$$P(A \cup B) = \frac{3}{6} + \frac{2}{6} - \frac{1}{6}$$

$$= \frac{4}{6} = \frac{2}{3}$$

> This is the number 6 which is both even and greater than 4.

1 Three separate electrical components, switch, bulb and contact point, are used together in the construction of a pocket torch. Of 534 defective torches, examined to identify the cause of failure, 468 are found to have a defective bulb. For a given failure of the torch, what is the probability that either the switch or the contact point is responsible for the failure? State clearly any assumptions that you have made in making this calculation.

2 If a fair die is thrown, what is the probability that it shows

(i)   4

(ii) 4 or more

(iii) less than 4

(iv) an even number?

3 A bag containing Scrabble letters has the following letter distribution.

A	B	C	D	E	F	G	H	I	J	K	L	M
9	2	2	4	12	2	3	2	9	1	1	4	2

N	O	P	Q	R	S	T	U	V	W	X	Y	Z
6	8	2	1	6	4	6	4	2	2	1	2	1

The first letter is chosen at random from the bag; find the probability that it is

(i)   an E

(ii) in the first half of the alphabet

(iii) in the second half of the alphabet

(iv) a vowel

(v)   a consonant

(vi) the only one of its kind.

4 **A sporting chance**

(i)   Two players, A and B, play tennis. On the basis of their previous results, the probability of A winning, $P(A)$, is calculated to be 0.65. What is $P(B)$, the probability of B winning?

(ii) Two hockey teams, A and B, play a game. On the basis of their previous results, the probability of team A winning, $P(A)$, is calculated to be 0.65. Why is it not possible to calculate directly $P(B)$, the probability of team B winning, without further information?

(iii) In a tennis tournament, player A, the favourite, is estimated to have a 0.3 chance of winning the competition. Player B is estimated to have a 0.15 chance. Find the probability that either A or B will win the competition.

(iv) In the Six Nations Rugby Championship, France and England are each given a 25% chance of winning or sharing the championship cup. It is also estimated that there is a 5% chance that they will share the cup. Estimate the probability that either England or France will win or share the cup.

5 The diagram shows even (*E*), odd (*O*) and square (*S*) numbers.

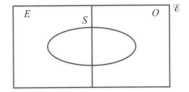

(i) Copy the diagram and place the numbers 1 to 20 on it.

The numbers 1 to 20 are written on separate cards.

(ii) A card is chosen at random. Find the probability that the number showing is:

(a) even, *E*

(b) square, *S*

(c) odd, *O*

(d) both even and square, $E \cap S$

(e) either even or square, $E \cup S$

(f) both even and odd, $E \cap O$

(g) either even or odd, $E \cup O$.

Write down equations connecting the probabilities of the following events.

(h) $E, S, E \cap S, E \cup S$

(i) $E, O, E \cap O, E \cup O$

Independent and dependent events

My lucky day!

Won $100 when the number on my newspaper came up in the daily draw and $50 in the weekly draw too. A chance in a million!

Veronica

This story describes two pieces of good fortune on the same day. Veronica said the probability was about $\frac{1}{1000000}$. What was it really?

The two events resulted from two different experiments, the daily draw and the weekly draw. Consequently this situation is different from those you met in the previous section. There you were looking at two events from a single experiment (like the number coming up when a die is thrown being even or being greater than 4).

The total number of entrants in the daily draw was 1245 and in the weekly draw 324. The draws were conducted fairly, that is each number had an equal chance of being selected. The following table sets out the two experiments and their corresponding events with associated probabilities.

Experiment	Events (and estimated probabilities)
Daily draw	Winning: $\frac{1}{1245}$
	Not winning: $\frac{1244}{1245}$
Weekly draw	Winning: $\frac{1}{324}$
	Not winning: $\frac{323}{324}$

The two events 'win daily draw' and 'win weekly draw' are *independent events*. Two events are said to be independent when the outcome of the first event does not affect the outcome of the second event. The fact that Veronica has won the daily draw does not alter her chances of winning the weekly draw.

● For two independent events, A and B, $P(A \cap B) = P(A) \times P(B)$.

In situations like this the possible outcomes resulting from the different experiments are often shown on a *tree diagram*.

EXAMPLE 3.6

Find, in advance of the results of the two draws, the probability that
(i) Veronica would win both draws
(ii) Veronica would fail to win either draw
(iii) Veronica would win one of the two draws.

SOLUTION

The possible results are shown on the tree diagram in figure 3.5.

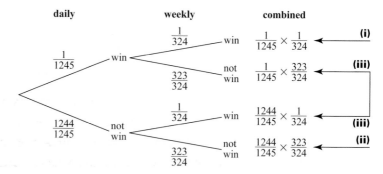

Figure 3.5

(i) The probability that Veronica wins both

$$= \frac{1}{1245} \times \frac{1}{324} = \frac{1}{403380}$$

This is not quite Veronica's 'one in a million' but it is not very far off it.

(ii) The probability that Veronica wins neither

$$= \frac{1244}{1245} \times \frac{323}{324} = \frac{401812}{403380}$$

This of course is much the most likely outcome.

(iii) The probability that Veronica wins one but not the other

$$= \underbrace{\frac{1}{1245} \times \frac{323}{324}}_{} + \underbrace{\frac{1244}{1245} \times \frac{1}{324}}_{} = \frac{1567}{403\,380}$$

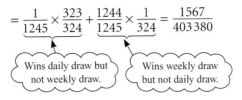

Wins daily draw but not weekly draw.

Wins weekly draw but not daily draw.

Look again at the structure of the tree diagram in figure 3.5.

There are two experiments, the daily draw and the weekly draw. These are considered as *First, then* experiments, and set out *First* on the left and *Then* on the right. Once you understand this, the rest of the layout falls into place, with the different outcomes or events appearing as branches. In this example there are two branches at each stage; sometimes there may be three or more. Notice that for a given situation the component probabilities sum to 1, as before.

$$\frac{1}{403\,380} + \frac{323}{403\,380} + \frac{1244}{403\,380} + \frac{401\,812}{403\,380} = \frac{403\,380}{403\,380} = 1$$

EXAMPLE 3.7

Some friends buy a six-pack of potato crisps. Two of the bags are snake flavoured (S), the rest are frog flavoured (F). They decide to allocate the bags by lucky dip.

Find the probability that

(i) the first two bags chosen are the same as each other

(ii) the first two bags chosen are different from each other.

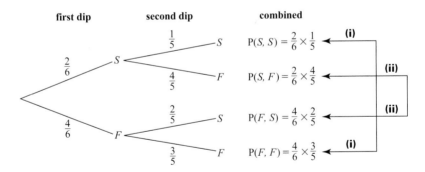

Figure 3.6

SOLUTION

Note: P(F, S) means the probability of drawing a frog bag (F) on the first dip and a snake bag (S) on the second.

(i) The probability that the first two bags chosen are the same as each other is

$$P(S, S) + P(F, F) = \frac{2}{6} \times \frac{1}{5} + \frac{4}{6} \times \frac{3}{5}$$

$$= \frac{1}{15} + \frac{6}{15}$$

$$= \frac{7}{15}$$

(ii) The probability that the first two bags chosen are different from each other is

$$P(S, F) + P(F, S) = \frac{2}{6} \times \frac{4}{5} + \frac{4}{6} \times \frac{2}{5}$$
$$= \frac{4}{15} + \frac{4}{15}$$
$$= \frac{8}{15}$$

Note

The answer to part **(ii)** above hinged on the fact that two orderings (*S* then *F*, and *F* then *S*) are possible for the same combined event (that the two bags selected include one snake and one frog bag).

The probabilities changed between the first dip and the second dip. This is because the outcome of the second dip is *dependent* on the outcome of the first one (with fewer bags remaining to choose from).

By contrast, the outcomes of the two experiments involved in tossing a coin twice are *independent*, and so the probability of getting a head on the second toss remains unchanged at 0.5, whatever the outcome of the first toss.

Although you may find it helpful to think about combined events in terms of how they would be represented on a tree diagram, you may not always actually draw them in this way. If there are several experiments and perhaps more than two possible outcomes from each, drawing a tree diagram can be very time-consuming.

EXAMPLE 3.8

www.freeourdavid.com

Is this justice?

In 2012, David Starr was sentenced to 12 years' imprisonment for armed robbery solely on the basis of an identification parade. He was one of 12 people in the parade and was picked out by one witness but not by three others.

Many people who knew David well believe he was incapable of such a crime. Please add your voice to the clamour for a review of his case by clicking on the 'Free David' button.

Free David

How conclusive is this sort of evidence, or, to put it another way, how likely is it that a mistake has been made?

Investigate the likelihood that David Starr really did commit the robbery.

SOLUTION

In this situation you need to assess the probability of an innocent individual being picked out by chance alone. Assume that David Starr was innocent and the witnesses were selecting in a purely random way (that is, with a probability of $\frac{1}{12}$ of selecting each person and a probability of $\frac{11}{12}$ of not selecting each person). If each of the witnesses selected just one of the twelve people in the identity parade in this random manner, how likely is it that David Starr would be picked out by at least one witness?

$$P(\text{at least one selection}) = 1 - P(\text{no selections})$$
$$= 1 - \frac{11}{12} \times \frac{11}{12} \times \frac{11}{12} \times \frac{11}{12}$$
$$= 1 - 0.706 = 0.294 \text{ (i.e. roughly 30%)}.$$

In other words, there is about a 30% chance of an innocent person being chosen in this way by at least one of the witnesses.

The website concluded:

> Is 30% really the sort of figure we have in mind when judges use the phrase 'beyond reasonable doubt'? Because if it is, many innocent people will be condemned to a life behind bars.

This raises an important statistical idea, which you will meet again if you study *Statistics 2* about how we make judgements and decisions.

Judgements are usually made under conditions of uncertainty and involve us in having to weigh up the plausibility of one explanation against that of another. Statistical judgements are usually made on such a basis. We choose one explanation if we judge the alternative explanation to be sufficiently unlikely, that is if the probability of its being true is sufficiently small. Exactly how small this probability has to be will depend on the individual circumstances and is called the *significance level*.

EXERCISE 3B

1 The probability of a pregnant woman giving birth to a girl is about 0.49.

Draw a tree diagram showing the possible outcomes if she has two babies (not twins).

From the tree diagram, calculate the following probabilities:

(i)   that the babies are both girls

(ii) that the babies are the same sex

(iii) that the second baby is of different sex to the first.

2 In a certain district of a large city, the probability of a household suffering a break-in in a particular year is 0.07 and the probability of its car being stolen is 0.12.

Assuming these two trials are independent of each other, draw a tree diagram showing the possible outcomes for a particular year.

Calculate, for a randomly selected household with one car, the following probabilities:

(i)   that the household is a victim of both crimes during that year

(ii) that the household suffers *only one* of these misfortunes during that year

(iii) that the household suffers *at least one* of these misfortunes during that year.

3 There are 12 people at an identification parade. Three witnesses are called to identify the accused person.

Assuming they make their choice purely by random selection, draw a tree diagram showing the possible events.

(i) From the tree diagram, calculate the following probabilities:

(a) that all three witnesses select the accused person

(b) that none of the witnesses selects the accused person

(c) that at least two of the witnesses select the accused person.

(ii) Suppose now that by changing the composition of people in the identification parade, the first two witnesses increase their chances of selecting the accused person to 0.25.

Draw a new tree diagram and calculate the following probabilities:

(a) that all three witnesses select the accused person

(b) that none of the witnesses selects the accused person

(c) that at least two of the witnesses select the accused person.

4 Ruth drives her car to work – provided she can get it to start! When she remembers to put the car in the garage the night before, it starts next morning with a probability of 0.95. When she forgets to put the car away, it starts next morning with a probability of 0.75. She remembers to garage her car 90% of the time.

What is the probability that Ruth drives her car to work on a randomly chosen day?

5 Around 0.8% of men are red–green colour-blind (the figure is slightly different for women) and roughly 1 in 5 men is left-handed.

Assuming these characteristics are inherited independently, calculate with the aid of a tree diagram the probability that a man chosen at random will

(i) be both colour-blind and left-handed

(ii) be colour-blind and not left-handed

(iii) be colour-blind or left-handed

(iv) be neither colour-blind nor left-handed.

6 Three dice are thrown. Find the probability of obtaining

(i) at least two 6s

(ii) no 6s

(iii) different scores on all the dice.

7 Explain the flaw in this argument and rewrite it as a valid statement.

The probability of throwing a 6 on a fair die $= \frac{1}{6}$. *Therefore the probability of throwing at least one 6 in six throws of the die is* $\frac{1}{6} + \frac{1}{6} + \frac{1}{6} + \frac{1}{6} + \frac{1}{6} + \frac{1}{6} = 1$ *so it is a certainty.*

8 Two dice are thrown. The scores on the dice are added.

(i) Copy and complete this table showing all the possible outcomes.

		First die					
		1	2	3	4	5	6
Second die	1						
	2						
	3						
	4						10
	5						11
	6	7	8	9	10	11	12

(ii) What is the probability of a score of 4?

(iii) What is the most likely outcome?

(iv) Criticise this argument:

There are 11 possible outcomes, 2, 3, 4, up to 12. Therefore each of them has a probability of $\frac{1}{11}$.

9 The probability of someone catching flu in a particular winter when they have been given the flu vaccine is 0.1. Without the vaccine, the probability of catching flu is 0.4. If 30% of the population has been given the vaccine, what is the probability that a person chosen at random from the population will catch flu over that winter?

10 Kevin hosts the TV programme *Thank Your Lucky Stars*. During the show he picks members of the large studio audience at random and asks them what star sign they were born under.

(There are 12 star signs in all and you may assume that the probabilities that a randomly chosen person will be born under each star sign are equal.)

(i) The first person Kevin picks says that he was born under the star sign Aries. What is the probability that the next person he picks was *not* born under Aries?

(ii) Show that the probability that the first three people picked were all born under different star signs is approximately 0.764.

(iii) Calculate the probability that the first five people picked were all born under different star signs.

(iv) What is the probability that at least two of the first five people picked were born under the same star sign?

[MEI, *part*]

11 One plastic toy aeroplane is given away free in each packet of cornflakes. Equal numbers of red, yellow, green and blue aeroplanes are put into the packets.

Faye, a customer, has collected three colours of aeroplane but still wants a yellow one.

Find the probability that

(i) she gets a yellow aeroplane by opening just one packet

(ii) she fails to get a yellow aeroplane in opening four packets

(iii) she needs to open *exactly* five packets to get the yellow aeroplane she wants.

Henry, a quality controller employed by the cornflakes manufacturer, opens a number of packets chosen at random to check on the distribution of colours. Find the probability that

(iv) the first two packets he opens both have red aeroplanes in

(v) the first two packets he opens have aeroplanes of different colours in

(vi) he gets all four different colours by opening just four packets.

[MEI]

Conditional probability

 Sad news

Myra My best friend had a heart attack while out shopping. Sachit was rushed to hospital but died on the way. He was only 47 – too young ...

What is the probability that somebody chosen at random will die of a heart attack in the next 12 months?

One approach would be to say that, since there are about 300 000 deaths per year from heart and circulatory diseases (H & CD) among the 57 000 000 population of the country where Sachit lived,

$$\text{probability} = \frac{\text{number of deaths from H \& CD per year}}{\text{total population}}$$

$$= \frac{300\,000}{57\,000\,000} = 0.0053.$$

However, if you think about it, you will probably realise that this is rather a meaningless figure. For a start, young people are much less at risk than those in or beyond middle age.

So you might wish to give two answers:

$$P_1 = \frac{\text{deaths from H \& CD among over-40s}}{\text{population of over-40s}}$$

$$P_2 = \frac{\text{deaths from H \& CD among under-40s}}{\text{population of under-40s}}$$

Typically only 1500 of the deaths would be among the under-40s, leaving (on the basis of these figures) 298 500 among the over-40s. About 25 000 000 people in the country are over 40, and 32 000 000 under 40 (40 years and 1 day counts as over 40). This gives

$$P_1 = \frac{\text{deaths from H \& CD among over-40s}}{\text{population of over-40s}} = \frac{298\,500}{25\,000\,000}$$

$$= 0.0119$$

and $\quad P_2 = \dfrac{\text{deaths from H \& CD among under-40s}}{\text{population of under-40s}} = \dfrac{1500}{32\,000\,000}$

$$= 0.000\,047.$$

So somebody in the older group is over 200 times more likely to die of a heart attack than somebody in the younger group. Putting them both together as an average figure resulted in a figure that was representative of neither group.

But why stop there? You could, if you had the figures, divide the population up into 10-year, 5-year, or even 1-year intervals. That would certainly improve the accuracy; but there are also more factors that you might wish to take into account, such as the following.

- Is the person overweight?

- Does the person smoke?

- Does the person take regular exercise?

The more conditions you build in, the more accurate will be the estimate of the probability.

You can see how the conditions are brought in by looking at P_1:

$$P_1 = \frac{\text{deaths from H \& CD among over-40s}}{\text{population of over-40s}} = \frac{298\,500}{25\,000\,000}$$

$$= 0.0119$$

You would write this in symbols as follows:

Event G: Somebody selected at random is over 40.
Event H: Somebody selected at random dies from H & CD.

The probability of someone dying from H & CD given that he or she is over 40 is given by the conditional probability $P(H \mid G)$.

$$P(H|G) = \frac{n(H \cap G)}{n(G)}$$

$$= \frac{n(H \cap G)/n(\mathscr{E})}{n(G)/n(\mathscr{E})}$$

$$= \frac{P(H \cap G)}{P(G)}.$$

P(H|G) means the probability of event H occurring *given that* event G has occurred.

This result may be written in general form for all cases of conditional probability for events A and B.

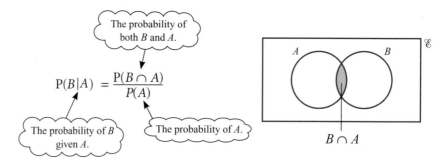

The probability of both B and A.

$$P(B|A) = \frac{P(B \cap A)}{P(A)}$$

The probability of B given A.

The probability of A.

$B \cap A$

Figure 3.7

Conditional probability is used when your estimate of the probability of an event is altered by your knowledge of whether some other event has occurred. In this case the estimate of the probability of somebody dying from heart and circulatory diseases, P(H), is altered by a knowledge of whether the person is over 40 or not.

Thus conditional probability addresses the question of whether one event is dependent on another one. If the probability of event B is not affected by the occurrence of event A, we say that B is *independent* of A. If, on the other hand, the probability of event B is affected by the occurrence (or not) of event A, we say that B is *dependent* on A.

- If A and B are independent, then P(B | A) = P(B | A') and this is just P(B).

- If A and B are dependent, then P(B | A) ≠ P(B | A').

As you have already seen, the probability of a combined event is the product of the separate probabilities of each event, provided the question of dependence between the two events is properly dealt with. Specifically:

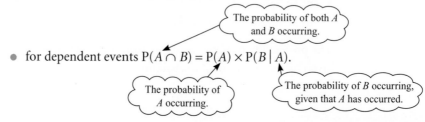

The probability of both A and B occurring.

- for dependent events P(A ∩ B) = P(A) × P(B | A).

The probability of A occurring.

The probability of B occurring, given that A has occurred.

When A and B are independent events, then, because $P(B \mid A) = P(B)$, this can be written as

- for independent events $P(A \cap B) = P(A) \times P(B)$.

EXAMPLE 3.9

A company is worried about the high turnover of its employees and decides to investigate whether they are more likely to stay if they are given training. On 1 January one year the company employed 256 people (excluding those about to retire). During that year a record was kept of who received training as well as who left the company. The results are summarised in this table.

	Still employed	Left company	Total
Given training	109	43	152
Not given training	60	44	104
Totals	169	87	256

(i) Find the probability that a randomly selected employee
  (a) received training
  (b) received training and did not leave the company.
(ii) Are the events T and S independent?
(iii) Find the probability that a randomly selected employee
  (a) did not leave the company, given that the person had received training
  (b) did not leave the company, given that the person had not received training.

SOLUTION

Using the notation T: The employee received training
S: The employee stayed in the company

(i) (a) $P(T) = \dfrac{n(T)}{n(\mathscr{E})} = \dfrac{152}{256} = 0.59$

(b) $P(T \cap S) = \dfrac{n(T \cap S)}{n(\mathscr{E})} = \dfrac{109}{256} = 0.43$

(ii) If T and S are independent events then $P(T \cap S) = P(T) \times P(S)$.

$P(S) = \dfrac{n(S)}{n(\mathscr{E})} = \dfrac{169}{256} = 0.66$

$P(T) \times P(S) = \dfrac{152}{256} \times \dfrac{169}{256} = 0.392$

As $P(T \cap S) \neq P(T) \times P(S)$, the events T and S are not independent.

(iii) (a) $P(S|T) = \dfrac{P(S \cap T)}{P(T)} = \dfrac{\frac{109}{256}}{\frac{152}{256}} = \dfrac{109}{152} = 0.72$

(b) $P(S|T') = \dfrac{P(S \cap T')}{P(T')} = \dfrac{\frac{60}{256}}{\frac{104}{256}} = \dfrac{60}{104} = 0.58$

Since $P(S|T)$ is not the same as $P(S|T')$, the event S is not independent of the event T. Each of S and T is dependent on the other, a conclusion which matches common sense. It is almost certainly true that training increases employees' job satisfaction and so makes them more likely to stay, but it is also probably true that the company is more likely to go to the expense of training the employees who seem less inclined to move on to other jobs.

? How would you show that the event T is not independent of the event S?

In some situations you may find it helps to represent a problem such as this as a Venn diagram.

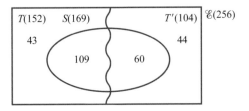

Figure 3.8

? What do the various numbers and letters represent?
Where is the region S'?
How are the numbers on the diagram related to the answers to parts (i) to (v)?

In other situations it may be helpful to think of conditional probabilities in terms of tree diagrams. Conditional probabilities are needed when events are *dependent,* that is when the outcome of one trial affects the outcomes from a subsequent trial, so, for dependent events, the probabilities of all but the first layer of a tree diagram will be conditional.

EXAMPLE 3.10

Rebecca is buying two goldfish from a pet shop. The shop's tank contains seven male fish and eight female fish but they all look the same.

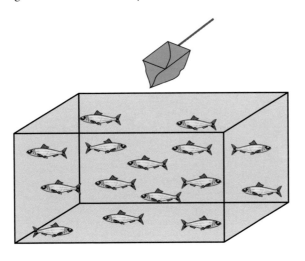

Figure 3.9

Find the probability that Rebecca's fish are

(i) both the same sex
(ii) both female
(iii) both female given that they are the same sex.

SOLUTION

The situation is shown on this tree diagram.

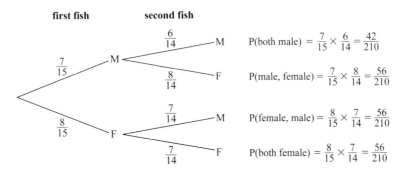

Figure 3.10

(i) P(both the same sex) = P(both male) + P(both female)

$$= \frac{42}{210} + \frac{56}{210} = \frac{98}{210} = \frac{7}{15}$$

(ii) P(both female) $= \frac{56}{210} = \frac{4}{15}$

(iii) P(both female | both the same sex)

= P(both female and the same sex) ÷ P(both the same sex) $= \dfrac{\frac{4}{15}}{\frac{7}{15}} = \frac{4}{7}$

This is the same as
P(both female).

The ideas in the last example can be expressed more generally for any two dependent events, A and B. The tree diagram would be as shown in figure 3.11.

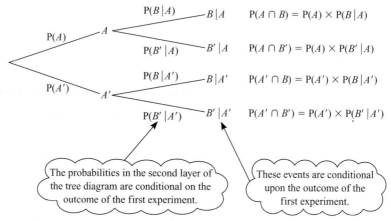

Figure 3.11

The tree diagram shows you that

- $P(B) = P(A \cap B) + P(A' \cap B)$
  $= P(A) \times P(B \mid A) + P(A') \times P(B \mid A')$

- $P(A \cap B) = P(A) \times P(B \mid A)$
  $\Rightarrow \quad P(B \mid A) = \dfrac{P(A \cap B)}{P(A)}$

❓ How were these results used in Example 3.10 about the goldfish?

---

1 In a school of 600 students, 360 are girls. There are 320 hockey players, of whom 200 are girls. Among the hockey players there are 28 goalkeepers, 19 of them girls. Find the probability that

(i) a student chosen at random is a girl

(ii) a girl chosen at random plays hockey

(iii) a hockey player chosen at random is a girl

(iv) a student chosen at random is a goalkeeper

(v) a goalkeeper chosen at random is a boy

(vi) a male hockey player chosen at random is a goalkeeper

(vii) a hockey player chosen at random is a male goalkeeper

(viii) two students chosen at random are both goalkeepers

(ix) two students chosen at random are a male goalkeeper and a female goalkeeper

(x) two students chosen at random are one boy and one girl.

2 100 cars are entered for a road-worthiness test which is in two parts, mechanical and electrical. A car passes only if it passes both parts. Half the cars fail the electrical test and 62 pass the mechanical. 15 pass the electrical but fail the mechanical test.

Find the probability that a car chosen at random

(i) passes overall

(ii) fails on one test only

(iii) given that it has failed, failed the mechanical test only.

3 Two dice are thrown. What is the probability that the total is

(i) 7

(ii) a prime number

(iii) 7, given that it is a prime number?

4 A cage holds two litters of rats. One litter comprises three females and four males, and the other comprises two females and six males. A random selection of two rats is made. Find, as fractions, the probabilities that the two rats are

(i) from the same litter

(ii) of the same sex

(iii) from the same litter and of the same sex

(iv) from the same litter given that they are of the same sex.

[MEI]

5 A and B are two events with probabilities given by $P(A) = 0.4$, $P(B) = 0.7$ and $P(A \cap B) = 0.35$.

(i) Find $P(A \mid B)$ and $P(B \mid A)$.

(ii) Show that the events A and B are not independent.

6 Quark hunting is a dangerous occupation. On a quark hunt, there is a probability of $\frac{1}{4}$ that the hunter is killed. The quark is twice as likely to be killed as the hunter. There is a probability of $\frac{1}{3}$ that both survive.

(i) Copy and complete this table of probabilities.

	Hunter dies	Hunter lives	Total
Quark dies			$\frac{1}{2}$
Quark lives		$\frac{1}{3}$	$\frac{1}{2}$
Totals	$\frac{1}{4}$		1

Find the probability that

(ii) both the hunter and the quark die

(iii) the hunter lives and the quark dies

(iv) the hunter lives, given that the quark dies.

7 In a tea shop 70% of customers order tea with milk, 20% tea with lemon and 10% tea with neither. Of those taking tea with milk $\frac{3}{5}$ take sugar, of those taking tea with lemon $\frac{1}{4}$ take sugar, and of those taking tea with neither milk nor lemon $\frac{11}{20}$ take sugar. A customer is chosen at random.

(i) Represent the information given on a tree diagram and use it to find the probability that the customer takes sugar.

(ii) Find the probability that the customer takes milk or sugar or both.

(iii) Find the probability that the customer takes sugar *and* milk. Hence find the probability that the customer takes milk *given that* the customer takes sugar.

[MEI]

8 Every year two teams, the *Ramblers* and the *Strollers*, meet each other for a quiz night. From past results it seems that in years when the *Ramblers* win, the probability of them winning the next year is 0.7 and in years when the *Strollers* win, the probability of them winning the next year is 0.5. It is not possible for the quiz to result in the scores being tied.

The *Ramblers* won the quiz in 2009.

(i) Draw a probability tree diagram for the three years up to 2012.

(ii) Find the probability that the *Strollers* will win in 2012.

(iii) If the *Strollers* win in 2012, what is the probability that it will be their first win for at least three years?

(iv) Assuming that the *Strollers* win in 2012, find the smallest value of *n* such that the probability of the *Ramblers* winning the quiz for *n* consecutive years after 2012 is less than 5%.

[MEI, *adapted*]

9 There are 90 players in a tennis club. Of these, 23 are juniors, the rest are seniors. 34 of the seniors and 10 of the juniors are male. There are 8 juniors who are left-handed, 5 of whom are male. There are 18 left-handed players in total, 4 of whom are female seniors.

(i) Represent this information in a Venn diagram.

(ii) What is the probability that

(a) a male player selected at random is left-handed?

(b) a left-handed player selected at random is a female junior?

(c) a player selected at random is either a junior or a female?

(d) a player selected at random is right-handed?

(e) a right-handed player selected at random is not a junior?

(f) a right-handed female player selected at random is a junior?

10 Data about employment for males and females in a small rural area are shown in the table.

	Unemployed	Employed
Male	206	412
Female	358	305

A person from this area is chosen at random. Let M be the event that the person is male and let E be the event that the person is employed.

(i) Find P(M).

(ii) Find P(M and E).

(iii) Are M and E independent events? Justify your answer.

(iv) Given that the person chosen is unemployed, find the probability that the person is female.

[Cambridge International AS and A Level Mathematics 9709, Paper 6 Q5 June 2005]

11 The probability that Henk goes swimming on any day is 0.2. On a day when he goes swimming, the probability that Henk has burgers for supper is 0.75. On a day when he does not go swimming, the probability that he has burgers for supper is x. This information is shown on the following tree diagram.

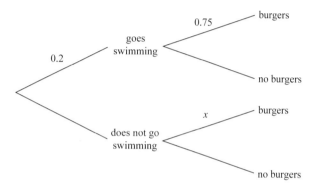

The probability that Henk has burgers for supper on any day is 0.5.

(i) Find x.

(ii) Given that Henk has burgers for supper, find the probability that he went swimming that day.

[Cambridge International AS and A Level Mathematics 9709, Paper 6 Q2 June 2006]

12 Boxes of sweets contain toffees and chocolate. Box A contains 6 toffees and 4 chocolates, box B contains 5 toffees and 3 chocolates, and box C contains 3 toffees and 7 chocolates. One of the boxes is chosen at random and two sweets are taken out, one after the other, and eaten.

(i) Find the probability that they are both toffees.

(ii) Given that they are both toffees, find the probability that they both come from box A.

[Cambridge International AS and A Level Mathematics 9709, Paper 6 Q2 November 2005]

13 There are three sets of traffic lights on Karinne's journey to work. The independent probabilities that Karinne has to stop at the first, second and third set of lights are 0.4, 0.8 and 0.3 respectively.

(i) Draw a tree diagram to show this information.

(ii) Find the probability that Karinne has to stop at each of the first two sets of lights but does not have to stop at the third set.

(iii) Find the probability that Karinne has to stop at exactly two of the three sets of lights.

(iv) Find the probability that Karinne has to stop at the first set of lights, given that she has to stop at exactly two sets of lights.

[Cambridge International AS and A Level Mathematics 9709, Paper 6 Q6 November 2008]

KEY POINTS

1 The probability of an event A is

$$P(A) = \frac{n(A)}{n(\mathcal{E})}$$

where $n(A)$ is the number of ways that A can occur and $n(\mathcal{E})$ is the total number of ways that all possible events can occur, all of which are equally likely.

2 For any two events, A and B, of the same experiment,

$$P(A \cup B) = P(A) + P(B) - P(A \cap B).$$

Where the events are mutually exclusive (i.e. where the events do not overlap) the rule still holds but, since $P(A \cap B)$ is now equal to zero, the equation simplifies to:

$$P(A \cup B) = P(A) + P(B).$$

3 Where an experiment produces two or more mutually exclusive events, the probabilities of the separate events sum to 1.

4 $P(A) + P(A') = 1$

5 For two independent events, A and B,

$$P(A \cap B) = P(A) \times P(B).$$

6 $P(B \mid A)$ means the probability of event B occurring given that event A has already occurred,

$$P(B \mid A) = \frac{P(A \cap B)}{P(A)}.$$

7 The probability that event A and then event B occur, in that order, is $P(A) \times P(B \mid A)$.

8 If event B is independent of event A,

$$P(B \mid A) = P(B \mid A') = P(B).$$

4 Discrete random variables

An approximate answer to the right problem is worth a good deal more than an exact answer to an approximate problem.

John Tukey

Carshare.com

Share life's journey!

Towns and cities around the country are gridlocked with traffic – many of these cars have just one occupant.
To solve this problem, Carshare.com is launching a new scheme for people to car-share on journeys into all major cities. Our comprehensive database can put interested drivers into touch with each other and live updates via your mobile will display the number of car-shares available in any major city. Car-shares are available from centralised locations for maximum convenience.

Carshare.com is running a small trial scheme in a busy town just south of the capital. We will be conducting a survey to measure the success of the trial. Keep up to date with the trial via the latest news on our website.

❓ How would you collect information on the volume of traffic in the town?

A traffic survey, at critical points around the town centre, was conducted at peak travelling times over a period of a working week. The survey involved 1000 cars. The number of people in each car was noted, with the following results.

Number of people per car	1	2	3	4	5	> 5
Frequency	560	240	150	40	10	0

❓ How would you illustrate such a distribution?
What are the main features of this distribution?

The numbers of people per car are necessarily discrete. A discrete frequency distribution is best illustrated by a vertical line chart, as in figure 4.1. This shows you that the distribution has positive skew, with most of the data at the lower end of the distribution.

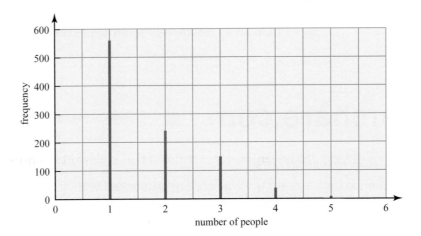

Figure 4.1

The survey involved 1000 cars. This is a large sample and so it is reasonable to use the results to estimate the *probabilities* of the various possible outcomes: 1, 2, 3, 4, 5 people per car. You divide each frequency by 1000 to obtain the *relative frequency*, or probability, of each outcome (number of people).

Outcome (Number of people)	1	2	3	4	5	> 5
Probability (Relative frequency)	0.56	0.24	0.15	0.04	0.01	0

Discrete random variables

You now have a *mathematical model* to describe a particular situation. In statistics you are often looking for models to describe and explain the data you find in the real world. In this chapter you are introduced to some of the techniques for working with models for discrete data. Such models use *discrete random variables*.

The model is *discrete* since the number of passengers can be counted and takes positive integer values only. The number of passengers is a *random variable* since the actual value of the outcome is variable and can only be predicted with a given probability, i.e. the outcomes occur at random.

Discrete random variables may have a *finite* or an *infinite* number of outcomes.

The distribution we have outlined so far is finite – in the survey the maximum number of people observed was five, but the maximum could be, say, eight, depending on the size of car. In this case there would be eight possible outcomes. A well known example of a finite discrete random variable is the *binomial distribution*, which you will study in Chapter 6.

On the other hand, if you considered the number of hits on a website in a given day, there may be no theoretical maximum, in which case the distribution may be considered as infinite. A well known example of an infinite discrete random variable is the *Poisson distribution*, which you will meet if you study *Statistics 2*.

The study of discrete random variables in this chapter will be limited to finite cases.

Notation and conditions for a discrete random variable

A discrete random variable is usually denoted by an upper case letter, such as X, Y or Z. You may think of this as the name of the variable. The particular values that the variable takes are denoted by lower case letters, such as r. Sometimes these are given suffixes r_1, r_2, r_3, ... Thus $P(X = r_1)$ means the probability that the discrete random variable X takes a particular value r_1. The expression $P(X = r)$ is used to express a more general idea, as, for example, in a table heading.

Another, shorter way of writing probabilities is p_1, p_2, p_3, ... If a finite discrete random variable has n distinct outcomes r_1, r_2, ..., r_n, with associated probabilities p_1, p_2, ..., p_n, then the sum of the probabilities must equal 1. Since the various outcomes cover all possibilities, they are *exhaustive*.

Formally we have:

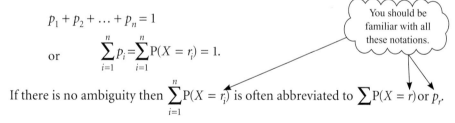

You should be familiar with all these notations.

$$p_1 + p_2 + ... + p_n = 1$$

or $$\sum_{i=1}^{n} p_i = \sum_{i=1}^{n} P(X = r_i) = 1.$$

If there is no ambiguity then $\sum_{i=1}^{n} P(X = r_i)$ is often abbreviated to $\sum P(X = r)$ or p_r.

You will often see an alternative notation used, in which the values that the variable takes are denoted by x rather than r. In this book x is used for a continuous variable (see *Statistics 2*) and r for a discrete variable.

Diagrams of discrete random variables

Just as with frequency distributions for discrete data, the most appropriate diagram to illustrate a discrete random variable is a vertical line chart. Figure 4.2 shows a diagram of the probability distribution of X, the number of people per car. Note that it is identical in shape to the corresponding frequency diagram in figure 4.1. The only real difference is the change of scale on the vertical axis.

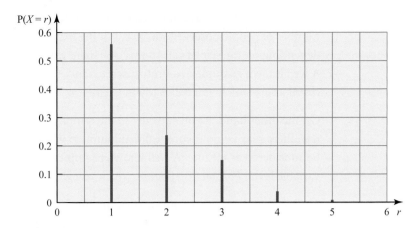

Figure 4.2

EXAMPLE 4.1 Two tetrahedral dice, each with faces labelled 1, 2, 3 and 4, are thrown and the random variable X represents the sum of the numbers shown on the dice.

(i) Find the probability distribution of X.

(ii) Illustrate the distribution and describe the shape of the distribution.

(iii) What is the probability that any throw of the dice results in a value of X which is an odd number?

SOLUTION

(i) The table shows all the possible totals when the two dice are thrown.

		First die			
		1	2	3	4
Second die	1	2	3	4	5
	2	3	4	5	6
	3	4	5	6	7
	4	5	6	7	8

You can use the table to write down the probability distribution for X.

r	2	3	4	5	6	7	8
$P(X=r)$	$\frac{1}{16}$	$\frac{2}{16}$	$\frac{3}{16}$	$\frac{4}{16}$	$\frac{3}{16}$	$\frac{2}{16}$	$\frac{1}{16}$

(ii) The vertical line chart in figure 4.3 illustrates this distribution, which is symmetrical.

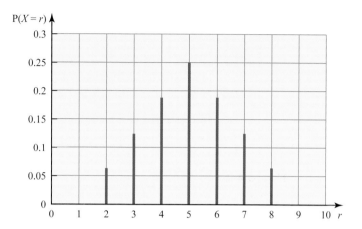

Figure 4.3

(iii) The probability that X is an odd number

$$= P(X = 3) + P(X = 5) + P(X = 7)$$
$$= \frac{2}{16} + \frac{4}{16} + \frac{2}{16}$$
$$= \frac{1}{2}$$

As well as defining a discrete random variable by tabulating the probability distribution, another effective way is to use an algebraic definition of the form $P(X = r) = f(r)$ for given values of r.

The following example illustrates how this may be used.

EXAMPLE 4.2

The probability distribution of a random variable X is given by

$$P(X = r) = kr \qquad \text{for } r = 1, 2, 3, 4$$
$$P(X = r) = 0 \qquad \text{otherwise.}$$

(i) Find the value of the constant k.
(ii) Illustrate the distribution and describe the shape of the distribution.
(iii) Two successive values of X are generated independently of each other. Find the probability that
  (a) both values of X are the same
  (b) the total of the two values of X is greater than 6.

SOLUTION

(i) Tabulating the probability distribution for X gives:

r	1	2	3	4
$P(X=r)$	k	$2k$	$3k$	$4k$

Since X is a random variable, $\sum P(X=r) = 1$

$\Rightarrow \quad k + 2k + 3k + 4k = 1$

$\Rightarrow \quad \qquad\qquad 10k = 1$

$\Rightarrow \quad \qquad\qquad k = 0.1$

Hence $P(X=r) = 0.1r$, for $r = 1, 2, 3, 4$, which gives the following probability distribution.

r	1	2	3	4
$P(X=r)$	0.1	0.2	0.3	0.4

(ii) The vertical line chart in figure 4.4 illustrates this distribution. It has negative skew.

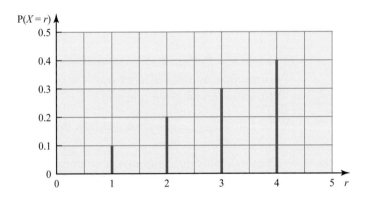

Figure 4.4

(iii) Let X_1 represent the first value generated and X_2 the second value generated.

(a) P(both values of X are the same)

$= P(X_1 = X_2 = 1 \text{ or } X_1 = X_2 = 2 \text{ or } X_1 = X_2 = 3 \text{ or } X_1 = X_2 = 4)$

$= P(X_1 = X_2 = 1) + P(X_1 = X_2 = 2) + P(X_1 = X_2 = 3) + P(X_1 = X_2 = 4)$

$= P(X_1 = 1) \times P(X_2 = 1) + P(X_1 = 2) \times P(X_2 = 2)$

$\quad + P(X_1 = 3) \times P(X_2 = 3) + P(X_1 = 4) \times P(X_2 = 4)$

$= (0.1)^2 + (0.2)^2 + (0.3)^2 + (0.4)^2$

$= 0.01 + 0.04 + 0.09 + 0.16$

$= 0.3$

(b) P(total of the two values is greater than 6)

$$= P(X_1 + X_2 > 6)$$

$$= P(X_1 + X_2 = 7 \text{ or } 8)$$

$$= P(X_1 + X_2 = 7) + P(X_1 + X_2 = 8)$$

$$= P(X_1 = 3) \times P(X_2 = 4) + P(X_1 = 4) \times P(X_2 = 3)$$

$$\quad + P(X_1 = 4) \times P(X_2 = 4)$$

$$= 0.3 \times 0.4 + 0.4 \times 0.3 + 0.4 \times 0.4$$

$$= 0.12 + 0.12 + 0.16$$

$$= 0.4$$

EXERCISE 4A

1 The random variable X is given by the sum of the scores when two ordinary dice are thrown.

(i) Find the probability distribution of X.

(ii) Illustrate the distribution and describe the shape of the distribution.

(iii) Find the values of

(a) $P(X > 8)$

(b) $P(X \text{ is even})$

(c) $P(|X - 7| < 3)$.

2 The random variable Y is given by the absolute difference between the scores when two ordinary dice are thrown.

(i) Find the probability distribution of Y.

(ii) Illustrate the distribution and describe the shape of the distribution.

(iii) Find the values of

(a) $P(Y < 3)$

(b) $P(Y \text{ is odd})$.

3 The probability distribution of a discrete random variable X is given by

$$P(X = r) = \frac{kr}{8} \qquad \text{for } r = 2, 4, 6, 8$$

$$P(X = r) = 0 \qquad \text{otherwise.}$$

(i) Find the value of k and tabulate the probability distribution.

(ii) If two successive values of X are generated independently find the probability that

(a) the two values are equal

(b) the first value is greater than the second value.

4 An irregular die with six faces produces scores, X, for which the probability distribution is given by

$$P(X = r) = \frac{k}{r} \qquad \text{for } r = 1, 2, 3, 4, 5, 6$$
$$P(X = r) = 0 \qquad \text{otherwise.}$$

(i) Find the value of k and illustrate the distribution.

(ii) Show that, when this die is thrown twice, the probability of obtaining two equal scores is very nearly $\frac{1}{4}$.

5 Three fair coins are tossed.

(i) By considering the set of possible outcomes, HHH, HHT, etc., tabulate the probability distribution for X, the number of heads occurring.

(ii) Illustrate the distribution and describe the shape of the distribution.

(iii) Find the probability that there are more heads than tails.

(iv) Without further calculation, state whether your answer to part (iii) would be the same if four fair coins were tossed. Give a reason for your answer.

6 Two fair tetrahedral dice, each with faces labelled 1, 2, 3 and 4, are thrown and the random variable X is the product of the numbers shown on the dice.

(i) Find the probability distribution of X.

(ii) What is the probability that any throw of the dice results in a value of X which is an odd number?

7 An ornithologist carries out a study of the number of eggs laid per pair by a species of rare bird in its annual breeding season. He concludes that it may be considered as a discrete random variable X with probability distribution given by

$$P(X = 0) = 0.2$$
$$P(X = r) = k(4r - r^2) \qquad \text{for } r = 1, 2, 3, 4$$
$$P(X = r) = 0 \qquad \text{otherwise.}$$

(i) Find the value of k and write the probability distribution as a table.

The ornithologist observes that the probability of survival (that is of an egg hatching and of the chick living to the stage of leaving the nest) is dependent on the number of eggs in the nest. He estimates the probabilities to be as follows.

r	Probability of survival
1	0.8
2	0.6
3	0.4

(ii) Find, in the form of a table, the probability distribution of the number of chicks surviving per pair of adults.

8 A sociologist is investigating the changing pattern of the number of children which women have in a country. She denotes the present number by the random variable X which she finds to have the following probability distribution.

r	0	1	2	3	4	5 +
$P(X = r)$	0.09	0.22	a	0.19	0.08	negligible

(i) Find the value of a.

She is keen to find an algebraic expression for the probability distribution and suggests the following model.

$$P(X = r) = k(r+1)(5-r) \quad \text{for } r = 0, 1, 2, 3, 4, 5$$
$$P(X = r) = 0 \quad \text{otherwise.}$$

(ii) Find the value of k for this model.

(iii) Compare the algebraic model with the probabilities she found, illustrating both distributions on one diagram.
Do you think it is a good model?

9 In a game, each player throws three ordinary six-sided dice. The random variable X is the largest number showing on the dice, so for example, for scores of 2, 5 and 4, $X = 5$.

(i) Find the probability that $X = 1$, i.e. $P(X = 1)$.
(ii) Find $P(X \leqslant 2)$ and deduce that $P(X = 2) = \frac{7}{216}$.
(iii) Find $P(X \leqslant r)$ and so deduce $P(X = r)$, for $r = 3, 4, 5, 6$.
(iv) Illustrate and describe the probability distribution of X.

10 A box contains six black pens and four red pens. Three pens are taken at random from the box.

(i) By considering the selection of pens as sampling without replacement, illustrate the various outcomes on a probability tree diagram.
(ii) The random variable X represents the number of red pens obtained. Find the probability distribution of X.

11 A vegetable basket contains 12 peppers, of which 3 are red, 4 are green and 5 are yellow. Three peppers are taken, at random and without replacement, from the basket.

(i) Find the probability that the three peppers are all different colours.
(ii) Show that the probability that exactly 2 of the peppers taken are green is $\frac{12}{55}$.
(iii) The number of **green** peppers taken is denoted by the discrete random variable X. Draw up a probability distribution table for X.

[Cambridge International AS and A Level Mathematics 9709, Paper 6 Q7 June 2007]

Expectation and variance

Carshare.com

Share life's journey!

Latest update …

Car-share trial a massive success. Traffic volume down and number of occupants per car up!

? What statistical evidence do you think Carshare.com's claim is based on?

A second traffic survey, at critical points around the town centre, was conducted at peak travelling times over a period of a working week. This time the survey involved 800 cars. The number of people in each car is shown in the table.

Number of people per car	1	2	3	4	5	> 5
Frequency	280	300	164	52	4	0

? How would you compare the results in the two traffic surveys?

The survey involved 800 cars. This is a fairly large sample and so, once again, it is reasonable to use the results to estimate the probabilities of the various possible outcomes: 1, 2, 3, 4 and 5 people per car, as before.

Outcome (Number of people)	1	2	3	4	5	> 5
Probability (Relative frequency)	0.35	0.375	0.205	0.065	0.005	0

One way to compare the two probability distributions, before and after the car-sharing campaign, is to calculate a measure of central tendency and a measure of spread.

The most useful measure of central tendency is the *mean* or *expectation* of the random variable and the most useful measure of spread is the *variance*. To a large extent the calculation of these statistics mirrors the corresponding statistics for a frequency distribution, $\bar{x}$ and sd^2.

ACTIVITY 4.1 Find the mean and variance of the frequency distribution for the people-per-car survey following the introduction of the car-sharing scheme.

Using relative frequencies generates an alternative approach which gives the *expectation* $E(X) = \mu$ and *variance* $\text{Var}(X) = \sigma^2$ for a discrete random variable.

We define the expectation, $E(X)$ as

$$E(X) = \mu = \sum r\,P(X = r) = \sum r p_r$$

Notice the notation, μ for the distribution's mean and σ for its standard deviation. Also notice the shortened notation for $P(X = r)$.

and Variance, $\text{Var}(X)$ as

$$\sigma^2 = E([X - \mu]^2) = \sum (r - \mu)^2 p_r$$

or $\qquad \sigma^2 = E(X^2) - \mu^2 = \sum r^2 p_r - \left[\sum r p_r\right]^2.$

σ^2 is read as 'sigma squared'.

The second version of the variance is often written as $E(X^2) - [E(X)]^2$, which can be remembered as 'the expectation of the squares minus the square of the expectation'.

These formulae can also be written as:

$$E(X) = \sum xp$$

$$\text{Var}(X) = \sum x^2 p - \left[E(X)\right]^2$$

Look at how expectation and variance are calculated using the probability distribution developed from the second survey of number of people per car. You can use these statistics to compare the distribution of number of people per car before and after the introduction of the car-sharing scheme.

When calculating the expectation and variance of a discrete probability distribution, you will find it helpful to set your work out systematically in a table.

			(a)	(b)
r	p_r	$r p_r$	$r^2 p_r$	$(r - \mu)^2 p_r$
1	0.35	0.35	0.35	0.35
2	0.375	0.75	1.5	0
3	0.205	0.615	1.845	0.205
4	0.065	0.26	1.04	0.26
5	0.005	0.025	0.125	0.045
Totals	$\Sigma p_r = 1$	$\mu = E(X) = 2$	4.86	$\text{Var}(X) = 0.86$

In this case:

$$E(X) = \mu = \sum r\,p_r$$
$$= 1 \times 0.35 + 2 \times 0.375 + 3 \times 0.205 + 4 \times 0.065 + 5 \times 0.005$$
$$= 2$$

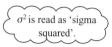

And *either* from **(a)**

This is μ.

$$\text{Var}(X) = \sigma^2 = \sum r^2 p_r - \left[\sum r p_r\right]^2$$

$$= 1^2 \times 0.35 + 2^2 \times 0.375 + 3^2 \times 0.205 + 4^2 \times 0.065 + 5^2 \times 0.005 - 2^2$$

$$= 4.86 - 4$$

$$= 0.86$$

or from **(b)**

$$\text{Var}(X) = \sigma^2 = \sum (r - \mu)^2 p_r$$

$$= (1 - 2)^2 \times 0.35 + (2 - 2)^2 \times 0.375 + (3 - 2)^2 \times 0.205$$

$$+ (4 - 2)^2 \times 0.065 + (5 - 2)^2 \times 0.005$$

$$= 0.86$$

The equivalence of the two methods is proved in Appendix 2 on the CD.

In practice, method **(a)** is to be preferred since the computation is usually easier, especially when the expectation is other than a whole number.

ACTIVITY 4.2

Carry out similar calculations for the expectation and variance of the probability distribution *before* the car-sharing experiment using the data on page 106. Using these two statistics, judge the success or otherwise of the scheme.

EXAMPLE 4.3

The discrete random variable X has the following probability distribution:

r	0	1	2	3
p_r	0.2	0.3	0.4	0.1

Find

(i) $\text{E}(X)$

(ii) $\text{E}(X^2)$

(iii) $\text{Var}(X)$ using   (a) $\text{E}(X^2) - \mu^2$ (b) $\text{E}([X - \mu]^2)$.

SOLUTION

			(a)	(b)
r	p_r	$r p_r$	$r^2 p_r$	$(r - \mu)^2 p_r$
0	0.2	0	0	0.392
1	0.3	0.3	0.3	0.048
2	0.4	0.8	1.6	0.144
3	0.1	0.3	0.9	0.256
Totals	1	1.4	2.8	0.84

(i) $E(X) = \mu = \sum r p_r$

$= 0 \times 0.2 + 1 \times 0.3 + 2 \times 0.4 + 3 \times 0.1 = 1.4$

(ii) $E(X^2) = \sum r^2 p_r$

$= 0 \times 0.2 + 1 \times 0.3 + 4 \times 0.4 + 9 \times 0.1 = 2.8$

(iii) (a) $Var(X) = E(X^2) - \mu^2$

$= 2.8 - 1.4^2 = 0.84$

(b) $Var(X) = E([X - \mu]^2)$

$= \sum (r - \mu)^2 p_r$

$= (0 - 1.4)^2 \times 0.2 + (1 - 1.4)^2 \times 0.3 + (2 - 1.4)^2 \times 0.4 + (3 - 1.4)^2 \times 0.1$

$= 0.392 + 0.048 + 0.144 + 0.256 = 0.84$

Notice that the two methods of calculating the variance in part (iii) give the same result, since one formula is just an algebraic rearrangement of the other.

? Look carefully at both methods for calculating the variance.
Are there any situations where one method might be preferred to the other?

As well as being able to carry out calculations for the expectation and variance you are often required to solve problems in context. The following example illustrates this idea.

EXAMPLE 4.4

Laura buys one litre of mango juice on three days out of every four and none on the fourth day. A litre of mango juice costs 40c. Let X represent her weekly juice bill.

(i) Find the probability distribution of her weekly juice bill.
(ii) Find the mean (μ) and standard deviation (σ) of her weekly juice bill.
(iii) Find (a) $P(X > \mu + \sigma)$ (b) $P(X < \mu - \sigma)$.

SOLUTION

(i) The pattern repeats every four weeks.

M	Tu	W	Th	F	Sa	Su	Number of litres	Juice bill
✓	✓	✓	✗	✓	✓	✓	6	$2.40
✗	✓	✓	✓	✗	✓	✓	5	$2.00
✓	✗	✓	✓	✓	✗	✓	5	$2.00
✓	✓	✗	✓	✓	✓	✗	5	$2.00

Tabulating the probability distribution for X gives the following.

r ($)	2.00	2.40
$P(X = r)$	0.75	0.25

(ii) $E(X) = \mu = \sum r P(X = r)$

$= 2 \times 0.75 + 2.4 \times 0.25$

$= 2.1$

$Var(X) = \sigma^2 = E(X^2) - \mu^2$

$= 4 \times 0.75 + 5.76 \times 0.25 - 2.1^2$

$= 0.03$

$\Rightarrow \quad \sigma = \sqrt{0.03} = 0.17$ (correct to 2 s.f.)

Hence her mean weekly juice bill is $2.10, with a standard deviation of about 17 cents.

(iii) (a) $P(X > \mu + \sigma) = P(X > 2.27) = 0.25$

(b) $P(X < \mu - \sigma) = P(X < 1.93) = 0$

EXERCISE 4B

1 Find by calculation the expectation of the outcome with the following probability distribution.

Outcome	1	2	3	4	5
Probability	0.1	0.2	0.4	0.2	0.1

2 The probability distribution of the discrete random variable X is given by

$P(X = r) = \dfrac{2r - 1}{16}$ for $r = 1, 2, 3, 4$

$P(X = r) = 0$ otherwise.

(i) Find $E(X) = \mu$.

(ii) Find $P(X < \mu)$.

3 (i) A discrete random variable X can take only the values 4 and 5, and has expectation 4.2.

By letting $P(X = 4) = p$ and $P(X = 5) = 1 - p$, solve an equation in p and so find the probability distribution of X.

(ii) A discrete random variable Y can take only the values 50 and 100. Given that $E(Y) = 80$, write out the probability distribution of Y.

4 The random variable X is given by the sum of the scores when two ordinary dice are thrown.

(i) Use the shape of the distribution to find $E(X) = \mu$. Confirm your answer by calculation.

(ii) Calculate $Var(X) = \sigma^2$.

(iii) Find the values of the following.

(a) $P(X < \mu)$ (b) $P(X > \mu + \sigma)$ (c) $P(|X - \mu| < 2\sigma)$

5   The random variable Y is given by the absolute difference between the scores when two ordinary dice are thrown.

   (i)   Find $E(Y)$ and $Var(Y)$.

   (ii) Find the values of the following.

      (a) $P(Y > \mu)$ (b) $P(Y > \mu + 2\sigma)$

6   Three fair coins are tossed. Let X represent the number of tails.

   (i)   Find $E(X)$. Show that this is equivalent to $3 \times \frac{1}{2}$.

   (ii) Find $Var(X)$. Show that this is equivalent to $3 \times \frac{1}{4}$.

   If instead ten fair coins are tossed, let Y represent the number of tails.

   (iii) Write down the values of $E(Y)$ and $Var(Y)$.

7   Birds of a particular species lay either 0, 1, 2 or 3 eggs in their nests with probabilities as shown in the table.

Number of eggs	0	1	2	3
Probability	0.25	0.35	0.30	k

   Find
   (i)   the value of k
   (ii) the expected number of eggs laid in a nest
   (iii) the standard deviation of the number of eggs laid in a nest.

8   An electronic device produces an output of 0, 1 or 3 volts, with probabilities $\frac{1}{2}, \frac{1}{3}$ and $\frac{1}{6}$ respectively. The random variable X denotes the result of adding the outputs for two such devices, which act independently.

   (i)   Show that $P(X = 4) = \frac{1}{9}$.

   (ii) Tabulate all the possible values of X with their corresponding probabilities.

   (iii) Hence calculate $E(X)$ and $Var(X)$, giving your answers as fractions in their lowest terms.

9   Bob earns \$80 per day, Monday to Friday inclusive. He works every alternate Saturday for which he earns 'time and a half' and every fourth Sunday, for which he is paid 'double time'.

   (i)   By considering a typical four-week period, find the probability distribution for his *daily* wage.

   (ii) Calculate the expectation and variance of his *daily* wage.

   (iii) Show that there are two possible patterns Bob could work over a typical four-week period, depending on which Saturdays and Sunday he works. Hence find the expectation and variance of his *weekly* wage under either pattern.

10 A hotel caters for business clients who make short stays. Past records suggest that the probability of a randomly chosen client staying X nights in succession is as follows.

r	1	2	3	4	5	6+
P($X = r$)	0.42	0.33	0.18	0.05	0.02	0

(i) Draw a sketch of this distribution.

(ii) Find the mean and standard deviation of X.

(iii) Find the probability that a randomly chosen client who arrives on Monday evening will still be in the hotel on Wednesday night.

(iv) Find the probability that a client who has already stayed two nights will stay at least one more night.

[MEI]

11 The probability distribution of the discrete random variable X is shown in the table below.

x	-3	-1	0	4
P($X = x$)	a	b	0.15	0.4

Given that E(X) = 0.75, find the values of a and b.

[Cambridge International AS and A Level Mathematics 9709, Paper 61 Q1 June 2010]

12 Every day Eduardo tries to phone his friend. Every time he phones there is a 50% chance that his friend will answer. If his friend answers, Eduardo does not phone again on that day. If his friend does not answer, Eduardo tries again in a few minutes' time. If his friend has not answered after 4 attempts, Eduardo does not try again on that day.

(i) Draw a tree diagram to illustrate this situation.

(ii) Let X be the number of unanswered phone calls made by Eduardo on a day. Copy and complete the table showing the probability distribution of X.

x	0	1	2	3	4
P($X = x$)		$\frac{1}{4}$			

(iii) Calculate the expected number of unanswered phone calls on a day.

[Cambridge International AS and A Level Mathematics 9709, Paper 6 Q6 June 2008]

13 Gohan throws a fair tetrahedral die with faces numbered 1, 2, 3, 4. If she throws an even number then her score is the number thrown. If she throws an odd number then she throws again and her score is the sum of both numbers thrown. Let the random variable X denote Gohan's score.

(i) Show that $P(X = 2) = \frac{5}{16}$.

(ii) The table below shows the probability distribution of X.

x	2	3	4	5	6	7
$P(X = x)$	$\frac{5}{16}$	$\frac{1}{16}$	$\frac{3}{8}$	$\frac{1}{8}$	$\frac{1}{16}$	$\frac{1}{16}$

Calculate $E(X)$ and $Var(X)$.

[Cambridge International AS and A Level Mathematics 9709, Paper 6 Q2 June 2009]

14 The probability distribution of the random variable X is shown in the following table.

x	-2	-1	0	1	2	3
$P(X = x)$	0.08	p	0.12	0.16	q	0.22

The mean of X is 1.05.

(i) Write down two equations involving p and q and hence find the values of p and q.

(ii) Find the variance of X.

[Cambridge International AS and A Level Mathematics 9709, Paper 6 Q2 November 2009]

15 The random variable X takes the values -2, 0 and 4 only. It is given that $P(X = -2) = 2p$, $P(X = 0) = p$ and $P(X = 4) = 3p$.

(i) Find p.

(ii) Find $E(X)$ and $Var(X)$.

[Cambridge International AS and A Level Mathematics 9709, Paper 6 Q2 November 2007]

16 A fair die has one face numbered 1, one face numbered 3, two faces numbered 5 and two faces numbered 6.

(i) Find the probability of obtaining at least 7 odd numbers in 8 throws of the die.

The die is thrown twice. Let X be the sum of the two scores. The following table shows the possible values of X.

		Second throw					
		1	3	5	5	6	6
First throw	1	2	4	6	6	7	7
	3	4	6	8	8	9	9
	5	6	8	10	10	11	11
	5	6	8	10	10	11	11
	6	7	9	11	11	12	12
	6	7	9	11	11	12	12

(ii) Draw up a table showing the probability distribution of X.

(iii) Calculate $E(X)$.

(iv) Find the probability that X is greater than $E(X)$.

[Cambridge International AS and A Level Mathematics 9709, Paper 6 Q7 November 2008]

KEY POINTS

1 For a discrete random variable, X, which can take only the values $r_1, r_2, \ldots, r_n$, with probabilities $p_1, p_2, \ldots, p_n$ respectively:

- $p_1 + p_2 + \ldots + p_n = \sum_{i=1}^{n} p_i = \sum_{i=1}^{n} P(X = r_i) = p_r = 1; \; p_i \geq 0$

2 A discrete probability distribution is best illustrated by a vertical line chart.

- The expectation $= E(X) = \mu = \sum r P(x = r) = \sum r p_r$

- The variance, where σ is the standard deviation, is

$$\text{Var}(X) = \sigma^2 = E(X - \mu)^2 = \sum (r - \mu)^2 p_r$$

or $\text{Var}(X) = \sigma^2 = E(X^2) - [E(X)]^2 = \sum r^2 p_r - \left[\sum r p_r\right]^2$

3 Another common notation is to denote the values the variable may take by x.

- The expectation $= E(X) = \sum x p$

- The variance $= \text{Var}(X) = \sum x^2 p - \left[E(X)\right]^2$

5

Permutations and combinations

An estate had seven houses;
Each house had seven cats;
Each cat ate seven mice;
Each mouse ate seven grains of wheat.
Wheat grains, mice, cats and houses,
How many were there on the estate?

Ancient Egyptian problem

ProudMum _____

My son is a genius!
I gave Oscar five bricks and straightaway he did this!
Is it too early to enrol him with MENSA?

What is the probability that Oscar chose the bricks at random and just happened by chance to get them in the right order?

There are two ways of looking at the situation. You can think of Oscar selecting the five bricks as five events, one after another. Alternatively, you can think of 1, 2, 3, 4, 5 as one outcome out of several possible outcomes and work out the probability that way.

Five events

Look at the diagram.

| 1 | | 2 | | 3 | | 4 | | 5 |

Figure 5.1

If Oscar had actually chosen them at random:

the probability of first selecting **1** is $\frac{1}{5}$

the probability of next selecting **2** is $\frac{1}{4}$ ◄── 1 correct choice from 4 remaining bricks.

the probability of next selecting **3** is $\frac{1}{3}$

the probability of next selecting **4** is $\frac{1}{2}$

then only **5** remains so the probability of selecting it is 1.

So the probability of getting the correct numerical sequence at random is

$$\tfrac{1}{5} \times \tfrac{1}{4} \times \tfrac{1}{3} \times \tfrac{1}{2} \times 1 = \tfrac{1}{120}.$$

Outcomes

How many ways are there of putting five bricks in a line?

To start with there are five bricks to choose from, so there are five ways of choosing brick 1. Then there are four bricks left and so there are four ways of choosing brick 2. And so on.

The total number of ways is

5	×	4	×	3	×	2	×	1	= 120.
Brick 1		Brick 2		Brick 3		Brick 4		Brick 5	

Only one of these is the order 1, 2, 3, 4, 5, so the probability of Oscar selecting it at random is $\frac{1}{120}$. ← Number of possible outcomes.

❓ Do you agree with Oscar's mother that he is a child prodigy, or do you think it was just by chance that he put the bricks down in the right order?

What further information would you want to be convinced that he is a budding genius?

Factorials

In the last example you saw that the number of ways of placing five different bricks in a line is $5 \times 4 \times 3 \times 2 \times 1$. This number is called 5 *factorial* and is written 5!. You will often meet expressions of this form.

In general the number of ways of placing n different objects in a line is $n!$, where $n! = n \times (n-1) \times (n-2) \times ... \times 3 \times 2 \times 1.$

n must be a positive integer.

| EXAMPLE 5.1 | Calculate 7! |

SOLUTION

$7! = 7 \times 6 \times 5 \times 4 \times 3 \times 2 \times 1 = 5040$

Some typical relationships between factorial numbers are illustrated below:

$10! = 10 \times 9!$ or in general $n! = n \times [(n-1)!]$

$10! = 10 \times 9 \times 8 \times 7!$ or in general $n! = n \times (n-1) \times (n-2) \times [(n-3)!]$

These are useful when simplifying expressions involving factorials.

| EXAMPLE 5.2 | Calculate $\dfrac{5!}{3!}$ |

SOLUTION

$\dfrac{5!}{3!} = \dfrac{5 \times 4 \times 3!}{3!} = 5 \times 4 = 20$

| EXAMPLE 5.3 | Calculate $\dfrac{7! \times 5!}{3! \times 4!}$ |

SOLUTION

$\dfrac{7! \times 5!}{3! \times 4!} = \dfrac{7 \times 6 \times 5 \times 4 \times 3! \times 5 \times 4!}{3! \times 4!}$

$= 7 \times 6 \times 5 \times 4 \times 5 = 4200$

| EXAMPLE 5.4 | Write $37 \times 36 \times 35$ in terms of factorials only. |

SOLUTION

$37 \times 36 \times 35 = \dfrac{37 \times 36 \times 35 \times 34!}{34!}$

$= \dfrac{37!}{34!}$

| EXAMPLE 5.5 | (i) Find the number of ways in which all five letters in the word GREAT can be arranged.
(ii) In how many of these arrangements are the letters A and E next to each other? |

SOLUTION

(i) There are five choices for the first letter (G, R, E, A or T). Then there are four choices for the next letter, then three for the third letter and so on. So the number of arrangements of the letters is

$5 \times 4 \times 3 \times 2 \times 1 = 5! = 120$

(ii) The E and the A are to be together, so you can treat them as a single letter.

So there are four choices for the first letter (G, R, EA or T), three choices for the next letter and so on.

So the number of arrangements of these four 'letters' is

$$4 \times 3 \times 2 \times 1 = 4! = 24$$

However | EA | G | R | T |

is different from | AE | G | R | T |

So each of the 24 arrangements can be arranged into two different orders.

The total number of arrangements with the E and A next to each other is

$$2 \times 4! = 48$$

Note

The total number of ways of arranging the letters with the A and the E apart is

$$120 - 48 = 72$$

Sometimes a question will ask you to deal with repeated letters.

EXAMPLE 5.6

Find the number of ways in which all five letters in the word GREET can be arranged.

SOLUTION

There are 5! = 120 arrangements of five letters.

However, GREET has two repeated letters and so some of these arrangements are really the same.

For example, | E | E | G | R | T |

is the same as | E | E | G | R | T |

The two Es can be arranged in 2! = 2 ways, so the total number of arrangements is

$$\frac{5!}{2!} = 60.$$

EXAMPLE 5.7

How many different arrangements of the letters in the word MATHEMATICAL are there?

SOLUTION

There are 12 letters, so there are 12! = 479 001 600 arrangements.

However, there are repeated letters and so some of these arrangements are the same.

For example,

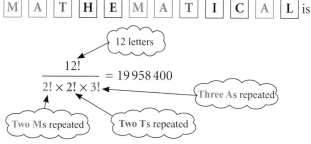

and

are the same.

In fact, there are 3! = 6 ways of arranging the As.

So the total number of arrangements of

M A T H E M A T I C A L is

$$\frac{12!}{2! \times 2! \times 3!} = 19\,958\,400$$

12 letters

Three As repeated

Two Ms repeated

Two Ts repeated

Example 5.7 illustrates how to deal with repeated objects. You can generalise from this example to obtain the following:

● The number of distinct arrangements of n objects in a line, of which p are identical to each other, q others are identical to each other, r of a third type are identical, and so on is $\dfrac{n!}{p!q!r!\ldots}$.

EXERCISE 5A

1 Calculate **(i)** 8! **(ii)** $\dfrac{8!}{6!}$ **(iii)** $\dfrac{5! \times 6!}{7! \times 4!}$

2 Simplify **(i)** $\dfrac{(n-1)!}{n!}$ **(ii)** $\dfrac{(n-1)!}{(n-2)!}$

3 Simplify **(i)** $\dfrac{(n+3)!}{(n+1)!}$ **(ii)** $\dfrac{n!}{(n-2)!}$

4 Write in factorial notation.

(i) $\dfrac{8 \times 7 \times 6}{5 \times 4 \times 3}$ **(ii)** $\dfrac{15 \times 16}{4 \times 3 \times 2}$ **(iii)** $\dfrac{(n+1)n(n-1)}{4 \times 3 \times 2}$

5 Factorise **(i)** $7! + 8!$ **(ii)** $n! + (n+1)!$

6 How many different four letter words can be formed from the letters A, B, C and D if letters cannot be repeated? (The words do not need to mean anything.)

7 How many different ways can eight books be arranged in a row on a shelf?

8 In a greyhound race there are six runners. How many different ways are there for the six dogs to finish?

9 In a 60-metre hurdles race there are five runners, one from each of the nations Austria, Belgium, Canada, Denmark and England.

(i)   How many different finishing orders are there?

(ii) What is the probability of predicting the finishing order by choosing first, second, third, fourth and fifth at random?

10 John has an MP3 player which can play tracks in 'shuffle' mode. If an album is played in 'shuffle' mode the tracks are selected in a random order with a different track selected each time until all the tracks have been played.

John plays a 14-track album in 'shuffle' mode.

(i)   In how many different orders could the tracks be played?

(ii) What is the probability that 'shuffle' mode will play the tracks in the normal set order listed on the album?

11 In a 'Goal of the season' competition, participants are asked to rank ten goals in order of quality.

The organisers select their 'correct' order at random. Anybody who matches their order will be invited to join the television commentary team for the next international match.

(i)   What is the probability of a participant's order being the same as that of the organisers?

(ii) Five million people enter the competition. How many people would be expected to join the commentary team?

12 The letters O, P, S and T are placed in a line at random. What is the probability that they form a word in the English language?

13 Find how many arrangements there are of the letters in each of these words.

(i) EXAM   (ii) MATHS   (iii) CAMBRIDGE

(iv) PASS   (v) SUCCESS   (vi) STATISTICS

14 How many arrangements of the word ACHIEVE are there if

(i)   there are no restrictions on the order the letters are to be in

(ii)   the first letter is an A

(iii) the letters A and I are to be together.

(iv)   the letters C and H are to be apart.

1 Solve the inequality $n! > 10^m$ for each of the cases $m = 3, 4, 5$.

2 In how many ways can you write 42 using factorials only?

3 **(i)** There are 4! ways of placing the four letters S, T, A, R in a line, if each of them must appear exactly once. How many ways are there if each letter may appear any number of times (i.e. between 0 and 4)? Formulate a general rule.

(ii) There are 4! ways of placing the letters S, T, A, R in line. How many ways are there of placing in line the letters
(a) S, T, A, A   **(b)** S, T, T, T?
Formulate a general rule for dealing with repeated letters.

Permutations

Joyetta

I should be one of the judges! When I heard the 16 songs in the competition, I knew which ones I thought were the best three. Last night they announced the results and I had picked the same three songs in the same order as the judges!

What is the probability of Joyeeta's result?

The winner can be chosen in 16 ways.
The second song can be chosen in 15 ways.
The third song can be chosen in 14 ways.

Thus the total number of ways of placing three songs in the first three positions is $16 \times 15 \times 14 = 3360$. So the probability that Joyeeta's selection is correct is $\frac{1}{3360}$.

In this example attention is given to the order in which the songs are placed. The solution required a *permutation* of three objects from sixteen.

In general the number of permutations, ^nP_r, of r objects from n is given by

$$^nP_r = n \times (n-1) \times (n-2) \times \ldots \times (n-r+1).$$

This can be written more compactly as

● $^nP_r = \dfrac{n!}{(n-r)!}$

EXAMPLE 5.8

Six people go to the cinema. They sit in a row with ten seats. Find how many ways can this be done if

(i) they can sit anywhere

(ii) all the empty seats are next to each other.

SOLUTION

(i) The first person to sit down has a choice of ten seats.
    The second person to sit down has a choice of nine seats.
    The third person to sit down has a choice of eight seats.
    ...
    The sixth person to sit down has a choice of five seats.

    So the total number of arrangements is $10 \times 9 \times 8 \times 7 \times 6 \times 5 = 151\,200$.
    This is a permutation of six objects from ten, so a quicker way to work this out is

    $$\text{number of arrangements} = {}^{10}P_6 = 151\,200$$

(ii) Since all four empty seats are to be together you can consider them to be a single 'empty seat', albeit a large one!
    So there are seven seats to seat six people.
    So the number of arrangements is ${}^{7}P_6 = 5040$

Combinations

It is often the case that you are not concerned with the order in which items are chosen, only with which ones are picked.

To take part in the UK National Lottery you fill in a ticket by selecting six numbers out of a possible 49 (numbers 1, 2, . . . , 49). When the draw is made a machine selects six numbers at random. If they are the same as the six on your ticket, you win the jackpot.

❓ You have the six winning numbers. Does it matter in which order the machine picked them?

The probability of a single ticket winning the jackpot is often said to be 1 in 14 million. How can you work out this figure?

The key question is, how many ways are there of choosing six numbers out of 49?

If the order mattered, the answer would be ${}^{49}P_6$, or $49 \times 48 \times 47 \times 46 \times 45 \times 44$.

However, the order does not matter. The selection 1, 3, 15, 19, 31 and 48 is the same as 15, 48, 31, 1, 19, 3 and as 3, 19, 48, 1, 15, 31, and lots more. For each set of six numbers there are 6! arrangements that all count as being the same.

So, the number of ways of selecting six balls, given that the order does not matter, is

$$\frac{49 \times 48 \times 47 \times 46 \times 45 \times 44}{6!}.$$

This is $\dfrac{{}^{49}P_6}{6!}$

This is called the number of *combinations* of 6 objects from 49 and is denoted by ${}^{49}C_6$.

? Show that ${}^{49}C_6$ can be written as $\dfrac{49!}{6! \times 43!}$.

Returning to the UK National Lottery, it follows that the probability of your one ticket winning the jackpot is $\dfrac{1}{{}^{49}C_6}$.

? Check that this is about 1 in 14 million.

This example shows a general result, that the number of ways of selecting r objects from n, when the order does not matter, is given by

$${}^{n}C_r = \frac{n!}{r!(n-r)!} = \frac{{}^{n}P_r}{r!}$$

? How can you prove this general result?

Another common notation for ${}^{n}C_r$ is $\begin{pmatrix} n \\ r \end{pmatrix}$. Both notations are used in this book to help you become familiar with both of them.

⚠ The notation $\begin{pmatrix} n \\ r \end{pmatrix}$ looks exactly like a column vector and so there is the possibility of confusing the two. However, the context should usually make the meaning clear.

EXAMPLE 5.9

A School Governors' committee of five people is to be chosen from eight applicants. How many different selections are possible?

SOLUTION

Number of selections $= \begin{pmatrix} 8 \\ 5 \end{pmatrix} = \dfrac{8!}{5! \times 3!} = \dfrac{8 \times 7 \times 6}{3 \times 2 \times 1} = 56$

EXAMPLE 5.10 In how many ways can a committee of four people be selected from four applicants?

SOLUTION

Common sense tells us that there is only one way to make the committee, that is by appointing all applicants. So $^4C_4 = 1$. However, if we work from the formula

$$^4C_4 = \frac{4!}{4! \times 0!} = \frac{1}{0!}$$

For this to equal 1 requires the convention that 0! is taken to be 1.

? Use the convention 0! = 1 to show that $^nC_0 = {}^nC_n = 1$ for all values of n.

The binomial coefficients

In the last section you met numbers of the form ^nC_r or $\binom{n}{r}$. These are called the binomial coefficients; the reason for this is explained in Appendix 3 (which you can find on the CD) and in the next chapter.

ACTIVITY 5.1 Use the formula $\binom{n}{r} = \dfrac{n!}{r!(n-r)!}$ and the results $\binom{n}{0} = \binom{n}{n} = 1$ to check that the entries in this table, for $n = 6$ and 7, are correct.

r	0	1	2	3	4	5	6	7
$n = 6$	1	6	15	20	15	6	1	–
$n = 7$	1	7	21	35	35	21	7	1

It is very common to present values of ^nC_r in a table shaped like an isosceles triangle, known as Pascal's triangle.

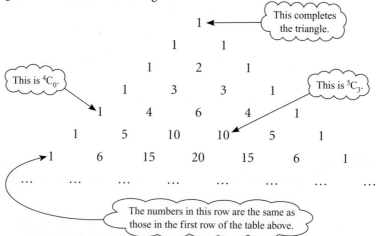

Pascal's triangle makes it easy to see two important properties of binomial coefficients.

1 Symmetry: $^nC_r = ^nC_{n-r}$

If you are choosing 11 players from a pool of 15 possible players you can either name the 11 you have selected or name the 4 you have rejected. Similarly, every choice of r objects included in a selection from n distinct objects corresponds to a choice of $(n-r)$ objects which are excluded. Therefore $^nC_r = ^nC_{n-r}$.

This provides a short cut in calculations when r is large. For example

$$^{100}C_{96} = {}^{100}C_4 = \frac{100 \times 99 \times 98 \times 97}{1 \times 2 \times 3 \times 4} = 3\,921\,225.$$

It also shows that the list of values of ^nC_r for any particular value of n is unchanged by being reversed. For example, when $n = 6$ the list is the seven numbers 1, 6, 15, 20, 15, 6, 1.

2 Addition: $^{n+1}C_{r+1} = ^nC_r + ^nC_{r+1}$

Look at the entry 15 in the bottom row of Pascal's triangle, towards the right. The two entries above and either side of it are 10 and 5,

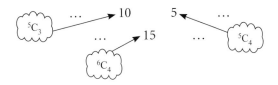

and $15 = 10 + 5$. In this case $^6C_4 = {}^5C_3 + {}^5C_4$. This is an example of the general result that $^{n+1}C_{r+1} = {}^nC_r + {}^nC_{r+1}$. Check that all the entries in Pascal's triangle (except the 1s) are found in this way.

This can be used to build up a table of values of ^nC_r without much calculation. If you know all the values of ^nC_r for any particular value of n you can add pairs of values to obtain all the values of $^{n+1}C_r$, i.e. the next row, except the first and last, which always equal 1.

Using binomial coefficients to calculate probabilities

EXAMPLE 5.11

A committee of 5 is to be chosen from a list of 14 people, 6 of whom are men and 8 women. Their names are to be put in a hat and then 5 drawn out.

What is the probability that this procedure produces a committee with no women?

SOLUTION

The probability of an all-male committee of 5 people is given by

> There are 6 men.

$$\frac{\text{the number of ways of choosing 5 people out of 6}}{\text{the number of ways of choosing 5 people out of 14}} = \frac{{}^6C_5}{{}^{14}C_5} = \frac{6}{2002} \approx 0.003$$

> There are 14 people.

🚌 GoByBus.com 🚐

Help decide our new bus routes

The exact route for our new bus service is to be announced in April. Rest assured our service will run from Amli to Chatra via Bawal and will be extended to include Dhar once our new fleet of buses arrives in September. As local people know, there are several roads connecting

these towns and we are keen to hear the views as to the most useful routes from our future passengers. Please post your views below!

 This consultation is a farce. The chance of getting a route that suits me is less than one

RChowdhry in a hundred :(

Is RChowdhry right? How many routes are there from Amli to Dhar? Start by looking at the first two legs, Amli to Bawal and Bawal to Chatra.

There are three roads from Amli to Bawal and two roads from Bawal to Chatra. How many routes are there from Amli to Chatra passing through Bawal on the way?

Look at figure 5.2.

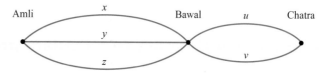

Figure 5.2

The answer is $3 \times 2 = 6$ because there are three ways of doing the first leg, followed by two for the second leg. The six routes are

$$x - u \qquad y - u \qquad z - u$$
$$x - v \qquad y - v \qquad z - v.$$

There are also four roads from Chatra to Dhar. So each of the six routes from Amli to Chatral has four possible ways of going on to Dhar. There are now $6 \times 4 = 24$ routes. See figure 5.3.

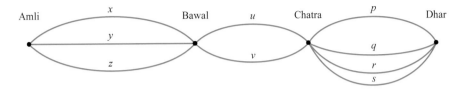

Figure 5.3

They can be listed systematically as follows:

$$
\begin{array}{cccccc}
x - u - p & y - u - p & z - u - p & x - v - p & y - v - p & z - v - p \\
x - u - q & \dots & \dots & \dots & \dots & \dots \\
x - u - r & \dots & \dots & \dots & \dots & \dots \\
x - u - s & \dots & \dots & \dots & \dots & z - v - s
\end{array}
$$

In general, if there are a outcomes from experiment A, b outcomes from experiment B and c outcomes from experiment C then there are $a \times b \times c$ different possible combined outcomes from the three experiments.

---

1 If GoByBus chooses its route at random, what is the probability that it will be the one RChowdhry wants? Is the comment justified?

2 In this example the probability was worked out by finding the number of possible routes. How else could it have been worked out?

EXAMPLE 5.12

A cricket team consisting of 6 batsmen, 4 bowlers and 1 wicket-keeper is to be selected from a group of 18 cricketers comprising 9 batsmen, 7 bowlers and 2 wicket-keepers. How many different teams can be selected?

SOLUTION

The batsmen can be selected in $^9C_6$ ways.
The bowlers can be selected in $^7C_4$ ways.
The wicket-keepers can be selected in $^2C_1$ ways.
Therefore total number of teams $= {}^9C_6 \times {}^7C_4 \times {}^2C_1$

$$
= \frac{9!}{3! \times 6!} \times \frac{7!}{3! \times 4!} \times \frac{2!}{1! \times 1!}
$$

$$
= \frac{9 \times 8 \times 7}{3 \times 2 \times 1} \times \frac{7 \times 6 \times 5}{3 \times 2 \times 1} \times 2
$$

$$
= 5880
$$

EXAMPLE 5.13

In a dance competition, the panel of ten judges sit on the same side of a long table. There are three female judges.

(i) How many different arrangements are there for seating the ten judges?

(ii) How many different arrangements are there if the three female judges all decide to sit together?

(iii) If the seating is at random, find the probability that the three female judges will **not** all sit together.

(iv) Four of the judges are selected at random to judge the final round of the competition. Find the probability that this final judging panel consists of two men and two women.

SOLUTION

(i) There are $10! = 3\,628\,800$ ways of arranging the judges in a line.

(ii) If the three female judges sit together then you can treat them as a single judge.

So there are eight judges and there are $8! = 40\,320$ ways of arranging the judges in a line.

However, there are $3! = 6$ ways of arranging the female judges.

So there are $3! \times 8! = 241\,920$ ways of arranging the judges so that all the female judges are together.

(iii) There are $3\,628\,800 - 241\,920 = 3\,386\,880$ ways of arranging the judges so that the female judges do not all sit together.

So the probability that the female judges do not all sit together is

$$\frac{3\,386\,880}{3\,628\,800} = 0.933 \text{ (to 3 s.f.).}$$

(iv) The probability of selecting two men and two women on the panel of four is

$$\frac{^3C_2 \times {}^7C_2}{^{10}C_4} = \frac{3!}{1! \times 2!} \times \frac{7!}{5! \times 2!} \div \frac{10!}{6! \times 4!}$$

$$= 3 \times 21 \div 210$$

$$= 0.3$$

EXERCISE 5B

1 (i) Find the values of (a) $^6P_2$ (b) $^8P_4$ (c) $^{10}P_4$.

(ii) Find the values of (a) $^6C_2$ (b) $^8C_4$ (c) $^{10}C_4$.

(iii) Show that, for the values of n and r in parts (i) and (ii),

$$^nC_r = \frac{^nP_r}{r!}.$$

2 There are 15 runners in a camel race. What is the probability of correctly guessing the first three finishers in their finishing order?

3 To win the jackpot in a lottery a contestant must correctly select six numbers from the numbers 1 to 30 inclusive. What is the probability that a contestant wins the jackpot with one selection of six numbers?

4 A group of 5 computer programmers is to be chosen to form the night shift from a set of 14 programmers. In how many ways can the programmers be chosen if the 5 chosen must include the shift-leader who is one of the 14?

5 My brother Mark decides to put together a rock band from amongst his year at school. He wants a lead singer, a guitarist, a keyboard player and a drummer. He invites applications and gets 7 singers, 5 guitarists, 4 keyboard players and 2 drummers. Assuming each person applies only once, in how many ways can Mark put the group together?

6 A touring party of cricket players is made up of 5 players from each of India, Pakistan and Sri Lanka and 3 from Bangladesh.

(i) How many different selections of 11 players can be made for a team?

(ii) In one match, it is decided to have 3 players from each of India, Pakistan and Sri Lanka and 2 from Bangladesh. How many different team selections can now be made?

7 A committee of four is to be selected from ten candidates, six men and four women.

(i) In how many distinct ways can the committee be chosen?

(ii) Assuming that each candidate is equally likely to be selected, determine the probabilities that the chosen committee contains

(a) no women

(b) two men and two women.

8 A committee of four is to be selected from five boys and four girls. The members are selected at random.

(i) How many different selections are possible?

(ii) What is the probability that the committee will be made up of

(a) all girls?

(b) more boys than girls?

9 Baby Imran has a set of alphabet blocks. His mother often uses the blocks I, M, R, A and N to spell Imran's name.

  (i) One day she leaves him playing with these five blocks. When she comes back into the room Imran has placed them in the correct order to spell his name. What is the probability of Imran placing the blocks in this order? (He is only 18 months old so he certainly cannot spell!)

  (ii) A couple of days later she leaves Imran playing with all 26 of the alphabet blocks. When she comes back into the room she again sees that he has placed the five blocks I, M, R, A and N in the correct order to spell his name. What is the probability of him choosing the five correct blocks and placing them in this order?

10 (i) A football team consists of 3 players who play in a defence position, 3 players who play in a midfield position and 5 players who play in a forward position. Three players are chosen to collect a gold medal for the team. Find in how many ways this can be done

    (a) if the captain, who is a midfield player, must be included, together with one defence and one forward player.

    (b) if exactly one forward player must be included, together with any two others.

  (ii) Find how many different arrangements there are of the nine letters in the words GOLD MEDAL

    (a) if there are no restrictions on the order of the letters,

    (b) if the two letters D come first and the two letters L come last.

[Cambridge International AS and A Level Mathematics 9709, Paper 6 Q7 June 2005]

11 The diagram shows the seating plan for passengers in a minibus, which has 17 seats arranged in 4 rows. The back row has 5 seats and the other 3 rows have 2 seats on each side. 11 passengers get on the minibus.

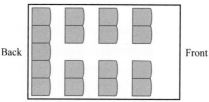

Back   Front

  (i) How many possible seating arrangements are there for the 11 passengers?

  (ii) How many possible seating arrangements are there if 5 particular people sit in the back row?

Of the 11 passengers, 5 are unmarried and the other 6 consist of 3 married couples.

  (iii) In how many ways can 5 of the 11 passengers on the bus be chosen if there must be 2 married couples and 1 other person, who may or may not be married?

[Cambridge International AS and A Level Mathematics 9709, Paper 6 Q4 June 2006]

12 Issam has 11 different CDs, of which 6 are pop music, 3 are jazz and 2 are classical.

    (i) How many different arrangements of all 11 CDs on a shelf are there if the jazz CDs are all next to each other?

    (ii) Issam makes a selection of 2 pop music CDs, 2 jazz CDs and 1 classical CD. How many different possible selections can be made?

[Cambridge International AS and A Level Mathematics 9709, Paper 6 Q3 June 2008]

13 A choir consists of 13 sopranos, 12 altos, 6 tenors and 7 basses. A group consisting of 10 sopranos, 9 altos, 4 tenors and 4 basses is to be chosen from the choir.

    (i) In how many different ways can the group be chosen?

    (ii) In how many ways can the 10 chosen sopranos be arranged in a line if the 6 tallest stand next to each other?

    (iii) The 4 tenors and the 4 basses in the group stand in a single line with all the tenors next to each other and all the basses next to each other. How many possible arrangements are there if three of the tenors refuse to stand next to any of the basses?

[Cambridge International AS and A Level Mathematics 9709, Paper 6 Q4 June 2009]

14 A staff car park at a school has 13 parking spaces in a row. There are 9 cars to be parked.

    (i) How many different arrangements are there for parking the 9 cars and leaving 4 empty spaces?

    (ii) How many different arrangements are there if the 4 empty spaces are next to each other?

    (iii) If the parking is random, find the probability that there will **not** be 4 empty spaces next to each other.

[Cambridge International AS and A Level Mathematics 9709, Paper 6 Q3 November 2005]

15 A builder is planning to build 12 houses along one side of a road. He will build 2 houses in style *A*, 2 houses in style *B*, 3 houses in style *C*, 4 houses in style *D* and 1 house in style *E*.

    (i) Find the number of possible arrangements of these 12 houses.

    (ii)

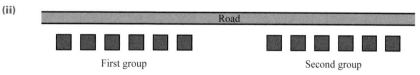

First group   Second group

    The 12 houses will be in two groups of 6 (see diagram). Find the number of possible arrangements if all the houses in styles *A* and *D* are in the first group and all the houses in styles *B*, *C* and *E* are in the second group.

    (iii) Four of the 12 houses will be selected for a survey. Exactly one house must be in style *B* and exactly one house in style *C*. Find the number of ways in which these four houses can be selected.

[Cambridge International AS and A Level Mathematics 9709, Paper 6 Q4 November 2008]

16 (i) Find how many numbers between 5000 and 6000 can be formed from the digits 1, 2, 3, 4, 5 and 6

    (a) if no digits are repeated,

    (b) if repeated digits are allowed.

(ii) Find the number of ways of choosing a school team of 5 pupils from 6 boys and 8 girls

    (a) if there are more girls than boys in the team,

    (b) if three of the boys are cousins and are either all in the team or all not in the team.

[Cambridge International AS and A Level Mathematics 9709, Paper 61 Q5 November 2009]

KEY POINTS

1 The number of ways of arranging n unlike objects in a line is $n!$

2 $n! = n \times (n-1) \times (n-2) \times (n-3) \times \ldots \times 3 \times 2 \times 1.$

3 The number of distinct arrangements of n objects in a line, of which p are identical to each other, q others are identical to each other, r of a third type are identical, and so on is

$$\frac{n!}{p!q!r!\ldots}.$$

4 The number of permutations of r objects from n is

$$^{n}P_{r} = \frac{n!}{(n-r)!}.$$

5 The number of combinations of r objects from n is

$$^{n}C_{r} = \frac{n!}{(n-r)!r!}.$$

6 For permutations the order matters. For combinations it does not.

7 By convention $0! = 1.$

6 The binomial distribution

To be or not to be, that is the question.

Shakespeare (Hamlet)

Innovate.com

Samantha's great invention

Mother of three, Samantha Weeks, has done more than her bit to protect the environment. She has invented the first full spectrum LED bulb to operate on stored solar energy.

Now Samantha is out to prove that she is not only a clever scientist but a smart business women as well. For Samantha is setting up her own factory to make and sell her bulbs.

Samantha admits there are still some technical problems ...

Samantha Weeks hopes to make a big success of her light industry

---

Samantha's production process is indeed not very good and there is a probability of 0.1 that any bulb will be substandard and so not last as long as it should.

She decides to sell her bulbs in packs of three. She believes that if one bulb in a pack is substandard the customers will not complain but that if two or more are substandard they will do so. She also believes that complaints should be kept down to no more than 2.5% of customers. Does she meet her target?

Imagine a pack of Samantha's bulbs. There are eight different ways that good (G) and substandard (S) bulbs can be arranged in Samantha's packs, each with its associated probability.

Arrangement	Probability	Good	Substandard
G G G	$0.9 \times 0.9 \times 0.9 = 0.729$	3	0
G G S	$0.9 \times 0.9 \times 0.1 = 0.081$	2	1
G S G	$0.9 \times 0.1 \times 0.9 = 0.081$	2	1
S G G	$0.1 \times 0.9 \times 0.9 = 0.081$	2	1
G S S	$0.9 \times 0.1 \times 0.1 = 0.009$	1	2
S G S	$0.1 \times 0.9 \times 0.1 = 0.009$	1	2
S S G	$0.1 \times 0.1 \times 0.9 = 0.009$	1	2
S S S	$0.1 \times 0.1 \times 0.1 = 0.001$	0	3

Putting these results together gives this table.

Good	Substandard	Probability
3	0	0.729
2	1	0.243
1	2	0.027
0	3	0.001

So the probability of more than one substandard bulb in a pack is

$$0.027 + 0.001 = 0.028 \text{ or } 2.8\%.$$

This is slightly more than the 2.5% that Samantha regards as acceptable.

❓ What business advice would you give Samantha?

In this example we wrote down all the possible outcomes and found their probabilities one at a time. Even with just three bulbs this was repetitive. If Samantha had packed her bulbs in boxes of six it would have taken 64 lines to list them all. Clearly you need a more efficient approach.

You will have noticed that in the case of two good bulbs and one substandard, the probability is the same for each of the three arrangements in the box.

Arrangement	Probability	Good	Substandard
G G S	$0.9 \times 0.9 \times 0.1 = 0.081$	2	1
G S G	$0.9 \times 0.1 \times 0.9 = 0.081$	2	1
S G G	$0.1 \times 0.9 \times 0.9 = 0.081$	2	1

So the probability of this outcome is $3 \times 0.081 = 0.243$. The number 3 arises because there are three ways of arranging two good and one substandard bulb in the box. This is a result you have already met in the previous chapter but written slightly differently.

EXAMPLE 6.1 How many different ways are there of arranging the letters GGS?

SOLUTION

Since all the letters are either G or S, all you need to do is to count the number of ways of choosing the letter G two times out of three letters. This is

$$^{3}C_{2} = \frac{3!}{2! \times 1!} = \frac{6}{2} = 3.$$

So what does this tell you? There was no need to list all the possibilities for Samantha's boxes of bulbs. The information could have been written down like this.

Good	Substandard	Expression	Probability
3	0	$^3C_3(0.9)^3$	0.729
2	1	$^3C_2(0.9)^2(0.1)^1$	0.243
1	2	$^3C_1(0.9)^1(0.1)^2$	0.027
0	3	$^3C_0(0.1)^3$	0.001

The binomial distribution

Samantha's light bulbs are an example of a common type of situation which is modelled by the binomial distribution. In describing such situations in this book, we emphasise the fact by using the word *trial* rather than the more general term *experiment*.

- You are conducting trials on random samples of a certain size, denoted by n.

- There are just two possible outcomes (in this case substandard and good). These are often referred to as *success* and *failure.*

- Both outcomes have fixed probabilities, the two adding to 1. The probability of success is usually called p, that of failure q, so $p + q = 1$.

- The probability of success in any trial is independent of the outcomes of previous trials.

You can then list the probabilities of the different possible outcomes as in the table above.

The method of the previous section can be applied more generally. You can call the probability of a substandard bulb p (instead of 0.1), the probability of a good bulb q (instead of 0.9) and the number of substandard bulbs in a packet of three, X.

Then the possible values of X and their probabilities are as shown in the table below.

r	0	1	2	3
$P(X = r)$	q^3	$3pq^2$	$3p^2q$	p^3

This package of values of X with their associated probabilities is called a *binomial probability distribution*, a special case of a discrete random variable.

If Samantha decided to put five bulbs in a packet the probability distribution would be as shown in the following table.

r	0	1	2	3	4	5
$P(X = r)$	q^5	$5pq^4$	$10p^2q^3$	$10p^3q^2$	$5p^4q$	p^5

10 is $^5C_2$.

The entry for $X = 2$, for example, arises because there are two 'successes' (substandard bulbs), giving probability p^2, and three 'failures' (good bulbs), giving probability q^3, and these can happen in $^5C_2 = 10$ ways. This can be written as $P(X = 2) = 10p^2q^3$.

If you are already familiar with the binomial theorem, you will notice that the probabilities in the table are the terms of the binomial expansion of $(q + p)^5$. This is why this is called a binomial distribution. Notice also that the sum of these probabilities is $(q + p)^5 = 1^5 = 1$, since $q + p = 1$, which is to be expected since the distribution covers all possible outcomes.

Note

The binomial theorem on the expansion of powers such as $(q + p)^n$ is covered in *Pure Mathematics 1*. The essential points are given in Appendix 3 on the CD.

The general case

The general binomial distribution deals with the possible numbers of successes when there are n trials, each of which may be a success (with probability p) or a failure (with probability q); p and q are fixed positive numbers and $p + q = 1$. This distribution is denoted by $B(n, p)$. So, the original probability distribution for the number of substandard bulbs in Samantha's boxes of three is $B(3, 0.1)$.

For $B(n, p)$, the probability of r successes in n trials is found by the same argument as before. Each success has probability p and each failure has probability q, so the probability of r successes and $(n - r)$ failures in a particular order is $p^r q^{n-r}$. The positions in the sequence of n trials which the successes occupy can be chosen in ^nC_r ways. Therefore

$$P(X = r) = {}^nC_r p^r q^{n-r} \quad \text{for } 0 \leq r \leq n.$$

This can also be written as

$$p_r = \binom{n}{r} p^r (1 - p)^{n-r}.$$

The successive probabilities for $X = 0, 1, 2, ..., n$ are the terms of the binomial expansion of $(q + p)^n$.

Notes

1 The number of successes, *X*, is a variable which takes a restricted set of values ($X = 0, 1, 2, ..., n$) each of which has a known probability of occurring. This is an example of a *random variable*. Random variables are usually denoted by upper case letters, such as *X*, but the particular values they may take are written in lower case, such as *r*. To state that *X* has the binomial distribution B(*n*, *p*) you can use the abbreviation $X \sim$ B(*n*, *p*), where the symbol $\sim$ means 'has the distribution'.

2 It is often the case that you use a theoretical distribution, such as the binomial, to describe a random variable that occurs in real life. This process is called modelling and it enables you to carry out relevant calculations. If the theoretical distribution matches the real life variable perfectly, then the model is perfect. Usually, however, the match is quite good but not perfect. In this case the results of any calculations will not necessarily give a completely accurate description of the real life situation. They may, nonetheless, be very useful.

EXERCISE 6A

1 The recovery ward in a maternity hospital has six beds. What is the probability that the mothers there have between them four girls and two boys? (You may assume that there are no twins and that a baby is equally likely to be a girl or a boy.)

2 A typist has a probability of 0.99 of typing a letter correctly. He makes his mistakes at random. He types a sentence containing 200 letters. What is the probability that he makes exactly one mistake?

3 In a well-known game you have to decide which your opponent is going to choose: 'Paper', 'Stone' or 'Scissors'. If you guess entirely at random, what is the probability that you are right exactly 5 times out of 15?

4 There is a fault in a machine making microchips, with the result that only 80% of those it produces work. A random sample of eight microchips made by this machine is taken. What is the probability that exactly six of them work?

5 An airport is situated in a place where poor visibility (less than 800 m) can be expected 25% of the time. A pilot flies into the airport on ten different occasions.
   (i) What is the probability that he encounters poor visibility exactly four times?
   (ii) What other factors could influence the probability?

6 Three coins are tossed.
   (i) What is the probability of all three showing heads?
   (ii) What is the probability of two heads and one tail?
   (iii) What is the probability of one head and two tails?
   (iv) What is the probability of all three showing tails?
   (v) Show that the probabilities for the four possible outcomes add up to 1.

7 A coin is tossed ten times.
  (i) What is the probability of it coming down heads five times and tails five times?
  (ii) Which is more likely: exactly seven heads or more than seven heads?

8 In an election 30% of people support the Progressive Party. A random sample of eight voters is taken.
  (i) What is the probability that it contains
      (a) 0   (b) 1   (c) 2
      (d) at least 3 supporters of the Progressive Party?
  (ii) Which is the most likely number of Progressive Party supporters to find in a sample of size eight?

9 There are 15 children in a class.
  (i) What is the probability that
      (a) 0   (b) 1   (c) 2
      (d) at least 3 were born in January?
  (ii) What assumption have you made in answering this question? How valid is this assumption in your view?

10 Criticise this argument.

   If you toss two coins they can come down three ways: two heads, one head and one tail, or two tails. There are three outcomes and so each of them must have probability one third.

The expectation and variance of B(n, p)

EXAMPLE 6.2

The number of substandard bulbs in a packet of three of Samantha's bulbs is modelled by the random variable X where $X \sim B(3, 0.1)$.

(i) Find the expected frequencies of obtaining 0, 1, 2 and 3 substandard bulbs in 2000 packets.
(ii) Find the mean number of substandard bulbs per packet.

SOLUTION

(i) $P(X = 0) = 0.729$ (as on page 143), so the expected frequency of packets with no substandard bulbs is $2000 \times 0.729 = 1458$.

   Similarly, the other expected frequencies are

   for 1 substandard bulb: $2000 \times 0.243 = 486$
   for 2 substandard bulbs: $2000 \times 0.027 = 54$
   for 3 substandard bulbs: $2000 \times 0.001 = 2$.

   Check:
   $1458 + 486 + 54 + 2 = 2000$

(ii) The expected total of substandard bulbs in 2000 packets is

   $0 \times 1458 + 1 \times 486 + 2 \times 54 + 3 \times 2 = 600$.

   This is also called the *expectation*.

   Therefore the mean number of substandard bulbs per packet is $\frac{600}{2000} = 0.3$.

Notice in this example that to calculate the mean we have multiplied each probability by 2000 to get the frequency, multiplied each frequency by the number of faulty bulbs, added these numbers together and finally divided by 2000. Of course we could have obtained the mean with less calculation by just multiplying each number of faulty bulbs by its probability and then summing, i.e. by finding $\sum_{r=0}^{3} rP(X = r)$. This is the standard method for finding an expectation, as you saw in Chapter 4.

Notice also that the mean or expectation of X is $0.3 = 3 \times 0.1 = np$. The result for the general binomial distribution is the same:

- if $X \sim B(n, p)$ then the expectation or mean of $X = \mu = np$.

This seems obvious: if the probability of success in each single trial is p, then the expected numbers of successes in n independent trials is np. However, since what seems obvious is not always true, a proper proof is required.

Let us take the case when $n = 5$. The distribution table for $B(5, p)$ is as on page 144, and the expectation of X is

$$0 \times q^5 + 1 \times 5pq^4 + 2 \times 10p^2q^3 + 3 \times 10p^3q^2 + 4 \times 5p^4q + 5 \times p^5$$
$$= 5pq^4 + 20p^2q^3 + 30p^3q^2 + 20p^4q + 5p^5$$
$$= 5p(q^4 + 4pq^3 + 6p^2q^2 + 4p^3q + p^4) \qquad \text{Take out the common factor } 5p.$$
$$= 5p(q + p)^4$$
$$= 5p \qquad \text{Since } q + p = 1.$$

The proof in the general case follows the same pattern: the common factor is now np, and the expectation simplifies to $np(q + p)^{n-1} = np$. The details are more fiddly because of the manipulations of the binomial coefficients.

Similarly, you can show that in this case the variance of X is given by $5pq$. This is an example of the general results that for a binomial distribution

- mean $= \mu = np$

- variance, $\text{Var}(X) = \sigma^2 = npq = np(1 - p)$

- standard deviation $= \sigma = \sqrt{npq} = \sqrt{np(1 - p)}$.

ACTIVITY 6.1 If you want a challenge write out the details of the proof that if $X \sim B(n, p)$ then the expectation of X is np.

Using the binomial distribution

EXAMPLE 6.3 Which is more likely: that you get at least one 6 when you throw a die six times, or that you get at least two 6s when you throw it twelve times?

SOLUTION

On a single throw of a die the probability of getting a 6 is $\frac{1}{6}$ and that of not getting a 6 is $\frac{5}{6}$.

So the probability distributions for the two situations required are $B(6, \frac{1}{6})$ and $B(12, \frac{1}{6})$ giving probabilities of:

$$1 - {}^6C_0\left(\tfrac{5}{6}\right)^6 = 1 - 0.335 = 0.665 \text{ (at least one 6 in six throws)}$$

and
$$1 - \left[{}^{12}C_0\left(\tfrac{5}{6}\right)^{12} + {}^{12}C_1\left(\tfrac{5}{6}\right)^{11}\left(\tfrac{1}{6}\right)\right] = 1 - (0.112 + 0.269)$$
$$= 0.619 \text{ (at least two 6s in 12 throws)}$$

So at least one 6 in six throws is somewhat more likely.

EXAMPLE 6.4

Extensive research has shown that 1 person out of every 4 is allergic to a particular grass seed. A group of 20 university students volunteer to try out a new treatment.

(i) What is the expectation of the number of allergic people in the group?
(ii) What is the probability that
    (a) exactly two
    (b) no more than two of the group are allergic?
(iii) How large a sample would be needed for the probability of it containing at least one allergic person to be greater than 99.9%?
(iv) What assumptions have you made in your answer?

SOLUTION

This situation is modelled by the binomial distribution with $n = 20$, $p = 0.25$ and $q = 0.75$. The number of allergic people is denoted by X.

(i) Expectation $= np = 20 \times 0.25 = 5$ people.

(ii) $X \sim B(20, 0.25)$
    (a) $P(X = 2) = {}^{20}C_2(0.75)^{18}(0.25)^2 = 0.067$
    (b) $P(X \leqslant 2) = P(X = 0) + P(X = 1) + P(X = 2)$
$$= (0.75)^{20} + {}^{20}C_1(0.75)^{19}(0.25) + {}^{20}C_2(0.75)^{18}(0.25)^2$$
$$= 0.003 + 0.021 + 0.067$$
$$= 0.091$$

(iii) Let the sample size be n (people), so that $X \sim B(n, 0.25)$.

The probability that none of them is allergic is

$$P(X = 0) = (0.75)^n$$

and so the probability that at least one is allergic is

$$P(X \geqslant 1) = 1 - P(X = 0)$$
$$= 1 - (0.75)^n$$

So we need $1 - (0.75)^n > 0.999$

$(0.75)^n < 0.001$

Solving $(0.75)^n = 0.001$

gives $n \log 0.75 = \log 0.001$

$n = \log 0.001 \div \log 0.75$

$= 24.01$

You meet logarithms in *Pure Mathematics 2*.

So 25 people are required.

Notes

1 Although 24.01 is very close to 24 it would be incorrect to round down.
   $1 - (0.75)^{24} = 0.998\,996\,6$ which is just less than 99.9%.

2 You can also use trial and improvement on a calculator to solve for *n*.

(iv) The assumptions made are:
   (a) That the sample is random. This is almost certainly untrue. University students are nearly all in the 18–25 age range and so a sample of them cannot be a random sample of the whole population. They may well also be unrepresentative of the whole population in other ways. Volunteers are seldom truly random.
   (b) That the outcome for one person is independent of that for another. This is probably true unless they are a group of friends from, say, an athletics team, where those with allergies are less likely to be members.

EXPERIMENT

Does the binomial distribution really work?

In the first case in Example 6.3, you threw a die six times (or six dice once each, which amounts to the same thing).

$X \sim B(6, \frac{1}{6})$ and this gives the probabilities in the following table.

Number of 6s	Probability
0	0.335
1	0.402
2	0.201
3	0.054
4	0.008
5	0.001
6	0.000

So if you carry out the experiment of throwing six dice 1000 times and record the number of 6s each time, you should get no 6s about 335 times, one 6 about 402 times and so on. What does 'about' mean? How close an agreement can you expect between experimental and theoretical results?

 You could carry out the experiment with dice, but it would be very tedious even if several people shared the work. Alternatively you could simulate the experiment on a spreadsheet using a random number generator.

EXERCISE 6B

1 In a game five dice are rolled together.

   (i) What is the probability that
      (a) all five show 1
      (b) exactly three show 1
      (c) none of them shows 1?
   (ii) What is the most likely number of times for 6 to show?

2 A certain type of sweet comes in eight colours: red, orange, yellow, green, blue, purple, pink and brown and these normally occur in equal proportions. Veronica's mother gives each of her children 16 of the sweets. Veronica says that the blue ones are much nicer than the rest and is very upset when she receives less than her fair share of them.

   (i) How many blue sweets did Veronica expect to get?
   (ii) What was the probability that she would receive fewer blue ones than she expected?
   (iii) What was the probability that she would receive more blue ones than she expected?

3 In a particular area 30% of men and 20% of women are overweight and there are four men and three women working in an office there. Find the probability that there are

   (i) 0
   (ii) 1
   (iii) 2 overweight men;
   (iv) 0
   (v) 1
   (vi) 2 overweight women;
   (vii) 2 overweight people in the office.

   What assumption have you made in answering this question?

4 On her drive to work Stella has to go through four sets of traffic lights. She estimates that for each set the probability of her finding them red is $\frac{2}{3}$ and green $\frac{1}{3}$. (She ignores the possibility of them being amber.) Stella also estimates that when a set of lights is red she is delayed by one minute.

(i) Find the probability of
   (a) 0
   (b) 1
   (c) 2
   (d) 3 sets of lights being against her.
(ii) Find the expected extra journey time due to waiting at lights.

5 Pepper moths are found in two varieties, light and dark. The proportion of dark moths increases with certain types of atmospheric pollution. At the time of the question 30% of the moths in a particular town are dark. A research student sets a moth trap and catches nine moths, four light and five dark.

(i) What is the probability of that result for a sample of nine moths?
(ii) What is the expected number of dark moths in a sample of nine?

The next night the student's trap catches ten pepper moths.

(iii) What is the probability that the number of dark moths in this sample is the same as the expected number?

6 Bella Cicciona, a fortune teller, claims to be able to predict the sex of unborn children. In fact, on each occasion she is consulted, the probability that she makes a correct prediction is 0.6, independent of any other prediction.

One afternoon, Bella is consulted by ten expectant mothers. Find, correct to 2 significant figures, the probabilities that

(i) her first eight predictions are correct and her last two are wrong
(ii) she makes exactly eight correct predictions
(iii) she makes at least eight correct predictions
(iv) she makes exactly eight correct predictions given that she makes at least eight.

[MEI]

7 A general knowledge quiz has ten questions. Each question has three possible 'answers' of which one only is correct. A woman attempts the quiz by pure guesswork.

(i) Find the probabilities that she obtains
   (a) exactly two correct answers
   (b) not more than two correct answers.
(ii) What is the most likely number of correct answers and the probability that she just achieves this number?

[MEI]

8 Five unbiased dice are thrown. Calculate the probabilities that

(i) there will be exactly four 6s

(ii) there will be some one number appearing exactly four times

(iii) there will be some one number appearing exactly three times and a second number appearing twice.

[MEI]

9 Six fair coins are tossed and those landing heads uppermost are eliminated. The remainder are tossed again and the process of elimination is repeated. Tossing and elimination continue in this way until no coins are left.

Find the probabilities of the following events.

(i) All six coins are eliminated in the first round.

(ii) Exactly two coins are eliminated in the first round.

(iii) Exactly two coins are eliminated in the first round and exactly two coins are eliminated in the second round.

(iv) Exactly two coins are eliminated in each of the first three rounds.

(v) Exactly two coins are eliminated in the first round and exactly two coins are eliminated in the *third* round.

[MEI]

10 A supermarket gets eggs from a supplier in boxes of 12. The supermarket manager is concerned at the number of eggs which are broken on arrival. She has a random sample of 100 boxes checked and the numbers of broken eggs per box are as follows.

Number of eggs broken	0	1	2	3	4	5+
Number of boxes	35	39	19	6	1	0

(i) Calculate the mean and standard deviation of the number of broken eggs in a box.

(ii) Show that a reasonable estimate for p, the probability of an egg being broken on arrival, is 0.0825. Use this figure to calculate the probability that a randomly chosen box will contain no broken eggs. How does this probability relate to the observed number of boxes which contain no broken eggs?

(iii) The manager tells the suppliers that they must reduce p to the value which will ensure that, in the long run, 75% of boxes have no broken eggs. To what value must the suppliers reduce p?

[MEI]

11 A box contains 300 discs of different colours. There are 100 pink discs, 100 blue discs and 100 orange discs. The discs of each colour are numbered from 0 to 99. Five discs are selected at random, one at a time, with replacement. Find

(i) the probability that no orange discs are selected,

(ii) the probability that exactly 2 discs with numbers ending in a 6 are selected,

(iii) the probability that exactly 2 orange discs with numbers ending in a 6 are selected,

(iv) the mean and variance of the number of pink discs selected.

[Cambridge International AS and A Level Mathematics 9709, Paper 6 Q5 November 2005]

12 The mean number of defective batteries in packs of 20 is 1.6. Use a binomial distribution to calculate the probability that a randomly chosen pack of 20 will have more than 2 defective batteries.

[Cambridge International AS and A Level Mathematics 9709, Paper 61 Q1 November 2009]

KEY POINTS

1 The binomial distribution may be used to model situations in which:

- you are conducting trials on random samples of a certain size, n

- in each trial there are two possible outcomes, often referred to as success and failure

- both outcomes have fixed probabilities, p and q, and $p + q = 1$

- the probability of success in any trial is independent of the outcomes of previous trials.

2 The probability that the number of successes, X, has the value r, is given by

$$P(X = r) = \binom{n}{r} p^r q^{n-r} = \binom{n}{r} p^r (1 - p)^{n-r}$$

An alternative notation for $\binom{n}{r}$ is ^nC_r.

3 For $B(n, p)$

- the expectation or mean of the number of successes, $E(X) = \mu = np$.

- the variance, $\text{Var}(X) = \sigma^2 = npq = np(1 - p)$.

- the standard deviation, $\sigma = \sqrt{npq} = \sqrt{np(1 - p)}$.

To be and not be to, that is the answer.

Piet Hein

The normal distribution

The normal law of error stands out in the experience of mankind as one of the broadest generalisations of natural philosophy. It serves as the guiding instrument in researches in the physical and social sciences and in medicine, agriculture and engineering. It is an indispensable tool for the analysis and the interpretation of the basic data obtained by observation and experiment.

W. J. Youden

UK Beanpole _____

Just had my height measured at the doctor's – I'm 194.3 cm. Can't be many around as tall as me!

UK Beanpole is clearly exceptionally tall, but how much so? Is he one in a hundred, or a thousand or even a million? To answer that question you need to know the distribution of heights of adult British men.

The first point that needs to be made is that height is a continuous variable and not a discrete one. If you measure accurately enough it can take any value.

This means that it does not really make sense to ask 'What is the probability that somebody chosen at random has height exactly 194.3 cm?'. The answer is zero.

However, you can ask questions like 'What is the probability that somebody chosen at random has height between 194.25 cm and 194.35 cm?' and 'What is the probability that somebody chosen at random has height at least 194.3 cm?'. When the variable is continuous, you are concerned with a range of values rather than a single value.

Like many other naturally occurring variables, the heights of adult men may be modelled by a normal distribution, shown in figure 7.1. You will see that this has a distinctive bell-shaped curve and is symmetrical about its middle. The curve is continuous as height is a continuous variable.

On figure 7.1, area represents probability so the shaded area to the right of 194.3 cm represents the probability that a randomly selected adult male is over 194.3 cm tall.

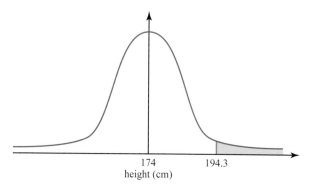

174   194.3
height (cm)

Figure 7.1

Before you can start to find this area, you must know the mean and standard deviation of the distribution, in this case about 174 cm and 7 cm respectively.

So UK Beanpole's height is 194.3 cm − 174 cm = 20.3 cm above the mean, and that is

$$\frac{20.3}{7} = 2.9 \text{ standard deviations.}$$

The number of standard deviations beyond the mean, in this case 2.9, is denoted by the letter z. Thus the shaded area gives the probability of obtaining a value of $z \geqslant 2.9$.

You find this area by looking up the value of $\Phi(z)$ when $z = 2.9$ in a normal distribution table of $\Phi(z)$ as shown in figure 7.2, and then calculating $1 - \Phi(z)$. (Φ is the Greek letter *phi*.)

z	0	1	2	3	4	5	6	7	8	9	1	2	3	4	5	6	7	8	9
															ADD				
0.0	0.5000	0.5040	0.5080	0.5120	0.5160	0.5199	0.5239	0.5279	0.5319	0.5359	4	8	12	16	20	24	28	32	36
0.1	0.5398	0.5438	0.5478	0.5517	0.5557	0.5596	0.5636	0.5675	0.5714	0.5753	4	8	12	16	20	24	28	32	36
0.2	0.5793	0.5832	0.5871	0.5910	0.5948	0.5987	0.6026	0.6064	0.6103	0.6141	4	8	12	15	19	23	27	31	35
0.3	0.6179	0.6217	0.6255	0.6293	0.6331	0.6368	0.6406	0.6443	06.480	0.6517	4	7	11	15	19	22	26	30	34
0.4	0.6554	0.6591	0.6628	0.6664	0.6700	0.6736	0.6772	0.6808	0.6844	0.6879	4	7	11	14	18	22	25	29	32
0.5	0.6915	0.6950	0.6985	0.7019	0.7054	0.7088	0.7123	0.7157	0.7190	0.7224	3	7	10	14	17	20	24	27	31
0.6	0.7257	0.7291	0.7324	0.7357	0.7389	0.7422	0.7454	0.7486	0.7517	0.7549	3	7	10	13	16	19	23	26	29
0.7	0.7580	0.7611	0.7642	0.7673	0.7704	0.7734	0.7764	0.7794	0.7823	0.7852	3	6	9	12	15	18	21	24	27
0.8	0.7881	0.7910	0.7939	0.7967	0.7995	0.8023	0.8051	0.8078	0.8106	0.8133	3	5	8	11	14	16	19	22	25
2.5	0.9938	0.9940	0.9941	0.9943	0.9945	0.9946	0.9948	0.9949	0.9951	0.9952	0	0	0	1	1	1	1	1	1
2.6	0.9953	0.9955	0.9956	0.9957	0.9959	0.9960	0.9961	0.9962	0.9963	0.9964	0	0	0	0	1	1	1	1	1
2.7	0.9965	0.9966	0.9967	0.9968	0.9969	0.9970	0.9971	0.9972	0.9973	0.9974	0	0	0	0	0	1	1	1	1
2.8	0.9974	0.9975	0.9976	0.9977	0.9977	0.9978	0.9979	0.9979	0.9980	0.9981	0	0	0	0	0	0	0	1	1
2.9	0.9981	0.9982	0.9982	0.9983	0.9984	0.9984	0.9985	0.9985	0.9986	0.9986	0	0	0	0	0	0	0	0	0

$\Phi(2.9) = 0.9981$

Figure 7.2 Extract from tables of $\Phi(z)$

This gives $\Phi(2.9) = 0.9981$, and so $1 - \Phi(2.9) = 0.0019$.

The probability of a randomly selected adult male being 194.3 cm or over is 0.0019. One man in slightly more than 500 is at least as tall as UK Beanpole.

Using normal distribution tables

The function $\Phi(z)$ gives the area under the normal distribution curve to the *left* of the value z, that is the shaded area in figure 7.3 (it is the cumulative distribution function). The total area under the curve is 1, and the area given by $\Phi(z)$ represents the probability of a value smaller than z.

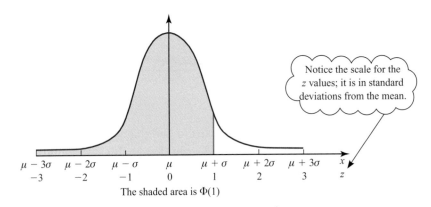

Notice the scale for the *z* values; it is in standard deviations from the mean.

The shaded area is $\Phi(1)$

Figure 7.3

If the variable X has mean μ and standard deviation σ then x, a particular value of X, is transformed into z by the equation

$$z = \frac{x - \mu}{\sigma}.$$

z is a particular value of the variable Z which has mean 0 and standard deviation 1 and is the *standardised* form of the normal distribution.

	Actual distribution, X	**Standardised distribution, Z**
Mean	μ	0
Standard deviation	σ	1
Particular value	x	$z = \dfrac{x - \mu}{\sigma}$

Notice how lower case letters, x and z, are used to indicate particular values of the random variables, whereas upper case letters, X and Z, are used to describe or name those variables.

Normal distribution tables are easy to use but you should always make a point of drawing a diagram and shading the region you are interested in.

It is often helpful to know that in a normal distribution, roughly

- 68% of the values lie within ±1 standard deviation of the mean
- 95% of the values lie within ±2 standard deviations of the mean
- 99.75% of the values lie within ±3 standard deviations of the mean.

EXAMPLE 7.1

Assuming the distribution of the heights of adult men is normal, with mean 174 cm and standard deviation 7 cm, find the probability that a randomly selected adult man is

(i) under 185 cm
(ii) over 185 cm
(iii) over 180 cm
(iv) between 180 cm and 185 cm
(v) under 170 cm

giving your answers to 2 significant figures.

SOLUTION

The mean height, $\mu = 174$ cm.

The standard deviation, $\sigma = 7$ cm.

(i) The probability that an adult man selected at random is under 185 cm. The area required is that shaded in figure 7.5.

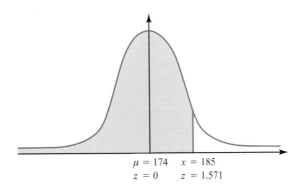

$\mu = 174 \quad x = 185$
$z = 0 \quad z = 1.571$

Figure 7.5

$$x = 185 \text{ cm}$$

and so $\qquad z = \dfrac{185 - 174}{7} = 1.571$

Look up the value of $\Phi(z)$ in a normal distribution table.

z	0	1	2	3	4	5	6	⑦	8	9	①	2	3	4	5	6	7	8	9
															ADD				
0.0	0.5000	0.5040	0.5080	0.5120	0.5160	0.5199	0.5239	0.5279	0.5319	0.5359	4	8	12	16	20	24	28	32	36
0.1	0.5398	0.5438	0.5478	0.5517	0.5557	0.5596	0.5636	0.5675	0.5714	0.5753	4	8	12	16	20	24	28	32	36
1.4	0.9192	0.9207	0.9222	0.9236	0.9251	0.9265	0.9279	0.9292	0.9306	0.9319	1	3	4	6	7	8	10	11	13
⑴.5	0.9332	0.9345	0.9357	0.9370	0.9382	0.9394	0.9406	⦅0.9418⦆	0.9429	0.9441	①	2	4	5	6	7	8	10	11
1.6	0.9452	0.9463	0.9474	0.9484	0.9495	0.9505	0.9515	0.9525	0.9535	0.9545	1	2	3	4	5	6	7	8	9
1.7	0.9554	0.9564	0.9573	0.9582	0.9591	0.9599	0.9608	0.9616	0.9625	0.9633	1	2	3	4	4	5	6	7	8
1.8	0.9641	0.9649	0.9656	0.9664	0.9671	0.9678	0.9686	0.9693	0.9699	0.9706	1	1	2	3	4	4	5	6	6

Figure 7.4 Extract from tables of $\Phi(z)$

$$\Phi(1.571) = 0.9418 + 0.0001$$
$$= 0.9419$$
$$= 0.94 \qquad \text{(2 s.f.)}$$

Answer: The probability that an adult man selected at random is under 185 cm is 0.94.

(ii) The probability that an adult man selected at random is over 185 cm. The area required is the complement of that for part (i) (see figure 7.6).

$$\text{Probability} = 1 - \Phi(1.571)$$
$$= 1 - 0.9419$$
$$= 0.0581$$
$$= 0.058 \qquad \text{(2 s.f.)}$$

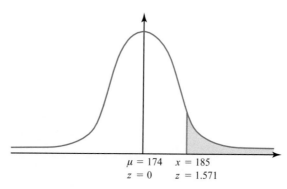

$$\mu = 174 \qquad x = 185$$
$$z = 0 \qquad z = 1.571$$

Figure 7.6

Answer: The probability that an adult man selected at random is over 185 cm is 0.058.

(iii) The probability that an adult man selected at random is over 180 cm.

$$x = 180 \text{ cm} \quad \text{and so} \quad z = \frac{180 - 174}{7} = 0.857$$

$$\begin{aligned} \text{The area required} &= 1 - \Phi(0.857) \\ &= 1 - 0.8042 \\ &= 0.1958 \\ &= 0.20 \quad (2 \text{ s.f.}) \end{aligned}$$

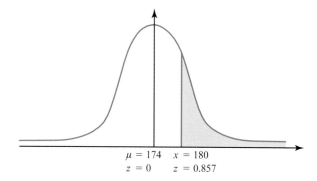

Figure 7.7

Answer: The probability that an adult man selected at random is over 180 cm is 0.20.

(iv) The probability that an adult man selected at random is between 180 cm and 185 cm.

The required area is shown in figure 7.8. It is

$$\begin{aligned} \Phi(1.571) - \Phi(0.857) &= 0.9419 - 0.8042 \\ &= 0.1377 \\ &= 0.14 \quad (2 \text{ s.f.}) \end{aligned}$$

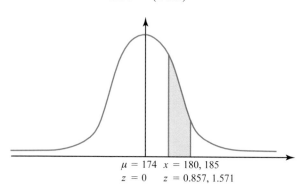

Figure 7.8

Answer: The probability that an adult man selected at random is over 180 cm but under 185 cm is 0.14.

(v) The probability that an adult man selected at random is under 170 cm.

In this case $x = 170$

and so $z = \dfrac{170 - 174}{7} = -0.571$

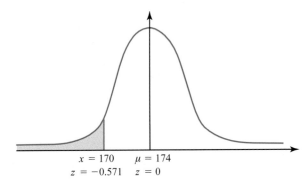

$$x = 170 \qquad \mu = 174$$
$$z = -0.571 \qquad z = 0$$

Figure 7.9

However, when you come to look up $\Phi(-0.571)$, you will find that only positive values of z are given in your tables. You overcome this problem by using the symmetry of the normal curve. The area you want in this case is that to the left of -0.571 and this is clearly just the same as that to the right of $+0.571$ (see figure 7.10).

So $\Phi(-0.571) = 1 - \Phi(0.571)$
$$= 1 - 0.716$$
$$= 0.284$$
$$= 0.28 \ (2 \text{ s.f.})$$

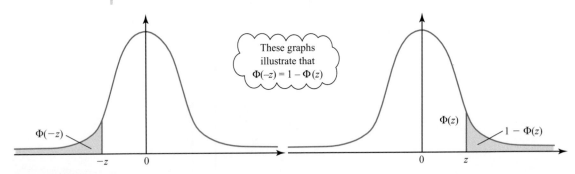

These graphs illustrate that $\Phi(-z) = 1 - \Phi(z)$

$\Phi(-z)$

$-z \qquad 0$

$\Phi(z)$

$1 - \Phi(z)$

$0 \qquad z$

Figure 7.10

Answer: The probability that an adult man selected at random is under 170 cm is 0.28.

e The normal curve

All normal curves have the same basic shape, so that by scaling the two axes suitably you can always fit one normal curve exactly on top of another one.

The curve for the normal distribution with mean μ and standard deviation σ (i.e. variance σ^2) is given by the function $\phi(x)$ in

$$\phi(x) = \frac{1}{\sigma\sqrt{2\pi}}e^{-\frac{1}{2}\left(\frac{x-\mu}{\sigma}\right)^2}$$

The notation $N(\mu, \sigma^2)$ is used to describe this distribution. The mean, μ, and standard deviation, σ (or variance, σ^2), are the two parameters used to define the distribution. Once you know their values, you know everything there is to know about the distribution. The standardised variable Z has mean 0 and variance 1, so its distribution is $N(0, 1)$.

After the variable X has been transformed to Z using $z = \dfrac{x - \mu}{\sigma}$ the form of the curve (now standardised) becomes

$$\phi(z) = \frac{1}{\sqrt{2\pi}}e^{-\frac{1}{2}z^2}$$

However, the exact shape of the normal curve is often less useful than the area underneath it, which represents a probability. For example, the probability that $Z \leqslant 2$ is given by the shaded area in figure 7.11.

Easy though it looks, the function $\phi(z)$ cannot be integrated algebraically to find the area under the curve; this can only be found by using a numerical method. The values found by doing so are given as a table, and this area function is called $\Phi(z)$.

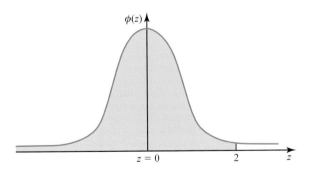

Figure 7.11

EXAMPLE 7.2

Skilled operators make a particular component for an engine. The company believes that the time taken to make this component may be modelled by the normal distribution with mean 95 minutes and standard deviation 4 minutes.

Assuming the company's belief to be true, find the probability that the time taken to make one of these components, selected at random, was

(i)   over 97 minutes

(ii) under 90 minutes

(iii) between 90 and 97 minutes.

Sheila believes that the company is allowing too long for the job and invites them to time her. They find that only 10% of the components take her over 90 minutes to make, and that 20% take her less than 70 minutes.

(iv) Estimate the mean and standard deviation of the time Sheila takes.

SOLUTION

According to the company $\mu = 95$ and $\sigma = 4$ so the distribution is N(95, 4^2).

(i)   The probability that a component required over 97 minutes.

$$z = \frac{97 - 95}{4} = 0.5$$

The probability is represented by the shaded area in figure 7.12 and is given by

$$1 - \Phi(0.5) = 1 - 0.6915$$
$$= 0.3085$$
$$= 0.309 \ \ (3 \ \text{s.f.})$$

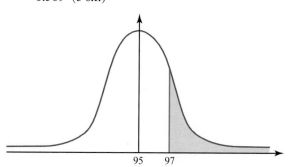

Figure 7.12

Answer: The probability it took the operator over 97 minutes to manufacture a randomly selected component is 0.309.

(ii) The probability that a component required under 90 minutes.

$$z = \frac{90 - 95}{4} = -1.25$$

The probability is represented by the shaded area in figure 7.13 and given by

$$1 - \Phi(1.25) = 1 - 0.8944$$
$$= 0.1056$$
$$= 0.106 \quad (3 \text{ s.f.})$$

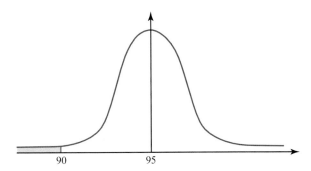

Figure 7.13

Answer: The probability it took the operator under 90 minutes to manufacture a randomly selected component is 0.106.

(iii) The probability that a component required between 90 and 97 minutes.

The probability is represented by the shaded area in figure 7.14 and given by

$$1 - 0.1056 - 0.3085 = 0.5859$$
$$= 0.586 \quad (3 \text{ s.f.})$$

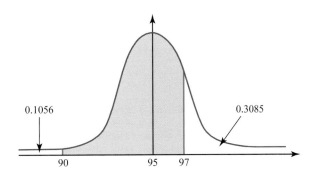

Figure 7.14

Answer: The probability it took the operator between 90 and 97 minutes to manufacture a randomly selected component is 0.586.

(iv) Estimate the mean and standard deviation of the time Sheila takes.

The question has now been put the other way round. You have to infer the mean, μ, and standard deviation, σ, from the areas under different parts of the graph.

10% take her 90 minutes or more. This means that the shaded area in figure 7.15 is 0.1.

$$z = \frac{90 - \mu}{\sigma}$$

$$\Phi(z) = 1 - 0.1 = 0.9$$

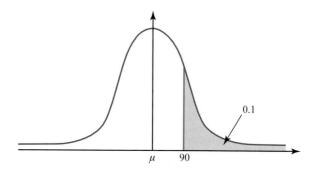

Figure 7.15

You now use the table of $\Phi(z) = p$ in reverse. $z = 1.28$ has a probability of 0.8997 which is as close to 0.9 as you can get using this middle part of the table. However, you can achieve greater accuracy by looking at the right-hand columns as well: $z = 1.281$ has a probability of 0.8999 and $z = 1.282$ has a probability of 0.9001. So the best value for z is 1.2815.

z	0	1	2	3	4	5	6	7	8	9	1	2	3	4	5	6	7	8	9
											\multicolumn{9}{c}{ADD}
0.0	0.5000	0.5040	0.5080	0.5120	0.5160	0.5199	0.5239	0.5279	0.5319	0.5359	4	8	12	16	20	24	28	32	36
0.1	0.5398	0.5438	0.5478	0.5517	0.5557	0.5596	0.5636	0.5675	0.5714	0.5753	4	8	12	16	20	24	28	32	36
0.2	0.5793	0.5832	0.5871	0.5910	0.5948	0.5987	0.6026	0.6064	0.6103	0.6141	4	8	12	15	19	23	27	31	35
0.3	0.6179	0.6217	0.6255	0.6293	0.6331	0.6368	0.6406	0.6443	0.6480	0.6517	4	7	11	15	19	22	26	30	34
0.4	0.6554	0.6591	0.6628	0.6664	0.6700	0.6736	0.6772	0.6808	0.6844	0.6879	4	7	11	14	18	22	25	29	32
0.5	0.6915	0.6950	0.6985	0.7019	0.7054	0.7088	0.7123	0.7157	0.7190	0.7224	3	7	10	14	17	20	24	27	31
0.6	0.7257	0.7291	0.7324	0.7357	0.7389	0.7422	0.7454	0.7486	0.7517	0.7549	3	7	10	13	16	19	23	26	29
0.7	0.7580	0.7611	0.7642	0.7673	0.7704	0.7734	0.7764	0.7794	0.7823	0.7852	3	6	9	12	15	18	21	24	27
0.8	0.7881	0.7910	0.7939	0.7967	0.7995	0.8023	0.8051	0.8078	0.8106	0.8133	3	5	8	11	14	16	19	22	25
0.9	0.8159	0.8186	0.8212	0.8238	0.8264	0.8289	0.8315	0.8340	0.8365	0.8389	3	5	8	10	13	15	18	20	23
1.0	0.8413	0.8438	0.8461	0.8485	0.8508	0.8531	0.8554	0.8577	0.8599	0.8621	2	5	7	9	12	14	16	19	21
1.1	0.8643	0.8665	0.8686	0.8708	0.8729	0.8749	0.8770	0.8790	0.8810	0.8830	2	4	6	8	10	12	14	16	18
1.2	0.8849	0.8869	0.8888	0.8907	0.8925	0.8944	0.8962	0.8980	0.8997	0.9015	2	4	6	7	9	11	13	15	17
1.3	0.9032	0.9049	0.9066	0.9082	0.9099	0.9115	0.9131	0.9147	0.9162	0.9177	2	3	5	6	8	10	11	13	14
1.4	0.9192	0.9207	0.9222	0.9236	0.9251	0.9265	0.9279	0.9292	0.9306	0.9319	1	3	4	6	7	8	10	11	13

$$\Phi^{-1}(0.9) = 1.2815$$

Figure 7.16 Extract from tables of $\Phi(z)$

Returning to the problem, you now know that

$$\frac{90 - \mu}{\sigma} = 1.2815 \quad \Rightarrow \quad 90 - \mu = 1.2815\sigma. \qquad \text{①}$$

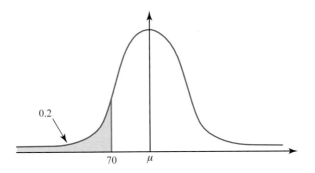

Figure 7.17

The second piece of information, that 20% of components took Sheila under 70 minutes, is illustrated in figure 7.17.

$$z = \frac{70 - \mu}{\sigma}$$

(z has a negative value in this case, the point being to the left of the mean.)

$$\Phi(z) = 0.2$$

and so, by symmetry,

$$\Phi(-z) = 1 - 0.2 = 0.8.$$

Using the table of the normal function gives

$$-z = 0.842 \quad \text{or} \quad z = -0.842$$

This gives a second equation for μ and σ.

$$\frac{70 - \mu}{\sigma} = -0.842 \quad \Rightarrow \quad 70 - \mu = -0.842\sigma. \qquad \text{②}$$

You now solve equations ① and ② simultaneously.

$$\begin{array}{rl} 90 - \mu = & 1.2815\sigma \qquad \text{①} \\ 70 - \mu = & -0.842\sigma \qquad \text{②} \end{array}$$

Subtract $\qquad 20 \quad = \quad 2.1235\sigma$

$$\sigma = 9.418 = 9.42 \quad (3 \text{ s.f.})$$

and $\qquad\qquad \mu = 77.930 = 77.9 \quad (3 \text{ s.f.})$

Answer: Sheila's mean time is 77.9 minutes with standard deviation 9.42 minutes.

1 The distribution of the heights of some plants is normal and has a mean of 40 cm and a standard deviation of 2 cm. Find the probability that a randomly selected plant is

(i)   under 42 cm

(ii) over 42 cm

(iii) over 40 cm

(iv) between 40 and 42 cm.

2 The distribution of the masses of some baby parrots is normal and has a mean of 60 g and a standard deviation of 5 g. Find the probability that a randomly selected bird is

(i)   under 63 g

(ii) over 63 g

(iii) over 68 g

(iv) between 63 and 68 g.

3 The distribution of the mass of sweets in a bag is normal and has a mean of 100 g and a standard deviation 2 g. Find the probability that a randomly selected bag is

(i)   under 98 g

(ii) over 98 g

(iii) under 102 g

(iv) between 98 and 102 g.

4 The distribution of the heights of 18-year-old girls may be modelled by the normal distribution with mean 162.5 cm and standard deviation 6 cm. Find the probability that the height of a randomly selected 18-year-old girl is

(i)   under 168.5 cm

(ii) over 174.5 cm

(iii) between 168.5 and 174.5 cm.

5 A pet shop has a tank of goldfish for sale. All the fish in the tank were hatched at the same time and their weights may be taken to be normally distributed with mean 100 g and standard deviation 10 g. Melanie is buying a goldfish and is invited to catch the one she wants in a small net. In fact the fish are much too quick for her to be able to catch any particular fish, and the one which she eventually nets is selected at random. Find the probability that its weight is

(i)   over 115 g

(ii) under 105 g

(iii) between 105 and 115 g.

6 When he makes instant coffee, Tony puts a spoonful of powder into a mug. The weight of coffee in grams on the spoon may be modelled by the normal distribution with mean 5 g and standard deviation 1 g. If he uses more than 6.5 g Julia complains that it is too strong and if he uses less than 4 g she tells him it is too weak. Find the probability that he makes the coffee

(i) too strong

(ii) too weak

(iii) all right.

7 A biologist finds a nesting colony of a previously unknown sea bird on a remote island. She is able to take measurements on 100 of the eggs before replacing them in their nests. She records their weights, w g, in this frequency table.

Weight, w	$25 < w \leqslant 27$	$27 < w \leqslant 29$	$29 < w \leqslant 31$	$31 < w \leqslant 33$	$33 < w \leqslant 35$	$35 < w \leqslant 37$
Frequency	2	13	35	33	17	0

(i) Find the mean and standard deviation of these data.

(ii) Assuming the weights of the eggs for this type of bird are normally distributed and that their mean and standard deviation are the same as those of this sample, find how many eggs you would expect to be in each of these categories.

(iii) Do you think the assumption that the weights of the eggs are normally distributed is reasonable?

8 The length of life of a certain make of tyre is normally distributed about a mean of 24 000 km with a standard deviation of 2500 km.

(i) What percentage of such tyres will need replacing before they have travelled 20 000 km?

(ii) As a result of improvements in manufacture, the length of life is still normally distributed, but the proportion of tyres failing before 20 000 km is reduced to 1.5%.

(a) If the standard deviation has remained unchanged, calculate the new mean length of life.

(b) If, instead, the mean length of life has remained unchanged, calculate the new standard deviation.

[MEI]

9 A machine is set to produce nails of length 10 cm, with standard deviation 0.05 cm. The lengths of the nails are normally distributed.

(i) Find the percentage of nails produced between 9.95 cm and 10.08 cm in length.

The machine's setting is moved by a careless apprentice with the consequence that 16% of the nails are under 5.2 cm in length and 20% are over 5.3 cm.

(ii) Find the new mean and standard deviation.

10 The concentration by volume of methane at a point on the centre line of a jet of natural gas mixing with air is distributed approximately normally with mean 20% and standard deviation 7%. Find the probabilities that the concentration

(i) exceeds 30%

(ii) is between 5% and 15%.

(iii) In another similar jet, the mean concentration is 18% and the standard deviation is 5%. Find the probability that in at least one of the jets the concentration is between 5% and 15%.

[MEI]

11 In a particular experiment, the length of a metal bar is measured many times. The measured values are distributed approximately normally with mean 1.340 m and standard deviation 0.021 m. Find the probabilities that any one measured value

(i) exceeds 1.370 m

(ii) lies between 1.310 m and 1.370 m

(iii) lies between 1.330 m and 1.390 m.

(iv) Find the length l for which the probability that any one measured value is less than l is 0.1.

[MEI]

12 A factory produces a very large number of steel bars. The lengths of these bars are normally distributed with 33% of them measuring 20.06 cm or more and 12% of them measuring 20.02 cm or less.

Write down two simultaneous equations for the mean and standard deviation of the distribution and solve to find values to 4 significant figures. Hence estimate the proportion of steel bars which measure 20.03 cm or more.

The bars are acceptable if they measure between 20.02 cm and 20.08 cm. What percentage are rejected as being outside the acceptable range?

[MEI]

13 The diameters D of screws made in a factory are normally distributed with mean 1 mm. Given that 10% of the screws have diameters greater than 1.04 mm, find the standard deviation correct to 3 significant figures, and hence show that about 2.7% of the screws have diameters greater than 1.06 mm.

Find, correct to 2 significant figures,

(i) the number d for which 99% of the screws have diameters that exceed d mm

(ii) the number e for which 99% of the screws have diameters that do not differ from the mean by more than e mm.

[MEI]

14 A machine produces crankshafts whose diameters are normally distributed with mean 5 cm and standard deviation 0.03 cm. Find the percentage of crankshafts it will produce whose diameters lie between 4.95 cm and 4.97 cm.

What is the probability that two successive crankshafts will both have a diameter in this interval?

Crankshafts with diameters outside the interval 5 ± 0.05 cm are rejected. If the mean diameter of the machine's production remains unchanged, to what must the standard deviation be reduced if only 4% of the production is to be rejected?

[MEI]

15 In a reading test for eight-year-old children, it is found that a reading score X is normally distributed with mean 5.0 and standard deviation 2.0.

(i) What proportion of children would you expect to score between 4.5 and 6.0?

(ii) There are about 700 000 eight-year-olds in the country. How many would you expect to have a reading score of more than twice the mean?

(iii) Why might educationalists refer to the reading score X as a 'score out of 10'?

The reading score is often reported, after scaling, as a value Y which is normally distributed, with mean 100 and standard deviation 15. Values of Y are usually given to the nearest integer.

(iv) Find the probability that a randomly chosen eight-year-old gets a score, after scaling, of 103.

(v) What range of Y scores would you expect to be attained by the best 20% of readers?

[MEI]

16 *Extralite* are testing a new long-life bulb. The lifetimes, in hours, are assumed to be normally distributed with mean μ and standard deviation σ. After extensive tests, they find that 19% of bulbs have a lifetime exceeding 5000 hours, while 5% have a lifetime under 4000 hours.

(i) Illustrate this information on a sketch.

(ii) Show that $\sigma = 396$ and find the value of μ.

In the remainder of this question take μ to be 4650 and σ to be 400.

(iii) Find the probability that a bulb chosen at random has a lifetime between 4250 and 4750 hours.

(iv) *Extralite* wish to quote a lifetime which will be exceeded by 99% of bulbs. What time, correct to the nearest 100 hours, should they quote?

A new school classroom has six light-fittings, each fitted with an *Extralite* long-life bulb.

(v) Find the probability that no more than one bulb needs to be replaced within the first 4250 hours of use.

[MEI]

17 Tyre pressures on a certain type of car independently follow a normal distribution with mean 1.9 bars and standard deviation 0.15 bars.

(i) Find the probability that all four tyres on a car of this type have pressures between 1.82 bars and 1.92 bars.

(ii) Safety regulations state that the pressures must be between $1.9 - b$ bars and $1.9 + b$ bars. It is known that 80% of tyres are within these safety limits. Find the safety limits.

[Cambridge International AS and A Level Mathematics 9709, Paper 6 Q6 June 2005]

18 The lengths of fish of a certain type have a normal distribution with mean 38 cm. It is found that 5% of the fish are longer than 50 cm.

(i) Find the standard deviation.

(ii) When fish are chosen for sale, those shorter than 30 cm are rejected. Find the proportion of fish rejected.

(iii) 9 fish are chosen at random. Find the probability that at least one of them is longer than 50 cm.

[Cambridge International AS and A Level Mathematics 9709, Paper 6 Q3 June 2006]

19 (i) The random variable X is normally distributed. The mean is twice the standard deviation. It is given that $P(X > 5.2) = 0.9$. Find the standard deviation.

(ii) A normal distribution has mean μ and standard deviation σ. If 800 observations are taken from this distribution, how many would you expect to be between $\mu - \sigma$ and $\mu + \sigma$?

[Cambridge International AS and A Level Mathematics 9709, Paper 6 Q3 June 2007]

20 In a certain country the time taken for a common infection to clear up is normally distributed with mean μ days and standard deviation 2.6 days. 25% of these infections clear up in less than 7 days.

(i) Find the value of μ.

In another country the standard deviation of the time taken for the infection to clear up is the same as in part **(i)** but the mean is 6.5 days. The time taken is normally distributed.

(ii) Find the probability that, in a randomly chosen case from this country, the infection takes longer than 6.2 days to clear up.

[Cambridge International AS and A Level Mathematics 9709, Paper 6 Q4 June 2008]

21 The random variable X has a normal distribution with mean 4.5. It is given that $P(X > 5.5) = 0.0465$ (see diagram).

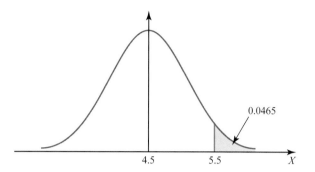

0.0465

4.5   5.5 X

(i) Find the standard deviation of X.

(ii) Find the probability that a random observation of X lies between 3.8 and 4.8.

[Cambridge International AS and A Level Mathematics 9709, Paper 6 Q4 November 2007]

22 (i) The daily minimum temperature in degrees Celsius (°C) in January in Ottawa is a random variable with distribution $N(-15.1, 62.0)$. Find the probability that a randomly chosen day in January in Ottawa has a minimum temperature above 0°C.

(ii) In another city the daily minimum temperature in °C in January is a random variable with distribution $N(\mu, 40.0)$. In this city the probability that a randomly chosen day in January has a minimum temperature above 0°C is 0.8888. Find the value of μ.

[Cambridge International AS and A Level Mathematics 9709, Paper 6 Q3 November 2008]

23 The times for a certain car journey have a normal distribution with mean 100 minutes and standard deviation 7 minutes. Journey times are classified as follows:

'short'   (the shortest 33% of times),
'long'   (the longest 33% of times),
'standard' (the remaining 34% of times).

(i) Find the probability that a randomly chosen car journey takes between 85 and 100 minutes.

(ii) Find the least and greatest times for 'standard' journeys.

[Cambridge International AS and A Level Mathematics 9709, Paper 61 Q3 November 2009]

Modelling discrete situations

Although the normal distribution applies strictly to a continuous variable, it is also common to use it in situations where the variable is discrete providing that

- the distribution is approximately normal; this requires that the steps in its possible values are small compared with its standard deviation

- *continuity corrections* are applied where appropriate.

The meaning of the term 'continuity correction' is explained in the following example.

EXAMPLE 7.3

The result of an Intelligence Quotient (IQ) test is an integer score, X. Tests are designed so that X has a mean value of 100 with standard deviation 15. A large number of people have their IQs tested. What proportion of them would you expect to have IQs measuring between 106 and 110 (inclusive)?

SOLUTION

Although the random variable X is an integer and hence discrete, the steps of 1 in its possible values are small compared with the standard deviation of 15. So it is reasonable to treat it as if it is continuous.

If you assume that an IQ test is measuring innate, natural intelligence (rather than the results of learning), then it is reasonable to assume a normal distribution.

If you draw the probability distribution function for the discrete variable X it looks like figure 7.18. The area you require is the total of the five bars representing 106, 107, 108, 109 and 110.

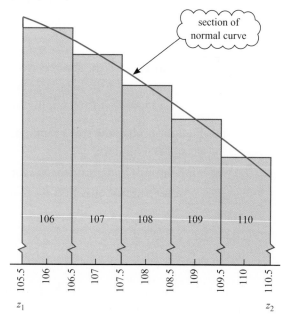

Figure 7.18

The equivalent section of the normal curve would run not from 106 to 110 but from 105.5 to 110.5, as you can see in figure 7.18. When you change from the discrete scale to the continuous scale, the numbers 106, 107, etc. no longer represent the whole intervals, just their centre points.

So the area you require under the normal curve is given by $\Phi(z_2) - \Phi(z_1)$

where $z_1 = \dfrac{105.5 - 100}{15}$ and $z_2 = \dfrac{110.5 - 100}{15}$.

This is

$$\Phi(0.7000) - \Phi(0.3667) = 0.7580 - 0.6431 = 0.1149$$

Answer: The proportion of IQs between 106 and 110 (inclusive) should be approximately 11%.

In this calculation, both end values needed to be adjusted to allow for the fact that a continuous distribution was being used to approximate a discrete one. These adjustments, $106 \to 105.5$ and $110 \to 110.5$, are called continuity corrections. Whenever a discrete distribution is approximated by a continuous one a continuity correction may need to be used.

You must always think carefully when applying a continuity correction. Should the corrections be added or subtracted? In this case 106 and 110 are inside the required area and so any value (like 105.7 or 110.4) which would round to them must be included. It is often helpful to draw a sketch to illustrate the region you want, like the one in figure 7.18.

If the region of interest is given in terms of inequalities, you should look carefully to see whether they are inclusive ($\leqslant$ or $\geqslant$) or exclusive ($<$ or $>$). For example $20 \leqslant X \leqslant 30$ becomes $19.5 \leqslant X < 30.5$ whereas $20 < X < 30$ becomes $20.5 \leqslant X < 29.5$.

Two particularly common situations are when the normal distribution is used to approximate the binomial and the Poisson distributions. (You will learn about the Poisson distribution if you study *Statistics 2*.)

Using the normal distribution as an approximation for the binomial distribution

You may use the normal distribution as an approximation for the binomial, $B(n, p)$ (where n is the number of trials each having probability p of success) when

- n is large
- p is not too close to 0 or 1.

A rough way of judging whether n is large enough is to require that both $np > 5$ and $nq > 5$, where $q = 1 - p$.

These conditions ensure that the distribution is reasonably symmetrical and not skewed away from either end, see figure 7.19.

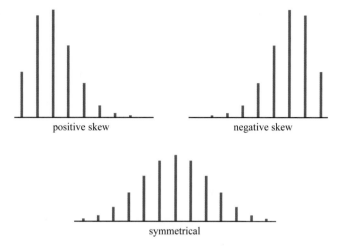

positive skew   negative skew

symmetrical

Figure 7.19

The parameters for the normal distribution are then

$$\text{Mean:} \quad \mu = np \quad \text{Variance:} \quad \sigma^2 = npq = np\,(1-p)$$

so that it can be denoted by N(np, npq).

EXAMPLE 7.4

This is a true story. During voting at an election, an exit poll of 1700 voters indicated that 50% of people had voted for a particular candidate. When the votes were counted it was found that he had in fact received 57% support.

850 of the 1700 people interviewed said they had voted for the candidate but 57% of 1700 is 969, a much higher number. What went wrong? Is it possible to be so far out just by being unlucky and asking the wrong people?

SOLUTION

The situation of selecting a sample of 1700 people and asking them if they voted for one candidate or not is one that is modelled by the binomial distribution, in this case B(1700, 0.57).

In theory you could multiply out $(0.43 + 0.57t)^{1700}$ and use that to find the probabilities of getting 0, 1, 2, ..., 850 supporters of this candidate in your sample of 1700. In practice such a method would be impractical because of the work involved.

What you can do is to use a normal approximation. The required conditions are fulfilled: at 1700, n is certainly not small; $p = 0.57$ is near neither 0 nor 1.

The parameters for the normal approximation are given by

$$\mu = np = 1700 \times 0.57 = 969$$

$$\sigma = \sqrt{npq} = \sqrt{1700 \times 0.57 \times 0.43} = 20.4$$

You will see that the standard deviation, 20.4, is large compared with the steps of 1 in the number of supporters of this candidate.

The probability of getting no more than 850 supporters of this candidate, $P(X \leqslant 850)$, is given by $\Phi(z)$, where

$$z = \frac{850.5 - 969}{20.4} = -5.8$$

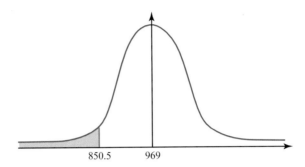

Figure 7.20

(Notice the continuity correction making 850 into 850.5.)

This is beyond the range of most tables and corresponds to a probability of about 0.000 01. The probability of a result as extreme as this is thus 0.000 02 (allowing for an equivalent result in the tail above the mean). It is clearly so unlikely that this was a result of random sampling that another explanation must be found.

? What do you think went wrong with the exit poll? Remember this really did happen.

1 A certain examination has a mean mark of 100 and a standard deviation of 15. The marks can be assumed to be normally distributed.

(i) What is the least mark needed to be in the top 35% of students taking this examination?

(ii) Between which two marks will the middle 90% of the students lie?

(iii) 150 students take this examination. Calculate the number of students likely to score 110 or over.

[MEI]

2 25% of Flapper Fish have red spots, the rest have blue spots. A fisherman nets 10 Flapper Fish. What are the probabilities that

(i) exactly 8 have blue spots

(ii) at least 8 have blue spots?

A large number of samples, each of 100 Flapper Fish, are taken.

(iii) What is the mean and the standard deviation of the number of red-spotted fish per sample?

(iv) What is the probability of a sample of 100 Flapper Fish containing over 30 with red spots?

3 A fair coin is tossed 10 times. Evaluate the probability that exactly half of the tosses result in heads.

The same coin is tossed 100 times. Use the normal approximation to the binomial to estimate the probability that exactly half of the tosses result in heads. Also estimate the probability that more than 60 of the tosses result in heads.

Explain why a continuity correction is made when using the normal approximation to the binomial and the reason for the adoption of this correction.

[MEI]

4 During an advertising campaign, the manufacturers of Wolfitt (a dog food) claimed that 60% of dog owners preferred to buy Wolfitt.

(i) Assuming that the manufacturer's claim is correct for the population of dog owners, calculate

(a) using the binomial distribution

(b) using a normal approximation to the binomial

the probability that at least 6 of a random sample of 8 dog owners prefer to buy Wolfitt. Comment on the agreement, or disagreement, between your two values. Would the agreement be better or worse if the proportion had been 80% instead of 60%?

(ii) Continuing to assume that the manufacturer's figure of 60% is correct, use the normal approximation to the binomial to estimate the probability that, of a random sample of 100 dog owners, the number preferring to buy Wolfitt is between 60 and 70 inclusive.

[MEI]

5 A multiple-choice examination consists of 20 questions, for each of which the candidate is required to tick as correct one of three possible answers. Exactly one answer to each question is correct. A correct answer gets 1 mark and a wrong answer gets 0 marks. Consider a candidate who has complete ignorance about every question and therefore ticks at random. What is the probability that he gets a particular answer correct? Calculate the mean and variance of the number of questions he answers correctly.

The examiners wish to ensure that no more than 1% of completely ignorant candidates pass the examination. Use the normal approximation to the binomial, working throughout to 3 decimal places, to establish the pass mark that meets this requirement.

[MEI]

6 A telephone exchange serves 2000 subscribers, and at any moment during the busiest period there is a probability of $\frac{1}{30}$ for each subscriber that he will require a line. Assuming that the needs of subscribers are independent, write down an expression for the probability that exactly N lines will be occupied at any moment during the busiest period.

Use the normal distribution to estimate the minimum number of lines that would ensure that the probability that a call cannot be made because all the lines are occupied is less than 0.01.

Investigate whether the total number of lines needed would be reduced if the subscribers were split into two groups of 1000, each with its own set of lines.

[MEI]

7 It is known that, on average, 2 people in 5 in a certain country are overweight. A random sample of 400 people is chosen. Using a suitable approximation, find the probability that fewer than 165 people in the sample are overweight.

[Cambridge International AS and A Level Mathematics 9709, Paper 6 Q1 June 2005]

8 A survey of adults in a certain large town found that 76% of people wore a watch on their left wrist, 15% wore a watch on their right wrist and 9% did not wear a watch.

(i) A random sample of 14 adults was taken. Find the probability that more than 2 adults did not wear a watch.

(ii) A random sample of 200 adults was taken. Using a suitable approximation, find the probability that more than 155 wore a watch on their left wrist.

[Cambridge International AS and A Level Mathematics 9709, Paper 6 Q7 June 2006]

9 On a certain road 20% of the vehicles are trucks, 16% are buses and the remainder are cars.

(i) A random sample of 11 vehicles is taken. Find the probability that fewer than 3 are buses.

(ii) A random sample of 125 vehicles is now taken. Using a suitable approximation, find the probability that more than 73 are cars.

[Cambridge International AS and A Level Mathematics 9709, Paper 6 Q3 June 2009]

10 On any occasion when a particular gymnast performs a certain routine, the probability that she will perform it correctly is 0.65, independently of all other occasions.

(i) Find the probability that she will perform the routine correctly on exactly 5 occasions out of 7.

(ii) On one day she performs the routine 50 times. Use a suitable approximation to estimate the probability that she will perform the routine correctly on fewer than 29 occasions.

(iii) On another day she performs the routine n times. Find the smallest value of n for which the expected number of correct performances is at least 8.

[Cambridge International AS and A Level Mathematics 9709, Paper 6 Q6 November 2007]

11 In the holidays Martin spends 25% of the day playing computer games. Martin's friend phones him once a day at a randomly chosen time.

(i) Find the probability that, in one holiday period of 8 days, there are exactly 2 days on which Martin is playing computer games when his friend phones.

(ii) Another holiday period lasts for 12 days. State with a reason whether it is appropriate to use a normal approximation to find the probability that there are fewer than 7 days on which Martin is playing computer games when his friend phones.

(iii) Find the probability that there are at least 13 days of a 40-day holiday period on which Martin is playing computer games when his friend phones.

[Cambridge International AS and A Level Mathematics 9709, Paper 61 Q5 June 2010]

KEY POINTS

1 The normal distribution with mean μ and standard deviation σ is denoted by $N(\mu, \sigma^2)$.

2 This may be given in standardised form by using the transformation

$$z = \frac{x - \mu}{\sigma}$$

3 In the standardised form, $N(0, 1)$, the mean is 0, and the standard deviation and variance are both 1.

4 The standard normal curve is given by

$$\Phi(z) = \frac{1}{\sqrt{2\pi}} e^{-\frac{1}{2}z^2}$$

5 The area to the left of the value z in the diagram below, representing the probability of a value less than z, is denoted by $\Phi(z)$ and is read from tables.

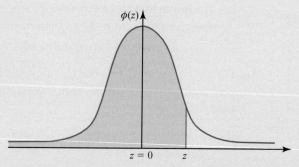

6 The normal distribution may be used to approximate suitable discrete distributions but continuity corrections are then required.

7 The binomial distribution $B(n, p)$ may be approximated by $N(np, npq)$, provided n is large and p is not close to 0 or 1, so that $np > 5$ and $nq > 5$.

Statistics 2

Hypothesis testing using the binomial distribution

You may prove anything by figures.

An anonymous salesman

Machoman Dan _____

Just became a father again! 8 boys in a row – how's that for macho chromosomes? Even at school I told people I was a real man!

What do you think?

There are two quite different points here.

Maybe you think that Dan is prejudiced, preferring boys to girls. However, you should not let your views on that influence your judgement on the second point, his claim to be biologically different from other people, with special chromosomes.

There are two ways this claim could be investigated, to look at his chromosomes under a high magnification microscope or to consider the statistical evidence. Since you have neither Dan nor a suitable microscope to hand, you must resort to the latter.

If you have eight children you would expect them to be divided about evenly between the sexes, $4 - 4$, $5 - 3$ or perhaps $6 - 2$. When you realised that a baby was on its way you would think it equally likely to be a boy or a girl until it was born, or a scan was carried out, when you would know for certain one way or the other.

In other words you would say that the probability of its being a boy was 0.5 and that of its being a girl was 0.5. So you can model the number of boys among eight children by the binomial distribution B(8, 0.5).

This gives the probabilities in the table, also shown in figure 8.1.

Boys	Girls	Probability
0	8	$\frac{1}{256}$
1	7	$\frac{8}{256}$
2	6	$\frac{28}{256}$
3	5	$\frac{56}{256}$
4	4	$\frac{70}{256}$
5	3	$\frac{56}{256}$
6	2	$\frac{28}{256}$
7	1	$\frac{8}{256}$
8	0	$\frac{1}{256}$

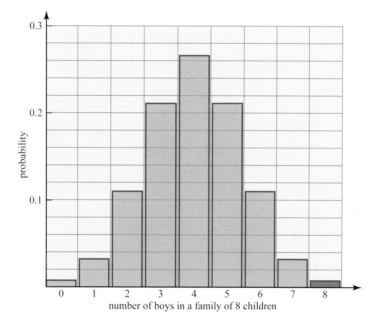

Figure 8.1

So you can say that, if a biologically normal man fathers eight children, the probability that they will all be boys is $\frac{1}{256}$ (dark green in figure 8.1).

This is unlikely but by no means impossible.

> *Note*
>
> The probability of a baby being a boy is not in fact 0.5 but about 0.503. Boys are less tough than girls and so more likely to die in infancy and this seems to be nature's way of compensating. In most societies men have a markedly lower life expectancy as well.

In some countries many people value boys more highly than girls. Medical advances mean that it will soon be possible for parents to decide in advance the sex of their next baby. What would be the effect of this on a country's population if, say, half the parents decided to have only boys and the other half to let nature take its course?

(This is a real problem. The social consequences could be devastating.)

Defining terms

In the last example we investigated Dan's claim by comparing it to the usual situation, the unexceptional. If we use p for the probability that a child is a boy then the normal state of affairs can be stated as

$p = 0.5.$

This is called the *null hypothesis*, denoted by H_0.

Dan's claim (made, he says, before he had any children) was that

$p > 0.5$

and this is called the *alternative hypothesis*, H_1.

The word hypothesis (plural *hypotheses*) means a theory which is put forward either for the sake of argument or because it is believed or suspected to be true. An investigation like this is usually conducted in the form of a test, called a *hypothesis test*. There are many different sorts of hypothesis test used in statistics; in this chapter you meet only one of them.

It is never possible to prove something statistically in the sense that, for example, you can prove that the angle sum of a triangle is 180°. Even if you tossed a coin a million times and it came down heads every single time, it is still possible that the coin is unbiased and just happened to land that way. What you can say is that it is very unlikely; the probability of it happening that way is $(0.5)^{1\,000\,000}$ which is a decimal that starts with over 300 000 zeros. This is so tiny that you would feel quite confident in declaring the coin biased.

There comes a point when the probability is so small that you say 'That's good enough for me. I am satisfied that it hasn't happened that way by chance.'

The probability at which you make that decision is called the *significance level* of the test. Significance levels are usually given as percentages; 0.05 is written as 5%, 0.01 as 1% and so on.

So in the case of Dan, the question could have been worded:

Test, at the 1% significance level, Dan's claim that his children are more likely to be boys than girls.

The answer would then look like this:

Null hypothesis, H_0: $p = 0.5$ (Boys and girls are equally likely)
Alternative hypothesis, H_1: $p > 0.5$ (Boys are more likely)
Significance level: 1%

Probability of 8 boys from 8 children $= \frac{1}{256} = 0.0039 = 0.39\%$.

Since $0.39\% < 1\%$ we reject the null hypothesis and accept the alternative hypothesis. We accept Dan's claim.

This example also illustrates some of the problems associated with hypothesis testing. Here is a list of points you should be considering.

Hypothesis testing checklist

1 Was the test set up before or after the data were known?

The test consists of a null hypothesis, an alternative hypothesis and a significance level.

In this case, the null hypothesis is the natural state of affairs and so does not really need to be stated in advance. Dan's claim 'Even at school I told people I was a real man' could be interpreted as the alternative hypothesis, $p > 0.5$.

The problem is that one suspects that whatever children Dan had he would find an excuse to boast. If they had all been girls, he might have been talking about 'my irresistible attraction for the opposite sex' and if they had been a mixture of girls and boys he would have been claiming 'super-virility' just because he had eight children.

Any test carried out retrospectively must be treated with suspicion.

2 Was the sample involved chosen at random and are the data independent?

The sample was not random and that may have been inevitable. If Dan had lots of children around the country with different mothers, a random sample of eight could have been selected. However, we have no knowledge that this is the case.

The data are the sexes of Dan's children. If there are no multiple births (for example, identical twins), then they are independent.

3 Is the statistical procedure actually testing the original claim?

Dan claims to have 'macho chromosomes' whereas the statistical test is of the alternative hypothesis that $p > 0.5$. The two are not necessarily the same. Even if this alternative hypothesis is true, it does not necessarily follow that Dan has macho chromosomes.

The ideal hypothesis test

In the ideal hypothesis test you take the following steps, in this order:

1 Establish the null and alternative hypotheses.

2 Decide on the significance level.

3 Collect suitable data using a random sampling procedure that ensures the items are independent.

4 Conduct the test, doing the necessary calculations.

5 Interpret the result in terms of the original claim, theory or problem.

There are times, however, when you need to carry out a test but it is just not possible to do so as rigorously as this.

If Dan been a laboratory rat you could have organised that he fathered further babies but this is not possible with a human.

Choosing the significance level

If, instead of 1%, we had set the significance level at 0.1%, then we would have rejected Dan's claim, since 0.39% > 0.1%. The lower the percentage in the significance level, the more stringent is the test.

The significance level you choose for a test involves a balanced judgement.

Imagine that you are testing the rivets on an plane's wing to see if they have lost their strength. Setting a small significance level, say 0.1%, means that you will only declare the rivets weak if you are very confident of your finding. The trouble with requiring such a high level of evidence is that even when they are weak you may well fail to register the fact, with the possible consequence that the plane crashes. On the other hand if you set a high significance level, such as 10%, you run the risk of declaring the rivets faulty when they are all right, involving the company in expensive and unnecessary maintenance work.

The question of how you choose the best significance level is, however, beyond the scope of this introductory chapter.

EXAMPLE 8.1

Leonora claims that a die is biased with a tendency to show the number 1. The die was thrown 20 times and the results were as follows.

$$
\begin{array}{cccccccccc}
1 & 6 & 6 & 5 & 5 & 1 & 2 & 3 & 2 & 3 \\
4 & 4 & 4 & 1 & 4 & 1 & 1 & 4 & 1 & 3
\end{array}
$$

Using a 5% significance level, test whether Leonora's claim is correct.

SOLUTION

Let p be the probability of getting 1 on any throw of the die.

Null hypothesis, H_0: $p = \frac{1}{6}$ (The die is unbiased)

Alternative hypothesis, H_1: $p > \frac{1}{6}$ (The die is biased towards 1)

Significance level: 5%

The results may be summarised as follows.

Score	1	2	3	4	5	6
Frequency	6	2	3	5	2	2

Under the null hypothesis, the number of 1s obtained is modelled by the binomial distribution, $B(20, \frac{1}{6})$ which gives these probabilities:

Number of 1s	Expression	Probability
0	$\left(\frac{5}{6}\right)^{20}$	0.0261
1	$^{20}C_1\left(\frac{5}{6}\right)^{19}\left(\frac{1}{6}\right)$	0.1043
2	$^{20}C_2\left(\frac{5}{6}\right)^{18}\left(\frac{1}{6}\right)^{2}$	0.1982
3	$^{20}C_3\left(\frac{5}{6}\right)^{17}\left(\frac{1}{6}\right)^{3}$	0.2379
4	$^{20}C_4\left(\frac{5}{6}\right)^{16}\left(\frac{1}{6}\right)^{4}$	0.2022
5	$^{20}C_5\left(\frac{5}{6}\right)^{15}\left(\frac{1}{6}\right)^{5}$	0.1294
6	$^{20}C_6\left(\frac{5}{6}\right)^{14}\left(\frac{1}{6}\right)^{6}$	0.0647
7	$^{20}C_7\left(\frac{5}{6}\right)^{13}\left(\frac{1}{6}\right)^{7}$	0.0259
8	$^{20}C_8\left(\frac{5}{6}\right)^{12}\left(\frac{1}{6}\right)^{8}$	0.0084
$\vdots$	$\vdots$	$\vdots$
20	$\left(\frac{1}{6}\right)^{20}$	0.0000

The probability of 1 coming up between 0 and 5 times is found by adding these probabilities. You get 0.8981 but working to more decimal places and then rounding gives 0.8982 which is correct to 4 decimal places.

If you worked out all these and added them you would get the probability that the number of 1s is 6 or more (up to a possible 20). It is much quicker, however, to find this as $1 - 0.8982$ (the answer above) $= 0.1018$.

Calling X the number of 1s occurring when a die is rolled 20 times, the probability of six or more 1s is given by

$$P(X \geqslant 6) = 1 - P(X \leqslant 5)$$
$$= 1 - 0.8982$$
$$= 0.1018,$$

about 10%.

Since 10% > 5%, the null hypothesis (the die is unbiased) is accepted. So Leonora's claim is rejected at the 5% significance level.

The probability of a result at least as extreme as that observed is greater than the 5% cut-off that was set in advance, that is, greater than the chosen significance level.

The alternative hypothesis (the die is biased in favour of the number 1) is rejected, even though the number 1 did come up more often than the other numbers.

❓ Does the procedure in Example 8.1 follow the steps of the ideal hypothesis test?

Note

Notice that this is a test not of the particular result (six 1s) but of a result at least as extreme as this (at least six 1s), the darker area in figure 8.2. A hypothesis test deals with the probability of an event 'as unusual as or more unusual than' what has occurred.

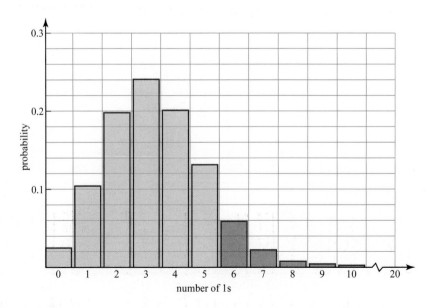

Figure 8.2

EXERCISE 8A

In all these questions you should apply this checklist to the hypothesis test.

a Was the test set up before or after the data were known?

b Was the sample used for the test chosen at random and are the data independent?

c Is the statistical procedure actually testing the original claim?

You should also comment critically on whether these steps have been followed.

- Establish the null and alternative hypotheses.

- Decide on the significance level.

- Collect suitable data using a random sampling procedure that ensures the items are independent.

- Conduct the test, doing the necessary calculations.

- Interpret the result in terms of the original claim, theory or problem.

1 Mrs da Silva is running for President. She claims to have 60% of the population supporting her.

She is suspected of overestimating her support and a random sample of 12 people are asked whom they support. Only four say Mrs da Silva.

Test, at the 5% significance level, the hypothesis that she has overestimated her support.

2 A company developed synthetic coffee and claim that coffee drinkers could not distinguish it from the real product. A number of coffee drinkers challenged the company's claim, saying that the synthetic coffee tasted synthetic. In a test, carried out by an independent consumer protection body, 20 people were given a mug of coffee. Ten had the synthetic brand and ten the natural, but they were not told which they had been given.

Out of the ten given the synthetic brand, eight said it was synthetic and two said it was natural. Use this information to test the coffee drinkers' claim (as against the null hypothesis of the company's claim), at the 5% significance level.

3 A group of 18 students decides to investigate the truth of the saying that if you drop a piece of toast it is more likely to land butter-side down. They each take one piece of toast, butter it on one side and throw it in the air. Fourteen land butter-side down, the rest butter-side up. Use their results to carry out a hypothesis test at the 1% significance level, stating clearly your null and alternative hypotheses.

4 On average 70% of people pass their driving test first time. There are complaints that Mr McTaggart is too harsh and so, unknown to himself, his work is monitored. It is found that he fails four out of ten candidates. Are the complaints justified at the 5% significance level?

5 A machine makes bottles. In normal running 5% of the bottles are expected to be cracked, but if the machine needs servicing this proportion will increase. As part of a routine check, 50 bottles are inspected and 5 are found to be unsatisfactory. Does this provide evidence, at the 5% significance level, that the machine needs servicing?

6 A firm producing mugs has a quality control scheme in which a random sample of 10 mugs from each batch is inspected. For 50 such samples, the numbers of defective mugs are as follows.

Number of defective mugs	0	1	2	3	4	5	6+
Number of samples	5	13	15	12	4	1	0

(i) Find the mean and standard deviation of the number of defective mugs per sample.

(ii) Show that a reasonable estimate for p, the probability that a mug is defective, is 0.2. Use this figure to calculate the probability that a randomly chosen sample will contain exactly two defective mugs. Comment on the agreement between this value and the observed data.

The management is not satisfied with 20% of mugs being defective and introduces a new process to reduce the proportion of defective mugs.

(iii) A random sample of 20 mugs, produced by the new process, contains just one which is defective. Test, at the 5% level, whether it is reasonable to suppose that the proportion of defective mugs has been reduced, stating your null and alternative hypotheses clearly.

(iv) What would the conclusion have been if the management had chosen to conduct the test at the 10% level?

[MEI]

7 An annual mathematics contest contains 15 questions, 5 short and 10 long. The probability that I get a short question right is 0.9. The probability that I get a long question right is 0.5. My performances on questions are independent of each other. Find the probability of the following:

(i) I get all the 5 short questions right.
(ii) I get exactly 8 of the 10 long questions right.
(iii) I get exactly 3 of the short questions and all of the long questions right.
(iv) I get exactly 13 of the 15 questions right.

After some practice, I hope that my performance on the long questions will improve this year. I intend to carry out an appropriate hypothesis test.

(v) State suitable null and alternative hypotheses for the test.

In this year's contest I get exactly 8 of the 10 long questions right.

(vi) Is there sufficient evidence, at the 5% significance level, that my performance on long questions has improved?

8 Isaac claims that 30% of cars in his town are red. His friend Hardip thinks that the proportion is less than 30%. The boys decided to test Isaac's claim at the 5% significance level and found that 2 cars out of the random sample of 18 were red. Carry out the hypothesis test and state your conclusion.

[Cambridge International AS and A Level Mathematics 9709, Paper 7 Q1 November 2007]

9 At the 2009 election, $\frac{1}{3}$ of the voters in Chington voted for the Citizens Party. One year later, a researcher questioned 20 randomly selected voters in Chington. Exactly 3 of these 20 voters said that if there were an election next week they would vote for the Citizens Party. Test at the 2.5% significance level whether there is evidence of a decrease in support for the Citizens Party in Chington, since the 2009 election.

[Cambridge International AS and A Level Mathematics 9709, Paper 73 Q1 June 2010]

Critical values and critical (rejection) regions

In Example 8.1 the number 1 came up six times and this was not enough for Leonora to show that the die was biased. What was the least number of times 1 would have had to come up for the test to give the opposite result?

We again use X to denote the number of times 1 comes up in the 20 throws and so $X = 6$ means that the number 1 comes up six times.

We know from our earlier work that the probability that $X \leqslant 5$ is 0.8982 and we can use the binomial distribution to work out the probabilities that $X = 6$, $X = 7$, etc.

$$P(X = 6) = {}^{20}C_2\left(\frac{5}{6}\right)^{14}\left(\frac{1}{6}\right)^6 = 0.0647$$

$$P(X = 7) = {}^{20}C_7\left(\frac{5}{6}\right)^{13}\left(\frac{1}{6}\right)^7 = 0.0259$$

${}^{20}C_2$ can also be written as $\binom{20}{2}$.

We know $P(X \geqslant 6) = 1 - P(X \leqslant 5) = 1 - 0.8982 = 0.1018$.

0.1018 is a little over 10% and so greater than the significance level of 5%. There is no reason to reject H_0.

What about the case when the number 1 comes up seven times, that is $X = 7$?

Since $\quad P(X \leqslant 6) = P(X \leqslant 5) + P(X = 6)$
$\qquad P(X \leqslant 6) = 0.8982 + 0.0647 = 0.9629$

So $\qquad P(X \geqslant 7) = 1 - P(X \leqslant 6)$
$\qquad\qquad = 1 - 0.9629 = 0.0371 = 3.71\%$

Since 3.7% < 5%, H_0 is now rejected in favour of H_1.

You can see that Leonora needed the 1 to come up seven or more times if her claim was to be upheld. She missed by just one. You might think Leonora's 'all or nothing' test was a bit harsh. Sometimes tests are designed so that if the result falls within a certain region further trials are recommended.

In this example the number 7 is the *critical value* (at the 5% significance level), the value at which you change from accepting the null hypothesis to rejecting it. The range of values for which you reject the null hypothesis, in this case $X \geqslant 7$, is called the *critical region* or the *rejection region*.

It is sometimes easier in hypothesis testing to find the critical region and see if your value lies in it, rather than working out the probability of a value at least as extreme as the one you have, the procedure used so far.

The quality control department of a factory tests a random sample of 20 items from each batch produced. A batch is rejected (or perhaps subject to further tests) if the number of faulty items in the sample, X, is more than 2.

This means that the rejection region is $X \geqslant 3$.

It is much simpler for the operator carrying out the test to be told the rejection region (determined in advance by the person designing the procedure) than to have to work out a probability for each test result.

> # Test procedure
>
> ## Take 20 pistons
>
> ## If 3 or more are faulty REJECT the batch

EXAMPLE 8.2

World-wide 25% of men are colour-blind but it is believed that the condition is less widespread among a group of remote hill tribes. An anthropologist plans to test this by sending field workers to visit villages in that area. In each village 30 men are to be tested for colour-blindness. Find the rejection region for the test at the 5% level of significance.

SOLUTION

Let p be the probability that a man in that area is colour-blind.

Null hypothesis, H_0: $p = 0.25$
Alternative hypothesis, H_1: $p < 0.25$ (Less colour-blindness in this area)
Significance level: 5%

With the hypothesis H_0, if the number of colour-blind men in a sample of 30 is X, then $X \sim B(30, 0.25)$.

The rejection region is the region $X \leqslant k$, where

$$P(X \leqslant k) \leqslant 0.05 \quad \text{and} \quad P(X \leqslant k+1) > 0.05.$$

$$P(X=0) = (0.75)^{30} = 0.00018$$

$$P(X=1) = 30(0.75)^{29}(0.25) = 0.00179$$

$$P(X=2) = \binom{30}{2}(0.75)^{28}(0.25)^2 = 0.00863$$

$$P(X=3) = \binom{30}{3}(0.75)^{27}(0.25)^3 = 0.02685$$

$$P(X=4) = \binom{30}{4}(0.75)^{26}(0.25)^4 = 0.06042.$$

So $P(X \leqslant 3) = 0.00018 + 0.00179 + 0.00863 + 0.02685 \approx 0.0375 \leqslant 0.05$

but $P(X \leqslant 4) \approx 0.0929 > 0.05.$

Therefore the rejection region is $X \leqslant 3$.

? What is the rejection region at the 10% significance level?

In many other hypothesis tests it is usual to find the critical values from tables.

EXPERIMENTS

Mind reading

Here is a simple experiment to see if you can read the mind of a friend whom you know well. The two of you face each other across a table on which is placed a coin. Your friend takes the coin and puts it in one or other hand under the table. You have to guess which one.

Play this game at least 20 times and test at the 10% significance level whether you can read your friend's mind.

Left and right

It is said that if people are following a route which brings them to a T-junction where they have a free choice between turning left and right the majority will turn right.

Design and carry out an experiment to test this hypothesis.

Note

This is taken very seriously by companies choosing stands at exhibitions. It is considered worth paying extra for a location immediately to the right of one of the entrances.

Coloured sweets

Get a large box of coloured sweets, such as Smarties, and taste the different colours. Choose the colour, *C*, which you think has the most distinctive flavour.

Now close your eyes and get a friend to feed you sweets. Taste each one and say if it is your chosen colour or not. Do this for at least 20 sweets and test at the 10% significance level whether you can pick out those with colour *C* by taste.

EXERCISE 8B

1 In a certain country, 90% of letters are delivered the day after posting.

A resident posts eight letters on a certain day.

Find the probability that

(i) all eight letters are delivered the next day

(ii) at least six letters are delivered the next day

(iii) exactly half the letters are delivered the next day.

It is later suspected that the service has deteriorated as a result of mechanisation. To test this, 17 letters are posted and it is found that only 13 of them arrive the next day. Let *p* denote the probability, after mechanisation, that a letter is delivered the next day.

(iv) Write down suitable null and alternative hypotheses for the value of *p*.

(v) Carry out the hypothesis test, at the 5% level of significance, stating your results clearly.

(vi) Write down the critical region for the test, giving a reason for your choice.

[MEI]

> **Hint:** You will find it easier to work out the probability that the number not arriving on time is 3, 2, 1 or 0 than to calculate the probability that the number arriving on time is 0, 1, 2, …, 13.

2 For most small birds, the ratio of males to females may be expected to be about 1:1. In one ornithological study birds are trapped by setting fine-mesh nets. The trapped birds are counted and then released. The catch may be regarded as a random sample of the birds in the area.

The ornithologists want to test whether there are more male blackbirds than females.

(i) Assuming that the sex ratio of blackbirds is 1:1, find the probability that a random sample of 16 blackbirds contains

(a) 12 males

(b) at least 12 males.

(ii) State the null and alternative hypotheses the ornithologists should use.

In one sample of 16 blackbirds there are 12 males and 4 females.

(iii) Carry out a suitable test using these data at the 5% significance level, stating your conclusion clearly. Find the critical region for the test.

(iv) Another ornithologist points out that, because female birds spend much time sitting on the nest, females are less likely to be caught than males. Explain how this would affect your conclusions.

[MEI]

3 A seed supplier advertises that, on average, 80% of a certain type of seed will germinate. Suppose that 18 of these seeds, chosen at random, are planted.

(i) Find the probability that 17 or more seeds will germinate if

(a) the supplier's claim is correct

(b) the supplier is incorrect and 82% of the seeds, on average, germinate.

Mr Brewer is the advertising manager for the seed supplier. He thinks that the germination rate may be higher than 80% and he decides to carry out a hypothesis test at the 10% level of significance. He plants 18 seeds.

(ii) Write down the null and alternative hypotheses for Mr Brewer's test, explaining why the alternative hypothesis takes the form it does.

(iii) Find the critical region for Mr Brewer's test. Explain your reasoning.

(iv) Determine the probability that Mr Brewer will reach the *wrong* conclusion if

(a) the true germination rate is 80%

(b) the true germination rate is 82%.

[MEI]

One-tail and two-tail tests

Think back to the two examples in the first part of this chapter.

What would Dan have said if his eight children had all been girls? What would Leonora have said if the number 1 had not come up at all?

In both our examples the claim was not only that something was unusual but that it was so in a particular direction. So we looked only at one side of the distributions when working out the probabilities, as you can see in figure 8.1 on page 181 and figure 8.2 on page 186. In both cases we applied one-tail tests. (The word 'tail' refers to the darker coloured part at the end of the distribution.)

If Dan had just claimed that there was something odd about his chromosomes, then you would have had to work out the probability of a result as extreme on either side of the distribution, in this case eight girls or eight boys, and you would then apply a two-tail test.

Here is an example of a two-tail test.

EXAMPLE 8.3

The producer of a television programme claims that it is politically unbiased. 'If you take somebody off the street it is 50 : 50 whether he or she will say the programme favours the government or the opposition', she says.

However, when ten people, selected at random, are asked the question 'Does the programme support the government or the opposition?', nine say it supports the government.

Does this constitute evidence, at the 5% significance level, that the producer's claim is inaccurate?

SOLUTION

Read the last sentence carefully and you will see that it does not say in which direction the bias must be. It does not ask if the programme is favouring the government or the opposition, only if the producer's claim is inaccurate. So you must consider both ends of the distribution, working out the probability of such an extreme result either way: 9 or 10 saying it favours the government, or 9 or 10 the opposition. This is a two-tail test.

If p is the probability that somebody believes the programme supports the government, you have

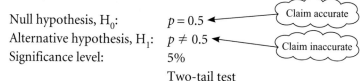

Null hypothesis, H_0: $p = 0.5$ Claim accurate

Alternative hypothesis, H_1: $p \neq 0.5$ Claim inaccurate

Significance level: 5%

               Two-tail test

The situation is modelled by the binomial distribution $B(10, 0.5)$ and is shown in figure 8.3.

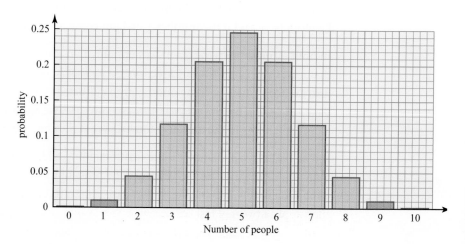

Figure 8.3

This gives

$$P(X=0) = \frac{1}{1024} \qquad P(X=1) = \frac{10}{1024}$$
$$P(X=10) = \frac{1}{1024} \qquad P(X=9) = \frac{10}{1024}$$

where X is the number of people saying the programme favours the government. Thus the total probability for the two tails is $\frac{22}{1024}$ or 2.15%.

Since 2.15% < 5% the null hypothesis is rejected in favour of the alternative, *that the producer's claim is inaccurate.*

Note

You have to look carefully at the way a test is worded to decide if it should be one-tail or two-tail.

Dan claimed his chromosomes made him more likely to father boys than girls. That requires a one-tail test.

Leonora claimed the die was biased in the direction of too many 1s. Again a one-tail test.

The test of the television producer's claim was for inaccuracy in either direction and so a two-tail test was needed.

EXERCISE 8C

1 To test the claim that a coin is biased, it is tossed 12 times. It comes down heads 3 times. Test at the 10% significance level whether this claim is justified.

2 A biologist discovers a colony of a previously unknown type of bird nesting in a cave. Out of the 16 chicks which hatch during his period of investigation, 13 are female. Test at the 5% significance level whether this supports the view that the sex ratio for the chicks differs from $1:1$.

3 People entering an exhibition have to choose whether to turn left or right. Out of the first twelve people, nine turn left and three right. Test at the 5% significance level whether people are more likely to turn one way than the other.

4 A multiple choice test has 15 questions, with the answer for each allowing five options, A, B, C, D and E. All the students in a class tell their teacher that they guessed all 15 answers. The teacher does not believe them. Devise a two-tail test at the 10% significance level to apply to a student's mark to test the hypothesis that the answers were not selected at random.

5 When a certain language is written down, 15% of the letters are Z. Use this information to devise a test at the 10% significance level which somebody who does not know the language could apply to a short passage, 50 letters long, to determine whether it is written in the same language.

6   A seed firm states on a packet of rare seeds that the germination rate is 20%. The packet contains 25 seeds.

(i)   How many seeds would you expect to germinate out of the packet?

(ii) What is the probability of exactly 5 seeds germinating?

A man buys a packet and only 1 seed germinates.

(iii) Is he justified in complaining?

7   Given that X has a binomial distribution in which $n = 15$ and $p = 0.5$, find the probability of each of the following events.

(i) $X = 4$

(ii) $X \leqslant 4$

(iii) $X = 4$ or $X = 11$

(iv) $X \leqslant 4$ or $X \geqslant 11$

A large company is considering introducing a new selection procedure for job applicants. The selection procedure is intended to result over a long period in equal numbers of men and women being offered jobs. The new procedure is tried with a random sample of applicants and 15 of them, 11 women and 4 men, are offered jobs.

(v)   Carry out a suitable test at the 5% level of significance to determine whether it is reasonable to suppose that the selection procedure is performing as intended. You should state the null and alternative hypotheses under test and explain carefully how you arrive at your conclusions.

(vi) Suppose now that, of the 15 applicants offered jobs, w are women. Find all the values of w for which the selection procedure should be judged acceptable at the 5% level.

[MEI]

Type I and Type II errors

There are two types of error that can occur when a hypothesis test is carried out. They are illustrated in the following example.

EXAMPLE 8.4

A gold coin is used for the toss at a country's football matches but it is suspected of being biased. It is suggested that it shows heads more often than it should. A test is planned in which the coin is to be tossed 19 times and the results recorded. It is decided to use a 5% significance level; so, if the coin shows heads 14 or more times, it will be declared biased.

What errors are possible in interpreting the test result?

SOLUTION

Two types of error are possible.

A Type I error

In this case the coin is actually unbiased, so the probability, p, of it showing heads is given by $p = 0.5$. However, it happens to come up heads 14 or more times and so is incorrectly declared to be biased.

The probabilities of possible outcomes from 19 tosses when $p = 0.5$ can be found using the binomial distribution. Some of them are given, to 2 significant figures, in the table below.

Number of heads	$\geqslant 10$	$\geqslant 11$	$\geqslant 12$	$\geqslant 13$	$\geqslant 14$	$\geqslant 15$	$\geqslant 16$
Probability	0.50	0.32	0.18	0.084	0.032	0.010	0.0022

The table shows that the probability of getting 14 or more heads, and so making the error of rejecting the true null hypothesis that $p = 0.5$, is 0.032 and so just less than the 5% significance level. This type of error, where a null hypothesis is rejected despite being correct, is called a Type I error. The figures in the table illustrate the fact that for a binomial test the probability of making a Type I error is either equal to the significance level of the test or slightly less than it. For most other hypothesis tests it is equal to the significance level; indeed that is the meaning of the term significance level, the probability of rejecting a true null hypothesis.

A Type II error

The other type of error occurs when the null hypothesis is in fact false but is nonetheless accepted. Imagine that the gold coin is actually biased with $p = 0.8$ and that it shows heads 12 times. In this test the null hypothesis is rejected if the number of heads is 14 or more, and so it is accepted if the number of heads is less than 14.

Since $12 < 14$, the null hypothesis is accepted, even though it is in fact false. This is called a Type II error, where a false null hypothesis is accepted.

In this case, it is possible to use the binomial distribution to work out the probability of a Type II error. When $p = 0.8$, the probability that when the coin is tossed 19 times the number of heads is less than 14 can be found to be 0.163, and so this is the probability of a Type II error in this example.

Notes

1 Notice that it was only possible to find the probability of a Type II error in Example 8.4 because the value of the population parameter under consideration was known: $p = 0.8$. Since finding out about this parameter is the object of the test, it would be unusual for it to be known. So, in practice, it is often not possible to calculate the probability of a Type II error. By contrast, no calculation at all is needed to find the probability of a Type I error; it is the significance level of the test.

2 For a given sample size, the probabilities of the two types of errors are linked. In Example 8.4, the probability of a Type II error could be reduced by making the test more severe; instead of requiring 14 or more heads to declare the coin biased, it could be reduced to 13 or perhaps 12. However, that would increase the probability of a Type I error.

3 The circumstances under which these errors occur is shown below.

		Decision	
		Accept H$_0$ (decide the coin is unbiased)	Reject H$_0$ (decide the coin is biased)
Reality	The null hypothesis, H$_0$, is true.	Correct decision	H$_0$ wrongly rejected: Type I error
	The null hypothesis, H$_0$, is false.	H$_0$ wrongly accepted: Type II error	Correct decision

In summary

● A type I error occurs when the sample leads you to wrongly reject H$_0$ when it is in fact true.

● A type II error occurs when the sample leads you to wrongly accept H$_0$ when it is in fact false.

EXAMPLE 8.5

It is known that 60% of the moths of a certain species are red; the rest are yellow. A biologist finds a new colony of these moths and observes that more of them seem to be red than she would expect. She designs an experiment in which she will catch 10 moths at random, observe their colour and then release them. She will then carry out a hypothesis test using a 5% significance level.

(i) State the null and alternative hypotheses for this test.

(ii) Find the rejection region.

(iii) Find the probability of a Type I error.

(iv) If in fact the proportion of red moths is 80%, find the probability that the test will result in a Type II error.

SOLUTION

(i) Let p be the probability that a randomly selected moth is red.

Null hypothesis: $H_0: p = 0.6$ The proportion of red moths in this colony is 60%.

Alternative hypothesis: $H_1: p > 0.6$ The proportion of red moths is greater than 60%.

(ii) Assuming H_0 is true, you can calculate the following probabilities for the 10 moths in the sample.

All 10 moths are red: $(0.6)^{10} = 0.0060...$

9 are red and 1 yellow: $^{10}C_1 \times (0.6)^9 \times 0.4 = 0.0403...$

8 are red and 2 yellow: $^{10}C_2 \times (0.6)^8 \times (0.4)^2 = 0.1209...$

There is no need to go any further.

The probability that there are nine or ten red moths is

$$0.0403... + 0.0060... = 0.0463...$$

and this is less than the 5% significance level.

The probability that there are eight, nine or ten red moths is

$$0.1209... + 0.0403... + 0.0060... = 0.167...$$

and this is greater than 5%.

So the rejection region for this test is 9 or 10 red moths.

(iii) A Type I error occurs when a true null hypothesis is rejected.

In this case if H_0 is true, and so $p = 0.6$, the probability of it being rejected because a particular sample has 9 or 10 red moths has already been worked out to be 0.0463... in part (ii). When rounded to 3 significant figures, this gives 0.0464.

So the probability of a Type 1 error is 0.0464 (to 3 s.f.).

(iv) If the proportion of red moths is 80%, the correct result from the test would be for the null hypothesis to be rejected in favour of the alternative hypothesis. The probability of this happening is

$$^{10}C_1 \times (0.8)^9 \times 0.2 + (0.8)^{10} = 0.376 \text{ (to 3 s.f.)}$$

A Type II error occurs when this result does not occur.

So in this situation the probability of a Type II error is $1 - 0.376 = 0.624$.

1 At a certain airport 20% of people take longer than an hour to check in. A new computer system is installed, and it is claimed that this will reduce the time to check in. It is decided to accept the claim if, from a random sample of 22 people, the number taking longer than an hour to check in is either 0 or 1.

(i) Calculate the significance level of the test.

(ii) State the probability that a Type I error occurs.

(iii) Calculate the probability that a Type II error occurs if the probability that a person takes longer than an hour to check in is now 0.09.

[Cambridge International AS and A Level Mathematics 9709, Paper 7 Q4 June 2007]

2 A manufacturer claims that 20% of sugar-coated chocolate beans are red. George suspects that this percentage is actually less than 20% and so he takes a random sample of 15 chocolate beans and performs a hypothesis test with the null hypothesis $p = 0.2$ against the alternative hypothesis $p < 0.2$. He decides to reject the null hypothesis in favour of the alternative hypothesis if there are 0 or 1 red beans in the sample.

(i) With reference to this situation, explain what is meant by a Type I error.

(ii) Find the probability of a Type I error in George's test.

[Cambridge International AS and A Level Mathematics 9709, Paper 7 Q2 November 2005]

3 In a certain city it is necessary to pass a driving test in order to be allowed to drive a car. The probability of passing the driving test at the first attempt is 0.36 on average. A particular driving instructor claims that the probability of his pupils passing at the first attempt is higher than 0.36. A random sample of 8 of his pupils showed that 7 passed at the first attempt.

(i) Carry out an appropriate hypothesis test to test the driving instructor's claim, using a significance level of 5%.

(ii) In fact, most of this random sample happened to be careful and sensible drivers. State which type of error in the hypothesis test (Type I or Type II) could have been made in these circumstances and find the probability of this type of error when a sample of size 8 is used for the test.

[Cambridge International AS and A Level Mathematics 9709, Paper 7 Q4 June 2009]

4 It is claimed that a certain 6-sided die is biased so that it is more likely to show a six than if it was fair. In order to test this claim at the 10% significance level, the die is thrown 10 times and the number of sixes is noted.

(i) Given that the die shows a six on 3 of the 10 throws, carry out the test.

On another occasion the same test is carried out again.

(ii) Find the probability of a Type I error.

(iii) Explain what is meant by a Type II error in this context.

[Cambridge International AS and A Level Mathematics 9709, Paper 71 Q6 November 2010]

1 **Hypothesis testing checklist**

- Was the test set up before or after the data were known?

- Was the sample involved chosen at random and are the data independent?

- Is the statistical procedure actually testing the original claim?

2 **Steps for conducting a hypothesis test**

- Establish the null and alternative hypotheses.

- Decide on the significance level.

- Collect suitable data using a random sampling procedure that ensures the items are independent.

- Conduct the test, doing the necessary calculations.

- Interpret the result in terms of the original claim, theory or problem.

3 A Type I error occurs when a true null hypothesis is rejected. The probability of a Type I error occurring is less than or equal to the significance level of the test.

4 A Type II error occurs when a false null hypothesis is accepted. The probability of a Type II error occurring depends on the (unknown) value of the population parameter; in a binomial test the parameter is p.

The Poisson distribution

9

If something can go wrong, sooner or later it will go wrong.

Murphy's Law

ElectricsExpress.com

Since our 'next day delivery guarantee' went live, the number of orders has increased dramatically. We are now one of the most popular websites for mail order electrical goods. We would like to reassure our customers that we have taken on more staff to cope with the increased demand for our products.
It is impossible to predict the level of demand, however, we do know that we are receiving an average of 150 orders per hour!

The appearance of this update on their website prompted a statistician to contact ElectricsExpress.com. She offered to analyse the data and see what suggestions she could come up with.

For her detailed investigation, she considered the distribution of the number of orders per minute. For a random sample of 1000 single-minute intervals during the last month, she collected the following data.

Number of orders per minute	0	1	2	3	4	5	6	7	>7
Frequency	70	215	265	205	125	75	30	10	5

Summary statistics for this frequency distribution are as follows.

$$n = 1000, \qquad \sum xf = 2525 \quad \text{and} \quad \sum x^2 f = 8885$$
$$\Rightarrow \quad \bar{x} = 2.525 \quad \text{and} \quad sd = 1.58 \text{ (to 3 s.f.)}$$

She also noted that

- orders made on the website appear at random and independently of each other

- the average number of orders per minute is about 2.5 which is equivalent to 150 per hour.

She suggested that the appropriate probability distribution to model the number of orders was the Poisson distribution.

The particular Poisson distribution, with an average number of 2.5 orders per minute, is defined as an *infinite* discrete random variable given by

$$P(X = r) = e^{-2.5} \times \frac{2.5^r}{r!} \quad \text{for} \quad r = 0, 1, 2, 3, 4, \ldots$$

where

- X represents the random variable 'number of orders per minute'

- e is the mathematical constant 2.718 281 828 459...

- $e^{-2.5}$ can be found from your calculator as 0.082 (to 3 d.p.)

- $r!$ means r *factorial*, for example $5! = 5 \times 4 \times 3 \times 2 \times 1 = 120$.

Values of the corresponding probability distribution may be tabulated using the formula, together with the expected frequencies this would generate. For example

$$P(X = 4) = e^{-2.5} \times \frac{2.5^4}{4!}$$

$$= 0.133\,60 \ldots$$

$$= 0.134 \text{ (to 3 s.f.)}$$

Number of orders per minute (r)	0	1	2	3	4	5	6	7	>7
Observed frequency	70	215	265	205	125	75	30	10	5
$P(X = r)$	0.082	0.205	0.257	0.214	0.134	0.067	0.028	0.010	0.003
Expected frequency	82	205	257	214	134	67	28	10	3

The closeness of the observed and expected frequencies (see figure 9.1) implies that the Poisson distribution is indeed a suitable model in this instance.

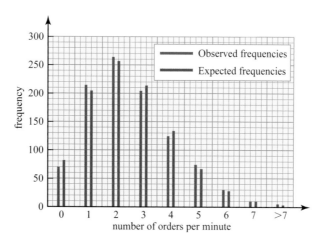

Figure 9.1

Note also that the sample mean, $\bar{x} = 2.525$, is very close to the sample variance, $s^2 = 2.509$ (to 4 s.f.). You will see later that, for a Poisson distribution, the expectation and variance are the same. So the closeness of these two summary statistics provides further evidence that the Poisson distribution is a suitable model.

The Poisson distribution

A discrete random variable may be modelled by a Poisson distribution provided

- events occur at random and independently of each other, in a given interval of time or space
- the average number events in the given interval, λ, is uniform and finite.

Let X represent the number of occurrences in a given interval, then

$$P(X = r) = e^{-\lambda} \times \frac{\lambda^r}{r!} \quad \text{for} \quad r = 0, 1, 2, 3, 4, \ldots$$

Like the discrete random variables you met in Chapter 4, the Poisson distribution may be illustrated by a vertical line chart. The shape of the Poisson distribution depends on the value of the parameter λ (pronounced 'lambda'). The letter μ (pronounced 'mu') is also commonly used to represent the Poisson parameter. If λ is small the distribution has positive skew, but as λ increases the distribution becomes progressively more symmetrical. Three typical Poisson distributions are illustrated in figure 9.2.

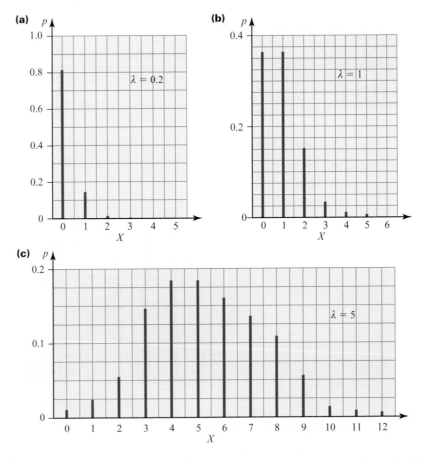

Figure 9.2 The shape of the Poisson distribution for **(a)** $\lambda = 0.2$ **(b)** $\lambda = 1$ **(c)** $\lambda = 5$

There are many situations in which events happen singly and the average number of occurrences per given interval of time or space is uniform and is known or can be easily found. Such events might include: the number of goals scored by a team in a football match, the number of telephone calls received per minute at an exchange, the number of accidents in a factory per week, the number of particles emitted in a minute by a radioactive substance whose half-life is relatively long, the number of typing errors per page in a document, the number of flaws per metre in a roll of cloth or the number of micro-organisms in 1 millilitre of pond water.

EXAMPLE 9.1

The number of defects in a wire cable can be modelled by the Poisson distribution with a uniform rate of 1.5 defects per kilometre.

Find the probability that

(i)   a single kilometre of wire will have exactly 3 defects
(ii) a single kilometre of wire will have at least 5 defects.

SOLUTION

Let X represent the number of defects per kilometre, then

$$P(X = r) = e^{-1.5} \times \frac{1.5^r}{r!} \quad \text{for} \quad r = 0, 1, 2, 3, 4, \dots.$$

(i) $P(X = 3) = e^{-1.5} \times \frac{1.5^3}{3!}$

$$= 0.125\,510\dots$$
$$= 0.126 \text{ (to 3 s.f.)}$$

(ii) $P(X \geqslant 5) = 1 - [P(X = 0) + P(X = 1) + P(X = 2) + P(X = 3) + P(X = 4)]$

$$= 1 - \left[e^{-1.5} \times \frac{1.5^0}{0!} + e^{-1.5} \times \frac{1.5^1}{1!} + e^{-1.5} \times \frac{1.5^2}{2!} + e^{-1.5} \times \frac{1.5^3}{3!} + e^{-1.5} \times \frac{1.5^4}{4!} \right]$$

$$= 1 - [0.223\,130\dots + 0.334\,695\dots + 0.251\,021\dots + 0.125\,510\dots$$
$$+ 0.047\,066\dots]$$

$$= 0.0186 \text{ (to 3 s.f.)}$$

Calculating Poisson distribution probabilities

In Example 9.1, about the defects in a wire cable, you had to work out $P(X \geqslant 5)$. To do this you used $P(X \geqslant 5) = 1 - P(X \leqslant 4)$ which saved you having to work out all the probabilities for five or more occurrences and adding them together. Such calculations can take a long time even though the terms eventually get smaller and smaller, so that after some time you will have gone far enough for the accuracy you require and may stop.

However, Example 9.1 did involve working out and summing five probabilities and so was quite time consuming. Here are two ways of cutting down on the amount of work, and so on the time you take.

Recurrence relations

Recurrence relations allow you to use the term you have obtained to work out the next one. For the Poisson distribution with parameter λ,

$$P(X=0) = e^{-\lambda} \qquad\qquad \text{You must use your calculator to find this term.}$$

$$P(X=1) = e^{-\lambda} \times \lambda = \lambda P(X=0) \qquad\qquad \text{Multiply the previous term by } \lambda.$$

$$P(X=2) = e^{-\lambda} \times \frac{\lambda^2}{2!} = \frac{\lambda}{2} P(X=1) \qquad\qquad \text{Multiply the previous term by } \frac{\lambda}{2}.$$

$$P(X=3) = e^{-\lambda} \times \frac{\lambda^3}{3!} = \frac{\lambda}{3} P(X=2) \qquad\qquad \text{Multiply the previous term by } \frac{\lambda}{3}.$$

$$P(X=4) = e^{-\lambda} \times \frac{\lambda^4}{4!} = \frac{\lambda}{4} P(X=3) \qquad\qquad \text{Multiply the previous term by } \frac{\lambda}{4}.$$

In general, you can find $P(X=r)$ by multiplying your previous probability, $P(X=r-1)$, by $\frac{\lambda}{r}$. You would expect to hold the latest value on your calculator and keep a running total in the memory.

Setting this out on paper with $\lambda = 1.5$ (the figure from Example 9.1) gives these figures.

No. of cases, r	Conversion	$P(X=r)$	Running total, $P(X \leqslant r)$
0		0.223 130...	0.223 130...
1	$\times 1.5$	0.334 695...	0.557 825...
2	$\times \dfrac{1.5}{2}$	0.251 021...	0.808 846...
3	$\times \dfrac{1.5}{3}$	0.125 510...	0.934 356...
4	$\times \dfrac{1.5}{4}$	0.047 066...	0.981 422...

Adapting the Poisson distribution for different time intervals

EXAMPLE 9.2

Jasmit is considering buying a telephone answering machine. He has one for five days' free trial and finds that 22 messages are left on it. Assuming that this is typical of the use it will get if he buys it, find:

(i) the mean number of messages per day
(ii) the probability that on one particular day there will be exactly six messages
(iii) the probability that there will be exactly six messages in two days.

SOLUTION

(i) Converting the total for five days to the mean for a single day gives

$$\text{daily mean} = \frac{22}{5} = 4.4 \text{ messages per day}$$

(ii) Calling X the number of messages per day,

$$P(X = 6) = e^{-4.4} \times \frac{4.4^6}{6!}$$

$$= 0.124$$

(iii) The mean for two days is

$$2 \times \frac{22}{5} = 8.8 \text{ messages}$$

So the probability of exactly six messages is

$$e^{-8.8} \times \frac{8.8^6}{6!} = 0.0972$$

Modelling with a Poisson distribution

In the example about ElectricsExpress.com, the mean and variance of the number of orders placed per minute on the website were given by $\bar{x} = 2.525$ and $s^2 = 2.51$ (to 3 s.f.). The corresponding Poisson parameter, λ, was then taken to be 2.5.

It can be shown that for any Poisson distribution

$$\text{Mean} = E(X) = \lambda \quad \text{and} \quad \text{Variance} = \text{Var}(X) = \lambda.$$

The notation $Po(\lambda)$ or $Poisson(\lambda)$ is used to describe this distribution. Formal derivations of the mean and variance of a Poisson distribution are given in Appendix 4 on the CD.

When modelling data with a Poisson distribution, the closeness of the mean and variance is one indication that the data fit the model well.

When you have collected the data, go through the following steps in order to check whether the data may be modelled by a Poisson distribution.

- Work out the mean and variance and check that they are roughly equal.

- Use the sample mean to work out the Poisson probability distribution and a suitable set of expected frequencies.

- Compare these expected frequencies with your observations.

EXERCISE 9A

1 If $X \sim Po(1.75)$, use the Poisson formula to calculate

(i) $P(X = 2)$ (ii) $P(X > 0)$.

2 If $X \sim Po(3.1)$, use the Poisson formula to calculate

(i) $P(X = 3)$ (ii) $P(X < 2)$ (iii) $P(X \geqslant 2)$.

3 The number of wombats that are killed on a particular stretch of road in Australia in any one day can be modelled by a Po(0.42) random variable.

(i) Calculate the probability that exactly two wombats are killed on a given day on this stretch of road.

(ii) Find the probability that exactly four wombats are killed over a 5-day period on this stretch of road.

4 A typesetter makes 1500 mistakes in a book of 500 pages. On how many pages would you expect to find (i) 0 (ii) 1 (iii) 2 (iv) 3 or more mistakes? State any assumptions in your workings.

5 In a country the mean number of deaths per year from lightning strike is 2.2.

(i) Find the probabilities of 0, 1, 2 and more than 2 deaths from lightning strike in any particular year.

In a neighbouring country, it is found that one year in twenty nobody dies from lightning strike.

(ii) Estimate the mean number of deaths per year in that country from lightning strike.

6 350 raisins are put into a mixture which is well stirred and made into 100 small buns. Estimate how many of these buns will

(i) be without raisins

(ii) contain five or more raisins.

In a second batch of 100 buns, exactly one has no raisins in it.

(iii) Estimate the total number of raisins in the second mixture.

7 A ferry takes cars and small vans on a short journey from an island to the mainland. On a representative sample of weekday mornings, the numbers of vehicles, X, on the 8 am sailing were as follows.

20	24	24	22	23	21	20	22	23	22
21	21	22	21	23	22	20	22	20	24

(i) Show that X does not have a Poisson distribution.

In fact 20 of the vehicles belong to commuters who use that sailing of the ferry every weekday morning. The random variable Y is the number of vehicles other than those 20 who are using the ferry.

(ii) Investigate whether Y may reasonably be modelled by a Poisson distribution.

The ferry can take 25 vehicles on any journey.

(iii) On what proportion of days would you expect at least one vehicle to be unable to travel on this particular sailing of the ferry because there was no room left and so have to wait for the next one?

8 Small hard particles are found in the molten glass from which glass bottles are made. On average, 15 particles are found per 100 kg of molten glass. If a bottle contains one or more such particles it has to be discarded.

Suppose bottles of mass 1 kg are made. It is required to estimate the percentage of bottles that have to be discarded. Criticise the following 'answer': *Since the material for 100 bottles contains 15 particles, approximately 15% will have to be discarded.*

Making suitable assumptions, which should be stated, develop a correct argument using a Poisson model, and find the percentage of faulty 1 kg bottles to three significant figures.

Show that about 3.7% of bottles of mass 0.25 kg are faulty.

[MEI]

9 People arrive randomly and independently at the elevator in a block of flats at an average rate of 4 people every 5 minutes.

(i) Find the probability that exactly two people arrive in a 1-minute period.

(ii) Find the probability that nobody arrives in a 15-second period.

(iii) The probability that at least one person arrives in the next t minutes is 0.9. Find the value of t.

[Cambridge International AS and A Level Mathematics 9709, Paper 7 Q6 June 2008]

10 A shopkeeper sells electric fans. The demand for fans follows a Poisson distribution with mean 3.2 per week.

(i) Find the probability that the demand is exactly 2 fans in any one week.

(ii) The shopkeeper has 4 fans in his shop at the beginning of a week. Find the probability that this will not be enough to satisfy the demand for fans in that week.

(iii) Given instead that he has n fans in his shop at the beginning of a week, find, by trial and error, the least value of n for which the probability of his not being able to satisfy the demand for fans in that week is less than 0.05.

[Cambridge International AS and A Level Mathematics 9709, Paper 7 Q6 November 2005]

11 People arrive randomly and independently at a supermarket checkout at an average rate of 2 people every 3 minutes.

(i) Find the probability that exactly 4 people arrive in a 5-minute period.

At another checkout in the same supermarket, people arrive randomly and independently at an average rate of 1 person each minute.

(ii) Find the probability that a total of fewer than 3 people arrive at the two checkouts in a 3-minute period.

[Cambridge International AS and A Level Mathematics 9709, Paper 71 Q2 November 2010]

e   **12** A manufacturer of rifle ammunition tests a large consignment for accuracy by firing 500 batches, each of 20 rounds, from a fixed rifle at a target. Those rounds that fall outside a marked circle on the target are classified as *misses*. For each batch of 20 rounds the number of misses is counted.

Misses, X	0	1	2	3	4	5	6–20
Frequency	230	189	65	15	0	1	0

(i)   Estimate the mean number of misses per batch.

(ii) Use your mean to estimate the probability of a batch producing 0, 1, 2, 3, 4 and 5 misses using the Poisson distribution as a model.

(iii) Use your answers to part (ii) to estimate expected frequencies of 0, 1, 2, 3, 4 and 5 misses per batch in 500 batches and compare your answers with those actually found.

(iv) Do you think the Poisson distribution is a good model for this situation?

The sum of two or more Poisson distributions

Safer crossing near our school?

A recent traffic survey has revealed that the number of vehicles using the main road outside the school has reached levels where crossing has become a hazard to our students.

The survey, carried out by a group of our students, show that the volume of traffic has increased so much that our students are almost taking their lives in their hands when crossing the road.

At 3 pm, usually one of quieter periods of the day, the average number of vehicles passing our school to go into the town is 3.5 per minute and the average number of vehicles heading out of town is 5.7 per minute. A safe crossing is a must!

The town council has told our students that if they can show that there is a greater than 1 in 4 chance of more than 10 vehicles passing per minute, then we should be successful in getting a safer crossing for outside the school.

Assuming that the flows of vehicles, into and out of town, can be modelled by independent Poisson distributions, you can model the flow of vehicles in both directions as follows.

Let X represent the number of vehicles travelling into town at 3 pm, then $X \sim \text{Po}(3.5)$.

Let Y represent the number of vehicles travelling out of town at 3 pm, then $Y \sim \text{Po}(5.7)$.

Let T represent the number of vehicles travelling in either direction at 3 pm, then $T = X + Y$.

You can find the probability distribution for T as follows.

$$P(T = 0) = P(X = 0) \times P(Y = 0)$$
$$= 0.0302 \times 0.0033 = 0.0001$$

$$P(T = 1) = P(X = 0) \times P(Y = 1) + P(X = 1) \times P(Y = 0)$$
$$= 0.0302 \times 0.0191 + 0.1057 \times 0.0033 = 0.0009$$

$$P(T = 2) = P(X = 0) \times P(Y = 2) + P(X = 1) \times P(Y = 1) + P(X = 2) \times P(Y = 0)$$
$$= 0.0302 \times 0.0544 + 0.1057 \times 0.0191 + 0.1850 \times 0.0033 = 0.0043$$

and so on.

You can see that this process is very time consuming. Fortunately, you can make life a lot easier by using the fact that if X and Y are two independent Poisson random variables, with means λ and μ respectively, then if $T = X + Y$ then T is a Poisson random variable with mean $\lambda + \mu$.

$$X \sim \text{Po}(\lambda) \text{ and } Y \sim \text{Po}(\mu) \quad \Rightarrow \quad X + Y \sim \text{Po}(\lambda + \mu)$$

Using $T \sim \text{Po}(9.2)$ gives the required probabilities straight away.

$$P(T = 0) = e^{-9.2} = 0.0001$$

$$P(T = 1) = e^{-9.2} \times 9.2 = 0.0009$$

$$P(T = 2) = e^{-9.2} \times \frac{9.2^2}{2!} = 0.0043$$

and so on.

You can now use the distribution for T to find the probability that the total traffic flow exceeds 10 vehicles per minute.

$$P(T > 10) = 1 - P(T \leqslant 10)$$
$$= 1 - 0.6820 = 0.318$$

Since there is a greater than 25% chance of more than 10 vehicles passing per minute, the case for the crossing has been made, based on the Poisson probability models.

EXAMPLE 9.3

A rare disease causes the death, on average, of 2.0 people per year in Sweden, 0.8 in Norway and 0.5 in Finland. As far as is known the disease strikes at random and cases are independent of one another.

What is the probability of 4 or more deaths from the disease in these three countries in any year?

SOLUTION

Notice first that:

- P(4 or more deaths) = 1 – P(3 or fewer deaths)

- each of the three distributions fulfils the conditions for it to be modelled by the Poisson distribution.

You can therefore add the three distributions together and treat the result as a single Poisson distribution.

The overall mean is given by
$$
\begin{array}{ccccccc}
2.0 & + & 0.8 & + & 0.5 & = & 3.3 \\
\text{Sweden} & & \text{Norway} & & \text{Finland} & & \text{Total}
\end{array}
$$

giving an overall distribution of Po(3.3).

The probability of 4 or fewer deaths is then

$$1 - e^{-3.3} \times \left(1 + 3.3 + \frac{3.3^2}{2!} + \frac{3.3^3}{3!} \right)$$

So the probability of 4 or more deaths is given by

$$1 - 0.580 = 0.420$$

Notes

1 You may only add Poisson distributions in this way if they are independent of each other.

2 The proof of the validity of adding Poisson distributions in this way is given in Appendix 5 on the CD.

EXAMPLE 9.4

On a lonely Highland road in Scotland, cars are observed passing at the rate of 6 per day and lorries at the rate of 3 per day. On the road is an old cattle grid which will soon need repair. The local works department decide that if the probability of more than 2 vehicles per hour passing is less than 1% then the repairs to the cattle grid can wait until next spring, otherwise it will have to be repaired before the winter.

When will the cattle grid have to be repaired?

SOLUTION

Let C be the number of cars per hour, L be the number of lorries per hour and V be the number of vehicles per hour.

$$V = L + C$$

Assuming that a car or a lorry passing along the road is a random event and the two are independent

$$C \sim \text{Po}(0.25), \ L \sim \text{Po}(0.125)$$

and so $\quad V \sim \text{Po}(0.25 + 0.125)$

$\Rightarrow \qquad V \sim \text{Po}(0.375)$

> 6 cars a day is $\dfrac{6}{24} = 0.25$ cars in an hour.
>
> Similarly, there are $\dfrac{3}{24} = 0.125$ lorries per hour.

The required probability is

$$P(V > 2) = 1 - P(V \leqslant 2)$$

$$= 1 - e^{-0.375} \times \left(1 + 0.375 + \frac{0.375^2}{2!} \right)$$

$$= 0.006\,65$$

This is less than 1% and so the repairs are left until spring.

❓ The modelling of this situation raises a number of questions.

1 Is it true that a car or lorry passing along the road is a random event, or are some of these regular users, like the lorry collecting the milk from the farms along the road? If, say, three of the cars and one lorry are regular daily users, what effect does this have on the calculation?

2 Is it true that every car or lorry travels independently of every other one?

3 Are vehicles more likely in some hours than others?

4 There are no figures for bicycles or motorcycles or other vehicles. Why might this be so?

EXERCISE 9B

1 The numbers of lorry drivers and car drivers visiting an all-night transport cafe between 2 am and 3 am on a Sunday morning have independent Poisson distributions with means 5.1 and 3.6 respectively.

(i) Find the probabilities that, between 2 am and 3 am on any Sunday,

  (a) exactly five lorry drivers visit the cafe

  (b) at least one car driver visits the cafe

  (c) exactly five lorry drivers and exactly two car drivers visit the cafe.

(ii) By using the distribution of the total number of drivers visiting the cafe, find the probability that exactly seven drivers visit the cafe between 2 am and 3 am on any Sunday. Given that exactly seven drivers visit the cafe between 2 am and 3 am on one Sunday, find the probability that exactly five of them are driving lorries.

[MEI]

2 Telephone calls reach a departmental administrator independently and at random, internal ones at a mean rate of two in any five-minute period, and external ones at a mean rate of one in any five-minute period.

(i) Find the probability that in a five-minute period, the administrator receives

(a) exactly three internal calls

(b) at least two external calls

(c) at most five calls in total.

(ii) Given that the administrator receives a total of four calls in a five-minute period, find the probability that exactly two were internal calls.

(iii) Find the probability that in any one-minute interval no calls are received.

3 Two random variables, X and Y, have independent Poisson distributions given by $X \sim Po(1.4)$ and $Y \sim Po(3.6)$ respectively.

(i) Using the distributions of X and Y *only*, calculate

(a) $P(X + Y = 0)$

(b) $P(X + Y = 1)$

(c) $P(X + Y = 2)$.

The random variable T is defined by $T = X + Y$.

(ii) Write down the distribution of T.

(iii) Use your distribution from part (ii) to check your results in part (i).

4 A boy is watching vehicles travelling along a motorway. All the vehicles he sees are either cars or lorries; the numbers of each may be modelled by two independent Poisson distributions. The mean number of cars per minute is 8.3 and the mean number of lorries per minute is 4.7.

(i) For a given period of one minute, find the probability that he sees

(a) exactly seven cars

(b) at least three lorries.

(ii) Calculate the probability that he sees a total of exactly ten vehicles in a given one-minute period.

(iii) Find the probability that he observes fewer than eight vehicles in a given period of 30 seconds.

5 The number of cats rescued by an animal shelter each day may be modelled by a Poisson distribution with parameter 2.5, while the number of dogs rescued each day may be modelled by an independent Poisson distribution with parameter 3.2.

(i) Calculate the probability that on a randomly chosen day the shelter rescues

(a) exactly two cats

(b) exactly three dogs

(c) exactly five cats and dogs in total.

(ii) Given that one day exactly five cats and dogs were rescued, find the conditional probability that exactly two of these animals were cats.

6 The numbers of emissions per minute from two radioactive substances, A and B, are independent and have Poisson distributions with means 2.8 and 3.25 respectively.

Find the probabilities that in a period of one minute there will be

(i) at least three emissions from substance A

(ii) one emission from one of the two substances and two emissions from the other substance

(iii) a total of five emissions.

7 The number of incoming telephone calls received per minute by a company's telephone exchange follows a Poisson distribution with mean 1.92.

(i) Find the probabilities of the following events.

(a) Exactly two calls are received in a one-minute interval.

(b) Exactly two calls are received each minute in a five-minute interval.

(c) At least five calls are received in a five-minute interval.

The number of outgoing telephone calls made per minute at the same exchange also follows a Poisson distribution, with mean λ. It is found that the proportion of one-minute intervals containing no outgoing calls is 20%. Incoming and outgoing calls occur independently.

(ii) Find the value of λ.

(iii) Find the probability that a total of four calls, incoming and outgoing, pass through the exchange in a one-minute interval.

(iv) Given that exactly four calls pass through the exchange in a one-minute interval, find the probability that two are incoming and two are outgoing.

[MEI]

8 The numbers of goals per game scored by teams playing at home and away in the Premier League are modelled by independent Poisson distributions with means 1.63 and 1.17 respectively.

(i) Find the probability that, in a game chosen at random,

(a) the home team scores at least two goals

(b) the result is a 1–1 draw

(c) the teams score five goals between them.

(ii) Give two reasons why the proposed model might not be suitable.

[MEI, *part*]

9 Every day I check the number of emails on my computer at home. The numbers of emails, x, received per day for a random sample of 100 days are summarised by

$$\sum x = 184, \qquad \sum x^2 = 514.$$

(i) Find the mean and variance of the data.

(ii) Give two reasons why the Poisson distribution might be thought to be a suitable model for the number of emails received per day.

(iii) Using the mean as found in part **(i)**, calculate the expected number of days, in a period of 100 days, on which I will receive exactly two emails.

On a working day, I also receive emails at the office. The number of emails received per day at the office follows a Poisson distribution with mean λ. On 1.5% of working days I receive no emails at the office.

(iv) Show that $\lambda = 4.2$, correct to 2 significant figures. Hence find the probability that on one working day I receive at least five emails at the office.

(v) Find the probability that on one working day I receive a total of ten emails (at home and at the office).

[MEI, *part*]

The Poisson approximation to the binomial distribution

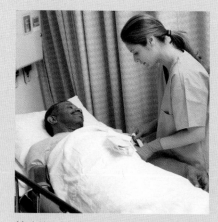

Rare disease blights town
Chemical plant blamed

A rare disease is attacking residents of Avonford. In the last year alone five people have been diagnosed as suffering from it. This is over three times the national average.

The disease (known as *Palfrey's condition*) causes nausea and fatigue. One sufferer, James Louth (32), of Harpers Lane, has been unable to work for the past six months. His wife Muriel (29) said 'I am worried sick, James has lost his job and I am frightened that the children (Mark, 4, and Samantha, 2) will catch it.'

Mrs Louth blames the chemical complex on the industrial estate for the disease. 'There were never any cases before *Avonford Chemicals* arrived.'

Local environmental campaigner Roy James supports Mrs Louth. 'I warned the local council when planning permission was sought that this would mean an increase in this sort of illness. Normally we would expect 1 case in every 40 000 of the population in a year.'

Avonford Chemicals spokesperson, Julia Millward said 'We categorically deny that our

Muriel Louth believes that the local chemical plant could destroy her family's lives

plant is responsible for the disease. Our record on safety is very good. None of our staff has had the disease. In any case five cases in a population of 60 000 can hardly be called significant.'

The expected number of cases is $60\,000 \times \frac{1}{40000}$ or 1.5, so 5 does seem rather high. Do you think that the chemical plant is to blame or do you think people are just looking for an excuse to attack it? How do you decide between the two points of view? Is 5 really that large a number of cases anyway?

The situation could be modelled by the binomial distribution. The probability of somebody getting the disease in any year is $\frac{1}{40000}$ and so that of not getting it is $1 - \frac{1}{40000} = \frac{39999}{40000}$.

The probability of 5 cases among 60 000 people (and so 59 995 people not getting the disease) is given by

$$^{60000}C_5 \left(\frac{39999}{40000} \right)^{59995} \left(\frac{1}{40000} \right)^5 \approx 0.0141.$$

What you really want to know, however, is not the probability of exactly 5 cases but that of 5 or more cases. If that is very small, then perhaps something unusual did happen in Avonford last year.

You can find the probability of 5 or more cases by finding the probability of up to and including 4 cases, and subtracting it from 1.

The probability of up to and including 4 cases is given by:

$$\left(\frac{39999}{40000} \right)^{60000} \qquad \text{0 cases}$$

$$+ \,^{60000}C_1 \left(\frac{39999}{40000} \right)^{59999} \left(\frac{1}{40000} \right) \qquad \text{1 case}$$

$$+ \,^{60000}C_2 \left(\frac{39999}{40000} \right)^{59998} \left(\frac{1}{40000} \right)^2 \qquad \text{2 cases}$$

$$+ \,^{60000}C_3 \left(\frac{39999}{40000} \right)^{59997} \left(\frac{1}{40000} \right)^3 \qquad \text{3 cases}$$

$$+ \,^{60000}C_4 \left(\frac{39999}{40000} \right)^{59996} \left(\frac{1}{40000} \right)^4 \qquad \text{4 cases}$$

It is messy but you can evaluate it on your calculator. It comes out to be

$$0.223 + 0.335 + 0.251 + 0.126 + 0.047 = 0.981.$$

(The figures are written to three decimal places but more places were used in the calculation.)

So the probability of 5 or more cases in a year is $1 - 0.981 = 0.019$. It is unlikely but certainly could happen, see figure 9.3 below.

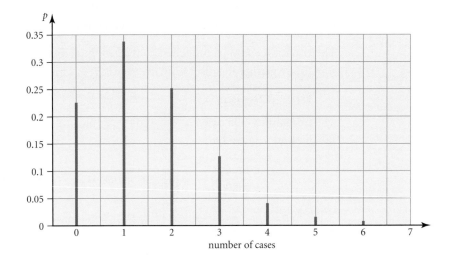

Figure 9.3 Probability distribution $B\left(60\,000, \frac{1}{40\,000}\right)$

Note

Two other points are worth making. First, the binomial model assumes the trials are independent. If this disease is at all infectious, that certainly would not be the case. Second, there is no evidence at all to link this disease with Avonford Chemicals. There are many other possible explanations.

Approximating the binomial terms

Although it was possible to do the calculation using results derived from the binomial distribution, it was distinctly cumbersome. In this section you will see how the calculations can be simplified, a process which turns out to be unexpectedly profitable. The work that follows depends upon the facts that the event is rare but there are many opportunities for it to occur: that is, p is small and n is large.

Start by looking at the first term, the probability of 0 cases of the disease. This is

$$\left(\frac{39999}{40000}\right)^{60000} = k, \text{ a constant.}$$

Now look at the next term, the probability of 1 case of the disease. This is

$$^{60000}C_1 \left(\frac{39999}{40000}\right)^{59999} \times \left(\frac{1}{40000}\right)$$

$$= \frac{60000 \times \left(\frac{39999}{40000}\right)^{60000} \times \left(\frac{40000}{39999}\right)}{40000}$$

$$= k \times \frac{60000}{39999}$$

$$\approx k \times \frac{60000}{40000}$$

$$= k \times 1.5.$$

Now look at the next term, the probability of 2 cases of the disease. This is

$$^{60000}C_2 \times \left(\frac{39999}{40000}\right)^{59998} \times \left(\frac{1}{40000}\right)^2$$

$$= \frac{60000 \times 59999}{2 \times 1} \times \left(\frac{39999}{40000}\right)^{60000} \times \left(\frac{40000}{39999}\right)^2 \times \left(\frac{1}{40000}\right)^2$$

$$= \frac{k \times 60000 \times 59999}{2 \times 1 \times 39999 \times 39999}$$

$$\approx \frac{k \times 60000 \times 60000}{2 \times 40000 \times 40000}$$

$$= k \times \frac{(1.5)^2}{2}.$$

Proceeding in this way leads to the following probability distribution for the number of cases of the disease.

Number of cases	0	1	2	3	4	...
Probability	k	$k \times 1.5$	$k \times \dfrac{(1.5)^2}{2!}$	$k \times \dfrac{(1.5)^3}{3!}$	$k \times \dfrac{(1.5)^4}{4!}$	...

Since the sum of the probabilities $= 1$,

$$k + k \times 1.5 + k \times \frac{(1.5)^2}{2!} + k \times \frac{(1.5)^3}{3!} + k \times \frac{(1.5)^4}{4!} + \ldots = 1$$

$$k\left[1 + 1.5 + \frac{(1.5)^2}{2!} + \frac{(1.5)^3}{3!} + \frac{(1.5)^4}{4!} + \ldots\right] = 1$$

The terms in the square brackets form a well known series in pure mathematics, the exponential series e^x.

$$e^x = 1 + x + \frac{x^2}{2!} + \frac{x^3}{3!} + \frac{x^4}{4!} + \ldots$$

Since $k \times e^{1.5} = 1$, $k = e^{-1.5}$.

This gives the probability distribution for the number of cases of the disease as

Number of cases	0	1	2	3	4	...
Probability	$e^{-1.5}$	$e^{-1.5} \times 1.5$	$e^{-1.5} \times \dfrac{(1.5)^2}{2!}$	$e^{-1.5} \times \dfrac{(1.5)^3}{3!}$	$e^{-1.5} \times \dfrac{(1.5)^4}{4!}$	...

and in general for r cases the probability is $e^{-1.5} \times \dfrac{(1.5)^r}{r!}$.

Accuracy

These expressions are clearly much simpler than those involving binomial coefficients. How accurate are they? The following table compares the results from the two methods, given to six decimal places.

Number of cases	Probability	
	Exact binomial method	Approximate method
0	0.223 126	0.223 130
1	0.334 697	0.334 695
2	0.251 025	0.251 021
3	0.125 512	0.125 511
4	0.047 066	0.047 067

You will see that the agreement is very good; there are no differences until the sixth decimal place.

The Poisson distribution may be used as an approximation to the binomial distribution, $B(n, p)$, when

- n is large (typically $n > 50$)

- p is small (and so the event is rare)

- np is not too large (typically $np < 5$).

EXAMPLE 9.5

It is known that nationally one person in a thousand is allergic to a particular chemical used in making a wood preservative. A firm that makes this wood preservative employs 500 people in one of its factories.

(i) What is the probability that more than two people at the factory are allergic to the chemical?

(ii) What assumption are you making?

SOLUTION

(i) Let X be the number of people in a random sample of 500 who are allergic to the chemical.

$$X \sim B(500, 0.001) \qquad n = 500 \qquad p = 0.001$$

Since n is large and p is small, the Poisson approximation to the binomial is appropriate.

$$\lambda = np$$
$$= 500 \times 0.001$$
$$= 0.5$$

Consequently $\qquad P(X = r) = e^{-\lambda} \times \dfrac{\lambda^r}{r!}$

$$= e^{-0.5} \times \dfrac{0.5^r}{r!}$$

$$\begin{aligned} P(X > 2) &= 1 - P(X \leqslant 2) \\ &= 1 - [P(X = 0) + P(X = 1) + P(X = 2)] \\ &= 1 - \left[e^{-0.5} + e^{-0.5} \times 0.5 + e^{-0.5} \times \dfrac{0.5^2}{2} \right] \\ &= 1 - [0.6065 + 0.3033 + 0.0758] \\ &= 1 - 0.9856 \\ &= 0.0144 \end{aligned}$$

(ii) The assumption made is that people with the allergy are just as likely to work in the factory as those without the allergy. In practice this seems rather unlikely: you would not stay in a job that made you unhealthy.

EXERCISE 9C

1 For each of the following binomial distributions, use the binomial formula to calculate $P(X = 3)$. *In each case* use an appropriate Poisson approximation to find $P(X = 3)$ and calculate the percentage error in using this approximation. Describe what you notice.

(i) $X \sim B(25, 0.2)$

(ii) $X \sim B(250, 0.02)$

(iii) $X \sim B(2500, 0.002)$

2 An automatic machine produces washers, 3% of which are defective according to a severe set of specifications. A sample of 100 washers is drawn at random from the production of this machine. Using a suitable approximating distribution, calculate the probabilities of observing

(i) exactly 3 defectives

(ii) between 2 and 4 defectives inclusive.

3 The number of civil lawsuits filed in state and federal courts on a given day is 500. The probability that any such lawsuit is settled within one week is 0.01. Use the Poisson approximation to find the probability that, of the original 500 lawsuits on a given day, the number that are settled within a week is

(i) exactly seven

(ii) at least five

(iii) at most six.

4 One per cent of the items produced by a certain process are defective. Using the Poisson approximation, determine the probability that in a random sample of 1000 articles

(i) exactly five are defective

(ii) at most five are defective.

5 Betty drives along a 50-kilometre stretch of road 5 days a week 50 weeks a year. She takes no notice of the $70\,\mathrm{km\,h^{-1}}$ speed limit and, when the traffic allows, travels between 95 and $105\,\mathrm{km\,h^{-1}}$. From time to time she is caught by the police and fined but she estimates the probability of this happening on any day is $\frac{1}{300}$. If she gets caught three times within three years she will be disqualified from driving. Use Betty's estimates of probability to answer the following questions.

(i) What is the probability of her being caught exactly once in any year?

(ii) What is the probability of her being caught less than three times in three years?

(iii) What is the probability of her being caught exactly three times in three years?

Betty is in fact caught one day and decides to be somewhat cautious, reducing her normal speed to between 85 and $95\,\mathrm{km\,h^{-1}}$. She believes this will reduce the probability of her being caught to $\frac{1}{500}$.

(iv) What is the probability that she is caught less than twice in the next three years?

6 Motorists in a particular part of Malaysia have a choice between a direct route and a one-way scenic detour. It is known that on average one in forty of the cars on the road will take the scenic detour. The road engineer wishes to do some repairs on the scenic detour. He chooses a time when he expects 100 cars an hour to pass along the road.

Find the probability that, in any one hour,

(i) no cars will turn on to the scenic detour

(ii) at most 4 cars will turn on to the scenic detour.

(iii) Between 10.30 am and 11.00 am it will be necessary to block the road completely. What is the probability that no car will be delayed?

7 A sociologist claims that only 3% of all suitably qualified students from inner city schools go on to university. Use his claim and the Poisson approximation to the binomial distribution to estimate the probability that in a randomly chosen group of 200 such students

(i) exactly five go to university

(ii) more than five go to university.

(iii) If the probability that more than n of the 200 students go to university is less than 0.2, find the lowest possible value of n.

Another group of 100 students is also chosen. Find the probability that

(iv) exactly five of each group go to university

(v) exactly ten of all the chosen students go to university.

[MEI, *adapted*]

8 In one part of the country, one person in 80 has blood of Type P. A random sample of 150 blood donors is chosen from that part of the country. Let X represent the number of donors in the sample having blood of Type P.

(i) State the distribution of X. Find the parameter of the Poisson distribution which can be used as an approximation. Give a reason why a Poisson approximation is appropriate.

(ii) Using the Poisson distribution, calculate the probability that in the sample of 150 donors at least two have blood of Type P.

[MEI, *part*]

9 An airline regularly sells more seats for its early morning flight from London to Paris than are available. On average, 5% of customers who have purchased tickets do not turn up. For this flight, the airline always sells 108 tickets. Let X represent the number of customers who do not turn up for this flight.

(i) State the distribution of X, giving one assumption you must make for it to be appropriate.

There is room for 104 passengers on the flight. For the rest of the question use a suitable Poisson approximation.

(ii) Find the probability that

(a) there are exactly three empty seats on Monday's flight

(b) Tuesday's flight is full

(c) from Monday to Friday inclusive the flight is full on just one day.

[MEI, *part*]

10 The manufacturers of *Jupiter Jellybabies* have launched a promotion to boost sales. One per cent of bags, chosen at random, contains a prize. A school tuck-shop takes delivery of 500 bags of *Jupiter Jellybabies*. Let X represent the number of bags in the delivery which contain a prize.

(i) State clearly the distribution which X takes.

(ii) Using a Poisson approximating distribution, find $P(3 \leqslant X \leqslant 7)$.

The values of the prizes are in the following proportions.

Value of prize	$10	$100	$1000
Proportion	90%	9%	1%

(iii) Suppose the tuck-shop receives five bags which contain prizes. Find the probability that at least one of these prizes has value $1000.

[MEI]

Using the normal distribution as an approximation for the Poisson distribution

You may use the normal distribution as an approximation for the Poisson distribution, provided that its parameter (mean) λ is sufficiently large for the distribution to be reasonably symmetrical and not positively skewed.

As a working rule λ should be at least 15.

If $\lambda = 15$, mean $= 15$

> The letter μ is also commonly used in place of λ for the Poisson parameter.

and standard deviation $= \sqrt{15} = 3.87$ (to 3 s.f.).

A normal distribution is almost entirely contained within 3 standard deviations of its mean and in this case the value 0 is between 3 and 4 standard deviations away from the mean value of 15.

The parameters for the normal distribution are then

Mean: $\mu = \lambda$
Variance: $\sigma^2 = \lambda$

so that it can be denoted by $N(\lambda, \lambda)$.

(Remember that, for a Poisson distribution, mean = variance.)

For values of λ larger than 15 the Poisson probability graph becomes less positively skewed and more bell-shaped in appearance thus making the normal approximation appropriate. Figure 9.4 shows the Poisson probability graph for the two cases $\lambda = 3$ and $\lambda = 25$. You will see that for $\lambda = 3$ the graph is positively skewed but for $\lambda = 25$ it is approximately bell-shaped.

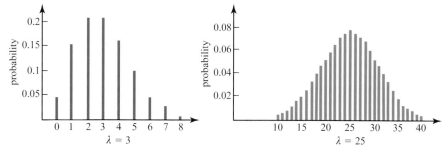

Figure 9.4

EXAMPLE 9.6

The annual number of deaths nationally from a rare disease, X, may be modelled by the Poisson distribution with mean 25. One year there are 31 deaths and it is suggested that the disease is on the increase.

What is the probability of 31 or more deaths in a year, assuming the mean has remained at 25?

SOLUTION

The Poisson distribution with mean 25 may be approximated by the normal distribution with parameters

    Mean: 25
    Standard deviation: $\sqrt{25} = 5$

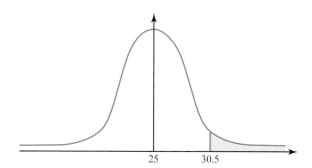

Figure 9.5

The probability of there being 31 or more deaths in a year, $P(X \geqslant 31)$, is given by $1 - \Phi(z)$, where

$$z = \frac{30.5 - 25}{5} = 1.1.$$

(Note the continuity correction, replacing 31 by 30.5.)

The required area is
$$1 - \Phi(1.1) = 1 - 0.8643$$
$$= 0.1357$$

This is not a particularly low probability; it is quite likely that there would be that many deaths in any one year.

Hypothesis test for the mean of a Poisson distribution

The next example shows you how to carry out a hypothesis test for the mean of a Poisson distribution.

EXAMPLE 9.7

An old university has a high tower that is quite often struck by lightning. Records going back over hundreds of years show that on average the tower is struck on 3.2 days per year.

It is suggested that a likely effect of global warming would be an increase in the number of days on which the tower is struck. The following year the tower is struck by lightning on 7 days.

Carry out a suitable hypothesis test at the 5% significance level and state your conclusion.

What is the probability of a Type I error in this test?

SOLUTION

The number of days per year that the tower is struck by lightning is modelled by X where

$$X \sim \text{Po}(3.2).$$

So the null and alternative hypotheses may be stated as follows.

H_0: $\mu = 3.2$ The population mean, μ, is unchanged.

H_1: $\mu > 3.2$ The population mean, μ, has increased.

One-tail test

Significance level: 0.05

The test is one-tailed because it is for an *increase* in lightning strikes. A test for a change would be two-tailed.

The probability of 7 or more days with lightning strikes is (1 – the probability of 6 or fewer such days).

The calculation is shown in the table.

Number of strikes	Probability
0	$e^{-3.2} = 0.040\,76...$
1	$3.2 \times e^{-3.2} = 0.130\,43...$
2	$\dfrac{3.2^2}{2!} \times e^{-3.2} = 0.208\,70...$
3	$\dfrac{3.2^3}{3!} \times e^{-3.2} = 0.222\,61...$
4	$\dfrac{3.2^4}{4!} \times e^{-3.2} = 0.178\,09...$
5	$\dfrac{3.2^5}{5!} \times e^{-3.2} = 0.113\,97...$
6	$\dfrac{3.2^6}{6!} \times e^{-3.2} = 0.060\,78...$
Total	$P(X \leqslant 6) = 0.955\,38...$

So the probability that $X \geqslant 7$ is

$$1 - 0.955\,38... = 0.044\,61... = 0.045 \ \ (3 \text{ d.p.})$$

Since $0.045 < 0.05$ (the significance level), the null hypothesis is rejected in favour of the alternative hypothesis at the 5% significance level.

The evidence does not support the hypothesis that there has been no change in the incidence of lightning strikes.

A Type I error occurs when a true null hypothesis is rejected. In this test, the rejection region is $X > 6$ and the probability of such a result is $0.044\,61...$ if $\mu = 3.2$. So the probability of a Type I error is 0.0446 (to 3 s.f.).

Note

Notice that the result in Example 9.7 does not *prove* that there has been an increase in the incidence of lightning strikes; it does, however, suggest that this may well be the case. The test was about lightning strikes and so in itself says nothing about global warming. Whether global warming is connected to the incidence of lightning strikes is not what was being tested; it formed no part of either the null or the alternative hypothesis.

EXERCISE 9D

1 The number of cars per minute entering a multi-storey car park can be modelled by a Poisson distribution with mean 2. What is the probability that three cars enter during a period of one minute?

What are the mean and the standard deviation of the number of cars entering the car park during a period of 30 minutes? Use the normal approximation to the Poisson distribution to estimate the probability that at least 50 cars enter in any one 30-minute period.

[MEI]

2 A large computer system which is in constant operation requires an average of 30 service calls per year.

(i) State the average number of service calls per month, taking a month to be $\frac{1}{12}$ of a year. What assumptions need to be made for the Poisson distribution to be used to model the number of calls in a given month?

(ii) Use the Poisson distribution to find the probability that at least one service call is required in January. Obtain the probability that there is at least one service call in each month of the year.

(iii) The service contract offers a discount if the number of service calls in the year is 24 or fewer. Use a suitable approximating distribution to find the probability of obtaining the discount in any particular year.

[MEI]

3 The number of night calls to a fire station in a small town can be modelled by a Poisson distribution with a mean of 4.2 per night.

Use the normal approximation to the Poisson distribution to estimate the probability that in any particular week (Sunday to Saturday inclusive) the number of night calls to the fire station will be

(i) at least 30

(ii) exactly 30

(iii) between 25 and 35 inclusive.

4 At a busy intersection of roads, accidents requiring the summoning of an ambulance occur with a frequency, on average, of 1.8 per week. These accidents occur randomly, so that it may be assumed that they follow a Poisson distribution.

Use a suitable approximating distribution to find the probability that in any particular year (of 52 weeks) the number of accidents at the intersection will be

(i)   at most 100

(ii) exactly 100

(iii) between 95 and 105 inclusive.

5 Tina is a traffic warden. The number of parking tickets she issues per day, from Monday to Saturday inclusive, may be modelled by a Poisson distribution with mean 11.5. By using suitable approximating distributions, find

(i)   the probability that on a particular Tuesday she issues at least 15 parking tickets

(ii) the probability that during any week (excluding Sunday) she issues at least 50 parking tickets

(iii) the probability that during four consecutive weeks she issues

  (a) at least 50 parking tickets each week

  (b) at least 200 parking tickets altogether.

  Account for the difference in the two answers.

6 The number of emails I receive per day on my computer may be modelled by a Poisson distribution with mean 8.5.

(i)   Use the most appropriate method to calculate the probability that I receive

  (a) at least 8 emails tomorrow

  (b) at least 240 emails next June.

(ii) What assumption do you have to make to find the probability in part (i) (b)?

(iii) Compare your answers to parts (i) (a) and (b) and account for the variation.

7 At a petrol station cars arrive independently and at random times at constant average rates of 8 cars per hour travelling east and 5 cars per hour travelling west.

(i)   Find the probability that, in a quarter-hour period

  (a) one or more cars travelling east and one or more cars travelling west will arrive,

  (b) a total of 2 or more cars will arrive.

(ii) Find the approximate probability that, in a 12-hour period, a total of more than 175 cars will arrive.

[Cambridge International AS and A Level Mathematics 9709, Paper 7 Q6 June 2005]

8 Some ancient documents from the pharaoh's astronomer are discovered in one of the pyramids. They include records, covering many years, of shooting stars during a certain part of one particular night of the year. The data are well modelled by a Poisson distribution with mean 5.6. A modern astronomer has a theory that there are now fewer shooting stars and so, on the right day and time, repeats the observation and carries out a suitable hypothesis test, using a 10% significance level.

(i) State the null and alternative hypotheses.

(ii) Find the rejection region for the test.

(iii) Find the probability of a Type I error.

The astronomer observes three shooting stars.

(iv) Carry out the hypothesis test.

9 A dressmaker makes dresses for Easifit Fashions. Each dress requires 2.5 m^2 of material. Faults occur randomly in the material at an average rate of 4.8 per 20 m^2.

(i) Find the probability that a randomly chosen dress contains at least 2 faults.

Each dress has a belt attached to it to make an outfit. Independently of faults in the material, the probability that a belt is faulty is 0.03. Find the probability that, in an outfit,

(ii) neither the dress nor its belt is faulty,

(iii) the dress has at least one fault and its belt is faulty.

The dressmaker attaches 300 randomly chosen belts to 300 randomly chosen dresses. An outfit in which the dress has at least one fault and its belt is faulty is rejected.

(iv) Use a suitable approximation to find the probability that fewer than 3 outfits are rejected.

[Cambridge International AS and A Level Mathematics 9709, Paper 7 Q6 June 2006]

10 It is proposed to model the number of people per hour calling a car breakdown service between the times 0900 and 2100 by a Poisson distribution.

(i) Explain why a Poisson distribution may be appropriate for this situation.

People call the car breakdown service at an average rate of 20 per hour, and a Poisson distribution may be assumed to be a suitable model.

(ii) Find the probability that exactly 8 people call in any half hour.

(iii) By using a suitable approximation, find the probability that exactly 250 people call in the 12 hours between 0900 and 2100.

[Cambridge International AS and A Level Mathematics 9709, Paper 7 Q5 June 2007]

11 Major avalanches can be regarded as randomly occurring events. They occur at a uniform average rate of 8 per year.

(i) Find the probability that more than 3 major avalanches occur in a 3-month period.

(ii) Find the probability that any two separate 4-month periods have a total of 7 major avalanches.

(iii) Find the probability that a total of fewer than 137 major avalanches occur in a 20-year period.

[Cambridge International AS and A Level Mathematics 9709, Paper 7 Q3 June 2009]

12 When a guitar is played regularly, a string breaks on average once every 15 months. Broken strings occur at random times and independently of each other.

(i) Show that the mean number of broken strings in a 5-year period is 4.

A guitar is fitted with a new type of string which, it is claimed, breaks less frequently. The number of broken strings of the new type was noted after a period of 5 years.

(ii) The mean number of broken springs of the new type in a 5-year period is denoted by λ. Find the rejection region for a test at the 10% significance level when the null hypothesis $\lambda = 4$ is tested against the alternative hypothesis $\lambda < 4$.

(iii) Hence calculate the probability of making a Type I error.

The number of broken guitar strings of the new type, in a 5-year period, was in fact 1.

(iv) State, with a reason, whether there is evidence at the 10% significance level that guitar strings of the new type break less frequently.

[Cambridge International AS and A Level Mathematics 9709, Paper 7 Q5 June 2008]

13 Every month Susan enters a particular lottery. The lottery company states that the probability, p, of winning a prize is 0.0017 each month. Susan thinks that the probability of winning is higher than this, and carries out a test based on her 12 lottery results in a one-year period. She accepts the null hypothesis $p = 0.0017$ if she has no wins in the year and accepts the alternative hypothesis $p > 0.0017$ if she wins a prize in at least one of the 12 months.

(i) Find the probability of the test resulting in a Type I error.

(ii) If in fact the probability of winning a prize each month is 0.0024, find the probability of the test resulting in a Type II error.

(iii) Use a suitable approximation, with $p = 0.0024$, to find the probability that in a period of 10 years Susan wins a prize exactly twice.

[Cambridge International AS and A Level Mathematics 9709, Paper 7 Q5 November 2008]

14 Pieces of metal discovered by people using metal detectors are found randomly in fields in a certain area at an average rate of 0.8 pieces per hectare. People using metal detectors in this area have a theory that ploughing the fields increases the average number of pieces of metal found per hectare. After ploughing, they tested this theory and found that a randomly chosen field of area 3 hectares yielded 5 pieces of metal.

(i) Carry out the test at the 10% level of significance.

(ii) What would your conclusion have been if you had tested at the 5% level of significance?

Jack decides that he will reject the null hypothesis that the average number is 0.8 pieces per hectare if he finds 4 or more pieces of metal in another ploughed field of area 3 hectares.

(iii) If the true mean after ploughing is 1.4 pieces per hectare, calculate the probability that Jack makes a Type II error.

[Cambridge International AS and A Level Mathematics 9709, Paper 7 Q6 November 2006]

15 A hospital patient's white blood cell count has a Poisson distribution. Before undergoing treatment the patient had a mean white blood cell count of 5.2. After the treatment a random measurement of the patient's white blood cell count is made, and is used to test at the 10% significance level whether the mean white blood cell count has decreased.

(i) State what is meant by a Type I error in the context of the question, and find the probability that the test results in a Type I error.

(ii) Given that the measured value of the white blood cell count after the treatment is 2, carry out the test.

(iii) Find the probability of a Type II error if the mean white blood cell count after the treatment is actually 4.1.

[Cambridge International AS and A Level Mathematics 9709, Paper 71 Q7 June 2010]

Historical note

Simeon Poisson was born in Pithiviers in France in 1781. Under family pressure he began to study medicine but after some time gave it up for his real interest, mathematics. For the rest of his life Poisson lived and worked as a mathematician in Paris. His contribution to the subject spanned a broad range of topics in both pure and applied mathematics, including integration, electricity and magnetism and planetary orbits as well as statistics. He was the author of between 300 and 400 publications and originally derived the Poisson distribution as an approximation to the binomial distribution.

When he was a small boy, Poisson had his hands tied by his nanny who then hung him from a hook on the wall so that he could not get into trouble while she went out. In later life he devoted a lot of time to studying the motion of a pendulum and claimed that this interest derived from his childhood experience of swinging against the wall.

1 The Poisson probability distribution

If $X \sim \text{Po}(\lambda)$, the parameter $\lambda > 0$.

$$P(X = r) = e^{-\lambda} \times \frac{\lambda^r}{r!} \qquad r \geqslant 0, \ r \text{ is an integer}$$
$$E(X) = \lambda$$
$$\text{Var}(X) = \lambda$$

2 Conditions under which the Poisson distribution may be used

- The Poisson distribution is generally thought of as the probability distribution for the number of occurrences of a rare event.

- Situations in which the mean number of occurrences is known (or can easily be found) but in which it is not possible, or even meaningful, to give values to n or p may be modelled using the Poisson distribution provided that the occurrences are
  - random
  - independent.

3 The sum of two Poisson distributions

If $X \sim \text{Po}(\lambda)$, $Y \sim \text{Po}(\mu)$ and X and Y are independent

$$X + Y \sim \text{Po}(\lambda + \mu)$$

4 Approximating to the binomial distribution

The Poisson distribution may be used as an approximation to the binomial distribution, $B(n, p)$, when

- n is large (typically $n > 50$)
- p is small (and so the event is rare)
- np is not too large (typically $np < 5$).

It would be unusual to use the Poisson distribution with parameter, λ, greater than about 20.

5 The Poisson distribution $\text{Po}(\lambda)$ may be approximated by $N(\lambda, \lambda)$, provided λ is about 15 or more.

10 Continuous random variables

A theory is a good theory if it satisfies two requirements: It must accurately describe a large class of observations on the basis of a model that contains only a few arbitrary elements, and it must make definite predictions about the results of future observations.

Stephen Hawking
A Brief History of Time

Lucky escape for local fisherman

Local fisherman Zhang Wei stared death in the face yesterday as he was plucked from his boat by a freak wave. Only the quick thinking of his brother Xiuying who grabbed hold of his legs, saved Wei from a watery grave.

'It was a bad day and suddenly this lump of water came down on us,' said Wei. 'It was a wave in a million. It must have been higher than our house, which is about 11 m high, and it caught me off guard'.

Hero Xiuying is a man of few words. 'All in the day's work' was his only comment.

Freak waves do occur and they can have serious consequences in terms of damage to shipping, oil rigs and coastal defences, sometimes resulting in loss of life. It is important to estimate how often they will occur, and how high they will be. Was Zhang Wei's one in a million estimate for a wave higher than 11 metres at all accurate?

Before you can answer this question, you need to know the *probability density* of the heights of waves at that time of the year in the area where the Zhang brothers were fishing. The graph in figure 10.1 shows this sort of information; it was collected in the same season of the year as the Zhang accident.

To obtain figure 10.1 a very large amount of wave data had to be collected. This allowed the class interval widths of the wave heights to be sufficiently small for the outline of the curve to acquire this shape. It also ensured that the sample data were truly representative of the population of waves at that time of the year.

In a graph such as figure 10.1 the vertical scale is a measure of probability density. Probabilities are found by estimating the area under the curve. The total area is 1.0, meaning that effectively all waves at this place have heights between 0.6 and 12.0 m, see figure 10.2.

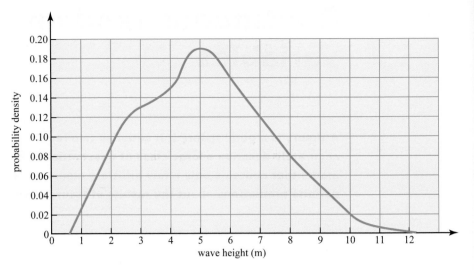

Figure 10.1

If this had been the place where the Zhang brothers were fishing, the probability of encountering a wave at least 11 m high would have been 0.003, about 1 in 300. Clearly Wei's description of it as 'a wave in a million' was not justified purely by its height. The fact that he called it a 'lump of water' suggests that perhaps it may have been more remarkable for its steep sides than its height.

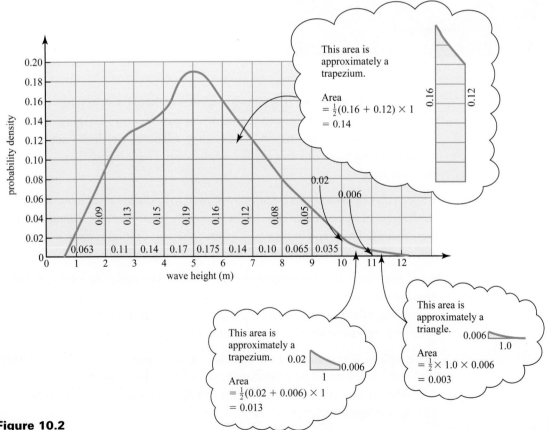

Figure 10.2

Probability density function

In the wave height example the curve was determined experimentally. The curve is continuous because the random variable, the wave height, is continuous and not discrete. The possible heights of waves are not restricted to particular steps (say every $\frac{1}{2}$ metre), but may take any value within a range.

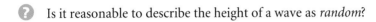

Is it reasonable to describe the height of a wave as *random*?

A function represented by a curve of this type is called a *probability density function*, often abbreviated to p.d.f.. The probability density function of a continuous random variable, X, is usually denoted by $f(x)$. If $f(x)$ is a p.d.f. it follows that:

- $f(x) \geq 0$ for all x You cannot have negative probabilities.

- $\displaystyle\int_{\substack{\text{All} \\ \text{values} \\ \text{of } x}} f(x)\,dx = 1$ The total area under the curve is 1.

For a continuous random variable with probability density function $f(x)$, the probability that X lies in the interval $[a, b]$ is given by

$$P(a \leq X \leq b) = \int_a^b f(x)\,dx$$

Looking at figure 10.1, you will see that in this case the probability density function has quite a complicated curve and so it is not possible to find a simple algebraic expression with which to model it.

Most of the techniques in this chapter assume that you do in fact have a convenient algebraic expression with which to work. However, the methods are still valid if this is not the case, but you would need to use numerical, rather than algebraic, techniques for integration and differentiation. In the high-wave incident mentioned on pages 233–234, the areas corresponding to wave heights of less than 2 m and of at least 11 m were estimated by treating the shape as a triangle: other areas were approximated by trapezia.

Note: Class boundaries

If you were to ask the question 'What is the probability of a randomly selected wave being exactly 2 m high?' the answer would be zero. If you measured a likely looking wave to enough decimal places (assuming you could do so), you would eventually come to a figure which was not zero. The wave height might be 2.01... m or 2.000 003... m but the probability of it being exactly 2 m is infinitesimally small. Consequently in theory it makes no difference whether you describe the class interval from 2 to 2.5 m as $2 < h < 2.5$ or as $2 \leq h \leq 2.5$.

However, in practice, measurements are always rounded to some extent. The reality of measuring a wave's height means that you would probably be quite happy to record it to the nearest 0.1 m and get on with the next wave. So, in practice, measurements of 2.0 m and 2.5 m probably will be recorded, and intervals have to be defined so that it is clear which class they belong to. You would normally expect < at one end of the interval and ≤ at the other: either $2 \leqslant h < 2.5$ or $2 < h \leqslant 2.5$. In either case the probability of the wave being within the interval would be given by

$$\int_2^{2.5} f(x)\,dx$$

Rufus foils council office break-in

Somewhere an empty-pocketed thief is nursing a sore leg and regretting the loss of a pair of trousers. Council porter Fred Lamming, and Rufus, a Jack Russell, were doing a late-night check round the council head office when they came upon the intruder on the ground floor.

'I didn't need to say anything,' Fred told me; 'Rufus went straight for him and grabbed him by the leg.' After a tussle the man's trousers tore, leaving Rufus with a mouthful of material while the man made good his escape out of the window.

Following the incident, the town council are looking at an electronic security system. 'Rufus won't live for ever,' explained Council leader Sandra Martin.

EXAMPLE 10.1

The town council are thinking of fitting an electronic security system inside head office. They have been told by manufacturers that the lifetime, X years, of the system they have in mind has the p.d.f.

$$f(x) = \frac{3x(20 - x)}{4000} \quad \text{for } 0 \leqslant x \leqslant 20,$$

and $\quad f(x) = 0 \qquad\qquad$ otherwise

(i) Show that the manufacturers' statement is consistent with $f(x)$ being a probability density function.

(ii) Find the probability that:

(a) it fails in the first year

(a) it lasts 10 years but then fails in the next year.

SOLUTION

(i) The condition $f(x) \geqslant 0$ for all values of x between 0 and 20 is satisfied, as shown by the graph of $f(x)$, figure 10.3.

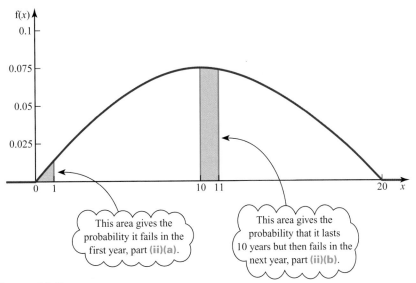

Figure 10.3

The other condition is that the area under the curve is 1.

$$\text{Area} = \int_{-\infty}^{\infty} f(x)\,dx = \int_{0}^{20} \frac{3x(20-x)}{4000}\,dx$$

$$= \frac{3}{4000} \int_{0}^{20} (20x - x^2)\,dx$$

$$= \frac{3}{4000} \left[10x^2 - \frac{x^3}{3} \right]_{0}^{20}$$

$$= \frac{3}{4000} \left[10 \times 20^2 - \frac{20^3}{3} \right]$$

$$= 1, \text{ as required.}$$

(ii) (a) *It fails in the first year.*

This is given by $P(X < 1) = \int_{0}^{1} \frac{3x(20-x)}{4000}\,dx$

$$= \frac{3}{4000} \int_{0}^{1} (20x - x^2)\,dx$$

$$= \frac{3}{4000} \left[10x^2 - \frac{x^3}{3} \right]_{0}^{1}$$

$$= \frac{3}{4000} \left(10 \times 1^2 - \frac{1^3}{3} \right)$$

$$= 0.007\,25$$

(b) *It fails in the 11th year.*

This is given by P$(10 \leqslant X < 11)$

$$= \int_{10}^{11} \frac{3x(20-x)}{4000} \, dx$$

$$= \frac{3}{4000} \left[10x^2 - \tfrac{1}{3}x^3 \right]_{10}^{11}$$

$$= \frac{3}{4000} \left(10 \times 11^2 - \tfrac{1}{3} \times 11^3 \right) - \frac{3}{4000} \left(10 \times 10^2 - \tfrac{1}{3} \times 10^3 \right)$$

$$= 0.07475$$

EXAMPLE 10.2   The continuous random variable X represents the amount of sunshine in hours between noon and 4 pm at a skiing resort in the high season. The probability density function, f(x), of X is modelled by

$$f(x) = \begin{cases} kx^2 & \text{for } 0 \leqslant x \leqslant 4 \\ 0 & \text{otherwise.} \end{cases}$$

(i) Find the value of k.

(ii) Find the probability that on a particular day in the high season there is more than two hours of sunshine between noon and 4 pm.

SOLUTION

(i) To find the value of k you must use the fact that the area under the graph of f(x) is equal to 1.

$$\int_{-\infty}^{\infty} f(x) \, dx = \int_{0}^{4} kx^2 \, dx = 1$$

Therefore

$$\left[\frac{kx^3}{3} \right]_{0}^{4} = 1$$

$$\frac{64k}{3} = 1$$

So

$$k = \frac{3}{64}$$

(ii)

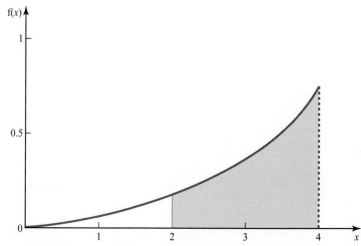

Figure 10.4

The probability of more than 2 hours of sunshine is given by

$$P(X > 2) = \int_2^\infty f(x)\,dx = \int_2^4 \frac{3x^2}{64}\,dx$$

$$= \left[\frac{x^3}{64}\right]_2^4$$

$$= \frac{64 - 8}{64}$$

$$= \frac{56}{64}$$

$$= 0.875$$

e In the next example, the probability density function is in two parts.

EXAMPLE 10.3 The number of hours Darren spends each day working in his garden is modelled by the continuous random variable X, with p.d.f. $f(x)$ defined by

$$f(x) = \begin{cases} kx & \text{for } 0 \leqslant x < 3 \\ k(6 - x) & \text{for } 3 \leqslant x \leqslant 6 \\ 0 & \text{otherwise.} \end{cases}$$

(i)   Find the value of k.
(ii) Sketch the graph of $f(x)$.
(iii) Find the probability that Darren will work between 2 and 5 hours in his garden on a randomly selected day.

SOLUTION

(i)   To find the value of k you must use the fact that the area under the graph of $f(x)$ is equal to 1. You may find the area by integration, as shown below.

$$\int_{-\infty}^\infty f(x)\,dx = \int_0^3 kx\,dx + \int_3^6 k(6 - x)\,dx = 1$$

$$\left[\frac{kx^2}{2}\right]_0^3 + \left[6kx - \frac{kx^2}{2}\right]_3^6 = 1$$

Therefore $\dfrac{9k}{2} + (36k - 18k) - \left(18k - \dfrac{9k}{2}\right) = 1$

$$9k = 1$$

So $$k = \tfrac{1}{9}$$

Note

In this case you could have found k without integration because the graph of the p.d.f. is a triangle, with area given by $\frac{1}{2} \times$ base $\times$ height, resulting in the equation

$$\tfrac{1}{2} \times 6 \times k(6 - 3) = 1$$

hence $$9k = 1$$

and $$k = \tfrac{1}{9}$$

S2
10

Probability density function

(ii) Sketch the graph of f(x).

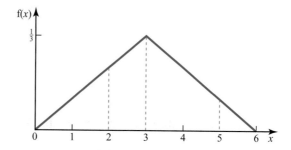

Figure 10.5

(iii) To find P($2 \leqslant X \leqslant 5$), you need to find both P($2 \leqslant X < 3$) and P($3 \leqslant X \leqslant 5$) because there is a different expression for each part.

$$P(2 \leqslant X \leqslant 5) = P(2 \leqslant X < 3) + P(3 \leqslant X \leqslant 5)$$

$$= \int_{2}^{3} \frac{1}{9}x\,dx + \int_{3}^{5} \frac{1}{9}(6-x)\,dx$$

$$= \left[\frac{x^2}{18}\right]_{2}^{3} + \left[\frac{2x}{3} - \frac{x^2}{18}\right]_{3}^{5}$$

$$= \frac{9}{18} - \frac{4}{18} + \left(\frac{10}{3} - \frac{25}{18}\right) - \left(2 - \frac{1}{2}\right)$$

$$= 0.72 \text{ to two decimal places.}$$

The probability that Darren works between 2 and 5 hours in his garden on a randomly selected day is 0.72.

EXERCISE 10A

1 The continuous random variable X has probability density function f(x) where

$$f(x) = kx \quad \text{for } 1 \leqslant x \leqslant 6$$
$$= 0 \quad \text{otherwise.}$$

(i) Find the value of the constant k.

(ii) Sketch $y = f(x)$.

(iii) Find P($X > 5$).

(iv) Find P($2 \leqslant X \leqslant 3$).

2 The continuous random variable X has p.d.f. f(x) where

$$f(x) = k(5 - x) \quad \text{for } 0 \leqslant x \leqslant 4$$
$$= 0 \quad \text{otherwise.}$$

(i) Find the value of the constant k.

(ii) Sketch $y = f(x)$.

(iii) Find P($1.5 \leqslant X \leqslant 2.3$).

3 The continuous random variable X has p.d.f. f(x) where

$$f(x) = ax^3 \quad \text{for } 0 \leqslant x \leqslant 3$$
$$= 0 \quad \text{otherwise.}$$

(i) Find the value of the constant a.

(ii) Sketch $y = f(x)$.

(iii) Find $P(X \leqslant 2)$.

4 The continuous random variable X has p.d.f. f(x) where

$$f(x) = c \quad \text{for } -3 \leqslant x \leqslant 5$$
$$= 0 \quad \text{otherwise.}$$

(i) Find c.

(ii) Sketch $y = f(x)$.

(iii) Find $P(|X| < 1)$.

(iv) Find $P(|X| > 2.5)$

5 A continuous random variable X has p.d.f

$$f(x) = k(x-1)(6-x) \quad \text{for } 1 \leqslant x \leqslant 6$$
$$= 0 \quad \text{otherwise.}$$

(i) Find the value of k.

(ii) Sketch $y = f(x)$.

(iii) Find $P(2 \leqslant X \leqslant 3)$.

6 A random variable X has p.d.f

$$f(x) = kx(3-x) \quad \text{for } 0 \leqslant x \leqslant 3$$
$$= 0 \quad \text{otherwise.}$$

(i) Find the value of k.

(ii) The lifetime (in years) of an electronic component is modelled by this distribution. Two such components are fitted in a radio which will only function if both devices are working. Find the probability that the radio will still function after two years, assuming that their failures are independent.

7 The planning officer in a council needs information about how long cars stay in the car park, and asks the attendant to do a check on the times of arrival and departure of 100 cars. The attendant provides the following data.

Length of stay	Under 1 hour	1–2 hours	2–4 hours	4–10 hours	More than 10 hours
Number of cars	20	14	32	34	0

The planning officer suggests that the length of stay in hours may be modelled by the continuous random variable X with probability density function of the form

$$f(x) = k(20 - 2x) \quad \text{for } 0 \leqslant x \leqslant 10$$
$$= 0 \quad \text{otherwise.}$$

(i) Find the value of k.

(ii) Sketch the graph of $f(x)$.

(iii) According to this model, how many of the 100 cars would be expected to fall into each of the four categories?

(iv) Do you think the model fits the data well?

(v) Are there any obvious weaknesses in the model? If you were the planning officer, would you be prepared to accept the model as it is, or would you want any further information?

8 A fish farmer has a very large number of trout in a lake. Before deciding whether to net the lake and sell the fish, she collects a sample of 100 fish and weighs them. The results (in kg) are as follows.

Weight, W	Frequency
$0 < W \leqslant 0.5$	2
$0.5 < W \leqslant 1.0$	10
$1.0 < W \leqslant 1.5$	23
$1.5 < W \leqslant 2.0$	26

Weight, W	Frequency
$2.0 < W \leqslant 2.5$	27
$2.5 < W \leqslant 3.0$	12
$3.0 < W$	0

(i) Illustrate these data on a histogram, with the number of fish on the vertical scale and W on the horizontal scale. Is the distribution of the data symmetrical, positively skewed or negatively skewed?

A friend of the farmer suggests that W can be modelled as a continuous random variable and proposes four possible probability density functions.

$$f_1(w) = \tfrac{2}{9}w(3 - w) \qquad f_2(w) = \tfrac{10}{81}w^2(3 - w)^2$$
$$f_3(w) = \tfrac{4}{27}w^2(3 - w) \qquad f_4(w) = \tfrac{4}{27}w(3 - w)^2$$

in each case for $0 < W \leqslant 3$.

(ii) Sketch the curves of the four p.d.f.s and state which one matches the data most closely in general shape.

(iii) Use this p.d.f. to calculate the number of fish which that model predicts should fall within each group.

(iv) Do you think it is a good model?

9 A random variable X has a probability density function f given by

$$f(x) = cx(5-x) \quad 0 \leqslant x \leqslant 5$$
$$= 0 \qquad\qquad \text{otherwise.}$$

(i) Show that $c = \frac{6}{125}$.

(ii) The lifetime X (in years) of an electric light bulb has this distribution. Given that a standard lamp is fitted with two such new bulbs and that their failures are independent, find the probability that neither bulb fails in the first year and the probability that exactly one bulb fails within two years.

[MEI]

10 This graph shows the probability density function, $f(x)$, for the heights, X, of waves at the point with Latitude 44°N Longitude 41°W.

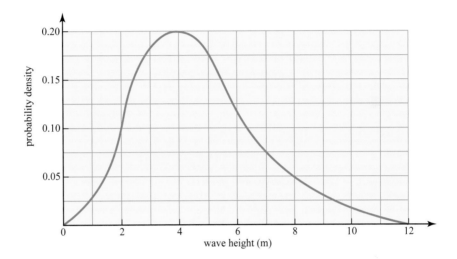

(i) Write down the values of $f(x)$ when $x = 0, 2, 4, \ldots, 12$.

(ii) Hence estimate the probability that the height of a randomly selected wave is in the interval

(a) 0–2 m   (b) 2–4 m   (c) 4–6 m

(d) 6–8 m   (e) 8–10 m   (f) 10–12 m.

A model is proposed in which

$$f(x) = kx(12-x)^2 \quad \text{for } 0 \leqslant x \leqslant 12$$
$$= 0 \qquad\qquad \text{otherwise.}$$

(iii) Find the value of k.

(iv) Find, according to this model, the probability that a randomly selected wave is in the interval

(a) 0–2 m   (b) 2–4 m   (c) 4–6 m

(d) 6–8 m   (e) 8–10 m   (f) 10–12 m.

(v) By comparing the figures from the model with the real data, state whether you think it is a good model or not.

11 The continuous random variable X has p.d.f. $f(x)$ where

$$f(x) = kx \qquad \text{for } 0 \leqslant x \leqslant 2$$
$$= 4k - kx \quad \text{for } 2 < x \leqslant 4$$
$$= 0 \qquad \text{otherwise.}$$

(i) Find the value of the constant k.

(ii) Sketch $y = f(x)$.

(iii) Find $P(1 \leqslant X \leqslant 3.5)$.

12 A random variable X has p.d.f.

$$f(x) = \begin{cases} (x-1)(2-x) & \text{for } 1 \leqslant x < 2 \\ a & \text{for } 2 \leqslant x \leqslant 4 \\ 0 & \text{otherwise.} \end{cases}$$

(i) Find the value of the constant a.

(ii) Sketch $y = f(x)$.

(iii) Find $P(1.5 \leqslant X \leqslant 2.5)$.

(iv) Find $P(|X - 2| < 1)$.

Mean and variance

You will recall from Chapter 4 that, for a discrete random variable, mean and variance are given by: μ

$$\mu = E(X) = \sum_i x_i p_i$$

$$\text{Var}(X) = \sum_i (x_i - \mu)^2 p_i = \sum_i x_i^2 p_i - [E(X)]^2$$

where μ is the mean and p_i is the probability of the outcome x_i for $i = 1, 2, 3, \ldots$, with the various outcomes covering all possibilities.

The expressions for the mean and variance of a continuous random variable are equivalent, but with summation replaced by integration.

$$\mu = E(X) = \int_{\substack{\text{All} \\ \text{values} \\ \text{of } x}} x\, f(x)\, dx$$

$$\text{Var}(X) = \int_{\substack{\text{All} \\ \text{values} \\ \text{of } x}} (x - \mu)^2\, f(x)\, dx = \int_{\substack{\text{All} \\ \text{values} \\ \text{of } x}} x^2\, f(x)\, dx - [E(X)]^2$$

$E(X)$ is the same as the population mean, μ, and is often called the mean of X.

EXAMPLE 10.4

The response time, in seconds, for a contestant in a general knowledge quiz is modelled by a continuous random variable X whose p.d.f. is

$$f(x) = \frac{x}{50} \quad \text{for } 0 < x \leqslant 10.$$

The rules state that a contestant who makes no answer is disqualified from the whole competition. This has the consequence that everybody gives an answer, if only a guess, to every question. Find

(i) the mean time in seconds for a contestant to respond to a particular question

(ii) the standard deviation of the time taken.

The organiser estimates the proportion of contestants who are guessing by assuming that they are those whose time is at least one standard deviation greater than the mean.

(iii) Using this assumption, estimate the probability that a randomly selected response is a guess.

SOLUTION

(i) Mean time: $E(X) = \displaystyle\int_0^{10} x\, f(x)\, dx$

$$= \int_0^{10} \frac{x^2}{50}\, dx$$

$$= \left[\frac{x^3}{150} \right]_0^{10} = \frac{1000}{150} = \frac{20}{3}$$

$$= 6\frac{2}{3}$$

The mean time is $6\frac{2}{3}$ seconds.

(ii) Variance: $\mathrm{Var}(X) = \displaystyle\int_0^{10} x^2\, f(x)\, dx - [E(X)]^2$

$$= \int_0^{10} \frac{x^3}{50}\, dx - \left(6\frac{2}{3} \right)^2$$

$$= \left[\frac{x^4}{200} \right]_0^{10} - \left(6\frac{2}{3} \right)^2$$

$$= 5\frac{5}{9}$$

Standard deviation $= \sqrt{\text{variance}} = \sqrt{5.\dot{5}}$

The standard deviation of the times is 2.357 seconds (to 3 d.p.).

(iii) All those with response times greater than $6.667 + 2.357 = 9.024$ seconds are taken to be guessing. The longest possible time is 10 seconds.

The probability that a randomly selected response is a guess is given by

$$\int_{9.024}^{10} \frac{x}{50}\, dx = \left[\frac{x^2}{100} \right]_{9.024}^{10}$$

$$= 0.186$$

So just under 1 in 5 answers are deemed to be guesses.

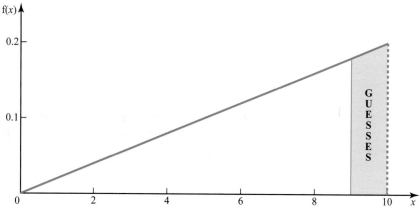

Figure 10.6

The median

The median value of a continuous random variable X with p.d.f. $f(x)$ is the value m for which

$$P(X < m) = P(X > m) = 0.5.$$

Consequently $\displaystyle\int_{-\infty}^{m} f(x)\,dx = 0.5$ and $\displaystyle\int_{m}^{\infty} f(x)\,dx = 0.5.$

The median is the value m such that the line $x = m$ divides the area under the curve $f(x)$ into two equal parts. In figure 10.7 a is the smallest possible value of X, b the largest. The line $x = m$ divides the shaded region into two regions A and B, both with area 0.5.

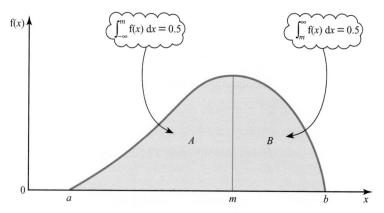

Figure 10.7

⚠ In general the *mean* does not divide the area into two equal parts but it will do so if the curve is symmetrical about it because, in that case, it is equal to the median.

The mode

The mode of a continuous random variable X whose p.d.f. is $f(x)$ is the value of x for which $f(x)$ has the greatest value. Thus the mode is the value of X where the curve is at its highest.

If the mode is at a local maximum of $f(x)$, then it may often be found by differentiating $f(x)$ and solving the equation

$$f'(x) = 0.$$

❓ For which of the distributions in figure 10.8 could the mode be found by differentiating the p.d.f.?

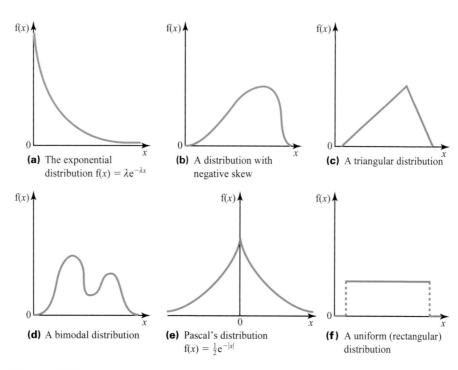

(a) The exponential distribution $f(x) = \lambda e^{-\lambda x}$

(b) A distribution with negative skew

(c) A triangular distribution

(d) A bimodal distribution

(e) Pascal's distribution $f(x) = \frac{1}{2}e^{-|x|}$

(f) A uniform (rectangular) distribution

Figure 10.8

EXAMPLE 10.5

The continuous random variable X has p.d.f. $f(x)$ where

$$f(x) = 4x(1-x^2) \quad \text{for } 0 \leqslant x \leqslant 1$$
$$= 0 \qquad\qquad \text{otherwise.}$$

Find

(i) the mode

(ii) the median.

SOLUTION

(i) The mode is found by differentiating $f(x) = 4x - 4x^3$

$$f'(x) = 4 - 12x^2$$

> $x = -0.577$ is also a root of $f'(x) = 0$ but is outside the range $0 \leqslant x \leqslant 1$.

Solving $f'(x) = 0$

$$x = \frac{1}{\sqrt{3}} = 0.577 \text{ to 3 decimal places.}$$

It is easy to see from the shape of the graph (see figure 10.9) that this must be a maximum, and so the mode is 0.577.

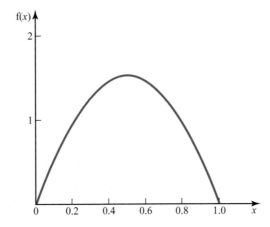

Figure 10.9

(ii) The median, m, is given by $\int_{-\infty}^{m} f(x)\,dx = 0.5$

$$\Rightarrow \int_0^m (4x - 4x^3)\,dx = 0.5 \quad\longleftarrow\quad \boxed{\text{Since } x \geqslant 0}$$

$$\left[2x^2 - x^4\right]_0^m = 0.5$$

$$2m^2 - m^4 = 0.5$$

Rearranging gives

$$2m^4 - 4m^2 + 1 = 0.$$

This is a quadratic equation in m^2. The formula gives

$$m^2 = \frac{4 \pm \sqrt{16 - 8}}{4}$$

$$m = 0.541 \text{ or } 1.307 \text{ to 3 decimal places.}$$

Since 1.307 is outside the domain of X, the median is 0.541.

The uniform (rectangular) distribution

It is common to describe distributions by the shapes of the graphs of their p.d.f.s: U-shaped, J-shaped, etc

The *uniform (rectangular) distribution* is particularly simple since its p.d.f. is constant over a range of values and zero elsewhere.

In figure 10.10, X may take values between a and b, and is zero elsewhere. Since the area under the graph must be 1, the height is $\dfrac{1}{b-a}$. The term 'uniform distribution' can be applied to both discrete and continuous variables so in the continuous case it is often written as 'uniform (rectangular)'.

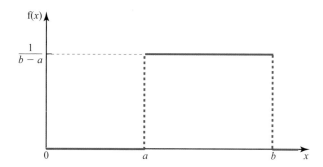

Figure 10.10

EXAMPLE 10.6

A junior gymnastics league is open to children who are at least five years old but have not yet had their ninth birthday. The age, X years, of a member is modelled by the uniform (rectangular) distribution over the range of possible values between five and nine. Age is measured in years and decimal parts of a year, rather than just completed years. Find

(i)   the p.d.f. f(x) of X
(ii) $P(6 \leqslant X \leqslant 7)$
(iii) $E(X)$
(iv) $Var(X)$
(v)   the percentage of the children whose ages are within one standard deviation of the mean.

SOLUTION

(i)   The p.d.f. $f(x) = \dfrac{1}{9-5} = \dfrac{1}{4}$ for $5 \leqslant x < 9$

$\qquad\qquad\qquad\quad = 0$ otherwise.

(ii) $P(6 \leqslant X \leqslant 7) = \frac{1}{4}$ by inspection of the rectangle in figure 10.11.

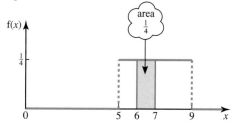

Figure 10.11

Alternatively, using integration

$$P(6 \leqslant X \leqslant 7) = \int_6^7 f(x)\,dx = \int_6^7 \frac{1}{4}\,dx$$

$$= \left[\frac{x}{4}\right]_6^7$$

$$= \frac{7}{4} - \frac{6}{4}$$

$$= \frac{1}{4}.$$

(iii) By the symmetry of the graph, $E(X) = 7$. Alternatively, using integration

$$E(X) = \int_{-\infty}^{\infty} x\,f(x)\,dx = \int_5^9 \frac{x}{4}\,dx$$

$$= \left[\frac{x^2}{8}\right]_5^9$$

$$= \frac{81}{8} - \frac{25}{8} = 7.$$

(iv) $$\text{Var}(X) = \int_{-\infty}^{\infty} x^2\,f(x)\,dx - [E(X)]^2 = \int_5^9 \frac{x^2}{4}\,dx - 7^2$$

$$= \left[\frac{x^3}{12}\right]_5^9 - 49$$

$$= \frac{729}{12} - \frac{125}{12} - 49$$

$$= 1.333 \text{ to 3 decimal places.}$$

(v) Standard deviation $= \sqrt{\text{variance}} = \sqrt{1.333} = 1.155$.

So the percentage within 1 standard deviation of the mean is

$$\frac{2 \times 1.155}{4} \times 100\% = 57.7\%.$$

? What percentage would be within 1 standard deviation of the mean for a normal distribution? Why is the percentage less in this example?

The mean and variance of the uniform (rectangular) distribution

In the previous example the mean and variance of a particular uniform distribution were calculated. This can easily be extended to the general uniform distribution given by:

$$f(x) = \frac{1}{b-a} \quad \text{for } a \leqslant x \leqslant b$$
$$= 0 \quad \text{otherwise.}$$

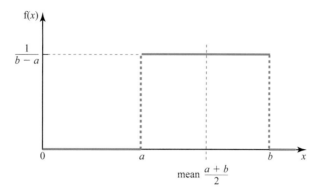

Figure 10.12

Mean   By symmetry the mean is $\dfrac{a+b}{2}$.

Variance $\displaystyle \text{Var}(X) = \int_{-\infty}^{\infty} x^2 \, f(x) \, dx - [E(X)]^2$

$$= \int_{a}^{b} x^2 \, f(x) \, dx - [E(X)]^2$$

$$= \int_{a}^{b} \frac{x^2}{b-a} \, dx - \left(\frac{a+b}{2}\right)^2$$

$$= \left[\frac{x^3}{3(b-a)}\right]_{a}^{b} - \frac{1}{4}(a^2 + 2ab + b^2)$$

$$= \frac{b^3 - a^3}{3(b-a)} - \frac{1}{4}(a^2 + 2ab + b^2)$$

$$= \frac{(b-a)}{3(b-a)}(b^2 + ab + a^2) - \frac{1}{4}(a^2 + 2ab + b^2)$$

$$= \frac{1}{12}(b^2 - 2ab + a^2)$$

$$= \frac{1}{12}(b-a)^2$$

1 The continuous random variable X has p.d.f. f(x) where

$$f(x) = \tfrac{1}{8}x \quad \text{for } 0 \leqslant x \leqslant 4$$
$$= 0 \quad \text{otherwise.}$$

Find

(i) E(X)

(ii) Var(X)

(iii) the median value of X.

2 The continuous random variable T has p.d.f. defined by

$$f(t) = \frac{6-t}{18} \quad \text{for } 0 \leqslant t \leqslant 6$$
$$= 0 \quad \text{otherwise.}$$

Find

(i) E(T)

(ii) Var(T)

(iii) the median value of T.

3 The continuous random variable Y has p.d.f. f(y) defined by

$$f(y) = 12y^2(1-y) \quad \text{for } 0 \leqslant y \leqslant 1$$
$$= 0 \quad \text{otherwise.}$$

(i) Find E(Y).

(ii) Find Var(Y).

(iii) Show that, to 2 decimal places, the median value of Y is 0.61.

4 The random variable X has p.d.f.

$$f(x) = \tfrac{1}{6} \quad \text{for } -2 \leqslant x \leqslant 4$$
$$= 0 \quad \text{otherwise.}$$

(i) Sketch the graph of f(x).

(ii) Find P($X < 2$).

(iii) Find E(X).

(iv) Find P($|X| < 1$).

5 The continuous random variable X has p.d.f. f(x) defined by

$$f(x) = \begin{cases} \tfrac{2}{9}x(3-x) & \text{for } 0 \leqslant x \leqslant 3 \\ 0 & \text{otherwise.} \end{cases}$$

(i) Find E(X).

(ii) Find Var(X).

(iii) Find the mode of X.

(iv) Find the median value of X.

(v) Draw a sketch graph of f(x) and comment on your answers to parts (i), (iii) and (iv) in the light of what it shows you.

6 The function $\mathrm{f}(x) = \begin{cases} k(3+x) & \text{for } 0 \leqslant x \leqslant 2 \\ 0 & \text{otherwise.} \end{cases}$

is the probability density function of the random variable X.

(i)   Show that $k = \frac{1}{8}$.

(ii) Find the mean and variance of X.

(iii) Find the probability that a randomly selected value of X lies between 1 and 2.

7 A continuous random variable X has a uniform (rectangular) distribution over the interval $(4, 7)$. Find

(i)   the p.d.f. of X

(ii) $\mathrm{E}(X)$

(iii) $\mathrm{Var}(X)$

(iv) $\mathrm{P}(4.1 \leqslant X \leqslant 4.8)$.

8 The distribution of the lengths of adult Martian lizards is uniform between 10 cm and 20 cm. There are no adult lizards outside this range.

(i)   Write down the p.d.f. of the lengths of the lizards.

(ii) Find the mean and variance of the lengths of the lizards.

(iii) What proportion of the lizards have lengths within

(a) one standard deviation of the mean

(b) two standard deviations of the mean?

9 The continuous random variable X has p.d.f. $\mathrm{f}(x)$ defined by

$$\mathrm{f}(x) = \begin{cases} \dfrac{a}{x} & \text{for } 1 \leqslant x \leqslant 2 \\ 0 & \text{otherwise.} \end{cases}$$

(i)   Find the value of a.

(ii) Sketch the graph of $\mathrm{f}(x)$.

(iii) Find the mean and variance of X.

(iv) Find the proportion of values of X between 1.5 and 2.

(v)   Find the median value of X.

10 The random variable X denotes the number of hours of cloud cover per day at a weather forecasting centre. The probability density function of X is given by

$$\mathrm{f}(x) = \begin{cases} \dfrac{(x-18)^2}{k} & 0 \leqslant x \leqslant 24, \\ 0 & \text{otherwise,} \end{cases}$$

where k is a constant.

(i)   Show that $k = 2016$.

(ii) On how many days in a year of 365 days can the centre expect to have less than 2 hours of cloud cover?

(iii) Find the mean number of hours of cloud cover per day.

[Cambridge International AS and A Level Mathematics 9709, Paper 7 Q7 June 2005]

11 The random variable X has probability density function given by

$$f(x) = \begin{cases} 4x^k & 0 \leqslant x \leqslant 1 \\ 0 & \text{otherwise.} \end{cases}$$

where k is a positive constant.

(i) Show that $k = 3$.

(ii) Show that the mean of X is 0.8 and find the variance of X.

(iii) Find the upper quartile of X.

(iv) Find the interquartile range of X.

[Cambridge International AS and A Level Mathematics 9709, Paper 7 Q5 June 2006]

12 If Usha is stung by a bee she always develops an allergic reaction. The time taken in minutes for Usha to develop the reaction can be modelled using the probability density function given by

$$f(t) = \begin{cases} \dfrac{k}{t+1} & 0 \leqslant t \leqslant 4, \\ 0 & \text{otherwise,} \end{cases}$$

where k is a constant.

(i) Show that $k = \dfrac{1}{\ln 5}$.

(ii) Find the probability that it takes more than 3 minutes for Usha to develop a reaction.

(iii) Find the median time for Usha to develop a reaction.

[Cambridge International AS and A Level Mathematics 9709, Paper 7 Q7 June 2008]

13 The time in minutes taken by candidates to answer a question in an examination has probability density function given by

$$f(t) = \begin{cases} k(6t - t^2) & 3 \leqslant t \leqslant 6, \\ 0 & \text{otherwise,} \end{cases}$$

where k is a constant.

(i) Show that $k = \frac{1}{18}$.

(ii) Find the mean time.

(iii) Find the probability that a candidate, chosen at random, takes longer than 5 minutes to answer the question.

(iv) Is the upper quartile of the times greater than 5 minutes, equal to 5 minutes or less than 5 minutes? Give a reason for your answer.

[Cambridge International AS and A Level Mathematics 9709, Paper 7 Q5 June 2009]

14 The time in hours taken for clothes to dry can be modelled by the continuous random variable with probability density function given by

$$f(t) = \begin{cases} k\sqrt{t} & 1 \leqslant t \leqslant 4, \\ 0 & \text{otherwise,} \end{cases}$$

where k is a constant.

(i) Show that $k = \frac{3}{14}$.

(ii) Find the mean time taken for clothes to dry.

(iii) Find the median time taken for clothes to dry.

(iv) Find the probability that the time taken for clothes to dry is between the mean time and the median time.

[Cambridge International AS and A Level Mathematics 9709, Paper 7 Q7 November 2008]

15 The random variable T denotes the time in seconds for which a firework burns before exploding. The probability density function of T is given by

$$f(t) = \begin{cases} ke^{0.2t} & 0 \leqslant t \leqslant 5, \\ 0 & \text{otherwise,} \end{cases}$$

where k is a positive constant.

(i) Show that $k = \dfrac{1}{5(e-1)}$.

(ii) Sketch the probability density function.

(iii) 80% of fireworks burn for longer than a certain time before they explode. Find this time.

[Cambridge International AS and A Level Mathematics 9709, Paper 71 Q5 June 2010]

KEY POINTS

1 If X is a continuous random variable with p.d.f. $f(x)$

- $\int f(x)\,dx = 1$

- $f(x) \geqslant 0$ for all x

- $P(c \leqslant x \leqslant d) = \int_c^d f(x)\,dx$

- $E(X) = \int x\,f(x)\,dx$

- $\text{Var}(X) = \int x^2\,f(x)\,dx - [E(X)]^2$

- The mode of X is the value for which $f(x)$ has its greatest magnitude.

2 **The uniform (rectangular) distribution over the interval (a, b)**

- $f(x) = \dfrac{1}{b-a}$

- $E(X) = \frac{1}{2}(a+b)$

- $\text{Var}(X) = \dfrac{(b-a)^2}{12}$

Linear combinations of random variables

11 Linear combinations of random variables

To approach zero defects, you must have statistical control of processes.

David Wilson

Unfair dismissal?

Janice

Just had one of those days. 'Everything went wrong. First the school bus arrived 5 minutes late to pick up my little boy. Then it was wet and slippery and there were so many people about that I just couldn't walk at my normal speed; usually I take 15 minutes but that day it took me 18 to get to work. And then when I got to work I had to wait $3\frac{1}{2}$ minutes for the lift instead of the usual $\frac{1}{2}$ minute. So instead of arriving my normal 10 minutes early I was one minute late.'

Mrs Dickens just wouldn't listen. She said she did not employ people to make excuses and told me to leave there and then.

Do you think I have a case for unfair dismissal?

Like Janice, we all have days when everything goes wrong at once. There were three random variables involved in her arrival time at work: the time she had to wait for the school bus, S; the time she took to walk to work, W, and the time she had to wait for the lift, L.

Her total time for getting to work, T, was the sum of all three: $T = S + W + L$.

Janice's case was essentially that the probability of T taking such a large value was very small. To estimate that probability you would need information about the distributions of the three random variables involved. You would also need to know how to handle the sum of two or more (in this case three) random variables.

The expectation (mean) of a function of *X*, E(g[*X*])

However, before you can do this, you need to extend some of the work you did in Chapter 4 on random variables. There you learnt that, for a discrete random variable X with $P(X = x_i) = p_i$,

its expectation $= E(X) = \mu = \sum x_i \times P(X = x_i) = \sum x_i p_i$

and its variance $= \sigma^2 = E[(X - \mu)^2] = \sum (x_i - \mu)^2 \times P(X = x_i) = \sum (x_i - \mu)^2 p_i$

$$= E(X^2) - E[(X)]^2 = \sum x_i^2 \times P(X = x_i) - \mu^2 = \sum x_i^2 p_i - \mu^2$$

This only finds the expected value and variance of a particular random variable.

Sometimes you will need to find the mean, i.e. the expectation, of a function of a random variable. That sounds rather forbidding and you may think the same of the definition given below at first sight. However, as you will see in the next two examples, the procedure is straightforward and common sense.

- If g[X] is a function of the discrete random variable X then E(g[X]) is given by

$$E(g[X]) = \sum_i g[x_i] \times P(X = x_i).$$

EXAMPLE 11.1

What is the expectation of the square of the number that comes up when a fair die is rolled?

SOLUTION

Let the random variable X be the number that comes up when the die is rolled.

$$g[X] = X^2$$

$$E(g[X]) = E(X^2) = \sum_i x_i^2 \times P(X = x_i)$$

$$= 1^2 \times \tfrac{1}{6} + 2^2 \times \tfrac{1}{6} + 3^2 \times \tfrac{1}{6} + 4^2 \times \tfrac{1}{6} + 5^2 \times \tfrac{1}{6} + 6^2 \times \tfrac{1}{6}$$

$$= 1 \times \tfrac{1}{6} + 4 \times \tfrac{1}{6} + 9 \times \tfrac{1}{6} + 16 \times \tfrac{1}{6} + 25 \times \tfrac{1}{6} + 36 \times \tfrac{1}{6}$$

$$= \tfrac{91}{6}$$

$$= 15.17$$

Note

This calculation could also have been set out in table form as shown below.

x	$P(X = x_i)$	x_i^2	$x_i^2 \times P(X = x_i)$
1	$\frac{1}{6}$	1	$\frac{1}{6}$
2	$\frac{1}{6}$	4	$\frac{4}{6}$
3	$\frac{1}{6}$	9	$\frac{9}{6}$
4	$\frac{1}{6}$	16	$\frac{16}{6}$
5	$\frac{1}{6}$	25	$\frac{25}{6}$
6	$\frac{1}{6}$	36	$\frac{36}{6}$
Total	1		$\frac{91}{6}$

$$E(g[X]) = \tfrac{91}{6} = 15.17$$

? E(X^2) is not the same as $[E(X)]^2$. In this case $15.57 \neq 3.5^2$ which is 12.25. In fact, the difference between E(X^2) and $[E(X)]^2$ is very important in statistics. Why is this?

EXAMPLE 11.2   A random variable X has the following probability distribution.

Outcome	1	2	3
Probability	0.4	0.4	0.2

(i) Calculate E($4X + 5$).

(ii) Calculate 4E(X) + 5.

(iii) Comment on the relationship between your answers to parts (i) and (ii).

SOLUTION

(i) $E(g[X]) = \sum_i g[x_i] \times P(X = x_i)$ with $g[X] = 4X + 5$

x_i	1	2	3
$g[x_i]$	9	13	17
$P(X = x_i)$	0.4	0.4	0.2

$$E(4X + 5) = E(g[X])$$
$$= 9 \times 0.4 + 13 \times 0.4 + 17 \times 0.2$$
$$= 12.2$$

(ii) $E(X) = 1 \times 0.4 + 2 \times 0.4 + 3 \times 0.2 = 1.8$

and so

$$4E(X) + 5 = 4 \times 1.8 + 5$$
$$= 12.2$$

(iii) Clearly E($4X + 5$) = 4E(X) + 5, both having the value 12.2.

Expectation: algebraic results

In Example 11.2 above you found that E($4X + 5$) = 4E(X) + 5.

The working was numerical, showing that both expressions came out to be 12.2, but it could also have been shown algebraically. This would have been set out as follows.

	Proof	Reasons (general rules)

$$E(4X + 5) = E(4X) + E(5) \qquad E(X \pm Y) = E(X) \pm E(Y)$$
$$\qquad\qquad = 4E(X) + E(5) \qquad E(aX) = aE(X)$$
$$\qquad\qquad = 4E(X) + 5 \qquad E(c) = c$$

Look at the general rules on the right-hand side of the page. (X and Y are random variables, a and c are constants.) They are important but they are also common sense.

Notice the last one, which in this case means the expectation of 5 is 5. Of course it is; 5 cannot be anything else but 5. It is so obvious that sometimes people find it confusing! In general

$$E(aX + c) = aE(X) + c$$

These rules can be extended to take in the expectation of the sum of two functions of a random variable.

$$E(f[X] + g[X]) = E(f[X]) + E(g[X])$$

where f and g are both functions of X.

EXAMPLE 11.3

The random variable X has the following probability distribution.

x	1	2	3	4
$P(X = x)$	0.6	0.2	0.1	0.1

Find

(i) $\text{Var}(X)$ (ii) $\text{Var}(7)$ (iii) $\text{Var}(3X)$ (iv) $\text{Var}(3X + 7)$.

What general rule do the answers to parts (ii) and (iv) illustrate?

SOLUTION

(i)

x	1	2	3	4
x^2	1	4	9	16
$P(X = x)$	0.6	0.2	0.1	0.1

$$E(X) = 1 \times 0.6 + 2 \times 0.2 + 3 \times 0.1 + 4 \times 0.1$$
$$= 1.7$$
$$E(X^2) = 1 \times 0.6 + 4 \times 0.2 + 9 \times 0.1 + 16 \times 0.1$$
$$= 3.9$$
$$\text{Var}(X) = E(X^2) - [E(X)]^2$$
$$= 3.9 - 1.7^2$$
$$= 1.01$$

(ii) $\text{Var}(7) = \text{E}(7^2) - [\text{E}(7)]^2$

$= \text{E}(49) - [7]^2$

$= 49 - 49$

$= 0$

General result

$\text{Var}(c) = 0$ for a constant c.

This result is obvious; a constant is constant and so can have no spread.

(iii) $\text{Var}(3X) = \text{E}[(3X)^2] - \mu^2$

$= \text{E}(9X^2) - [\text{E}(3X)]^2$

$= 9\text{E}(X^2) - [3\text{E}(X)]^2$

$= 9 \times 3.9 - (3 \times 1.7)^2$

$= 35.1 - 26.01$

$= 9.09$

General result

$\text{Var}(aX) = a^2 \text{Var}(X)$.

Notice that it is a^2 and not a on the right-hand side, but that taking the square root of each side gives the standard deviation of $(aX) = a \times$ standard deviation (X) as you would expect from common sense.

(iv) $\text{Var}(3X + 7)$

$= \text{E}[(3X + 7)^2]$

$\quad - [\text{E}(3X + 7)]^2$

$= \text{E}(9X^2 + 42X + 49)$

$\quad - [3\text{E}(X) + 7]^2$

$= \text{E}(9X^2) + \text{E}(42X) + \text{E}(49)$

$\quad - [3 \times 1.7 + 7]^2$

$= 9\text{E}(X^2) + 42\text{E}(X)$

$\quad + 49 - 12.1^2$

$= 9 \times 3.9 + 42 \times 1.7$

$\quad + 49 - 146.41$

$= 9.09$

General result

$\text{Var}(aX + c) = a^2 \text{Var}(X)$.

Notice that the constant c does not appear on the right-hand side.

EXERCISE 11A

1 The probability distribution of a random variable X is as follows.

x	1	2	3	4	5
$P(X = x)$	0.1	0.2	0.3	0.3	0.1

(i) Find
  (a) $\text{E}(X)$
  (b) $\text{Var}(X)$.

(ii) Verify that $\text{Var}(2X) = 4\text{Var}(X)$.

2 The probability distribution of a random variable X is as follows.

x	0	1	2
$P(X = x)$	0.5	0.3	0.2

(i) Find
  (a) $\text{E}(X)$
  (b) $\text{Var}(X)$.

(ii) Verify that $\text{Var}(5X + 2) = 25\text{Var}(X)$.

3 Prove that $\mathrm{Var}(aX - b) = a^2\,\mathrm{Var}(X)$ where a and b are constants.

4 A coin is biased so that the probability of obtaining a tail is 0.75. The coin is tossed four times and the random variable X is the number of tails obtained. Find

(i) $E(2X)$

(ii) $\mathrm{Var}(3X)$.

5 A discrete random variable W has the following distribution.

w	1	2	3	4	5	6
$P(W = w)$	0.1	0.2	0.1	0.2	0.1	0.3

Find the mean and variance of
(i) $W + 7$

(ii) $6W - 5$.

6 The random variable X is the number of heads obtained when four unbiased coins are tossed. Construct the probability distribution for X and find

(i) $E(X)$

(ii) $\mathrm{Var}(X)$

(iii) $\mathrm{Var}(3X + 4)$.

7 The discrete random variable X has probability distribution given by

$$P(X = x) = \frac{(4x + 7)}{68} \qquad \text{for } x = 1, 2, 3, 4.$$

(i) Find

   (a) $E(X)$

   (b) $E(X^2)$

   (c) $E(X^2 + 5X - 2)$.

(ii) Verify that $E(X^2 + 5X - 2) = E(X^2) + 5E(X) - 2$.

8 A bag contains four balls, numbered 2, 4, 6, 8 but identical in all other respects. One ball is chosen at random and the number on it is denoted by N, so that $P(N = 2) = P(N = 4) = P(N = 6) = P(N = 8) = \frac{1}{4}$.
Show that $\mu = E(N) = 5$ and $\sigma^2 = \mathrm{Var}(N) = 5$.

Two balls are chosen at random one after the other, with the first ball being replaced after it has been drawn. Let $\overline{N}$ be the arithmetic mean of the numbers on the two balls. List the possible values of $\overline{N}$ and their probabilities of being obtained. Hence evaluate $E(\overline{N})$ and $\mathrm{Var}(\overline{N})$.

[MEI]

The sums and differences of independent random variables

Sometimes, as in the case of Janice in the website forum thread on page 256, you may need to add or subtract a number of independent random variables. This process is illustrated in the next example.

EXAMPLE 11.4

The possible lengths (in cm) of the blades of cricket bats form a discrete uniform distribution:

> 38, 40, 42, 44, 46.

The possible lengths (in cm) of the handles of cricket bats also form a discrete uniform distribution:

> 22, 24, 26.

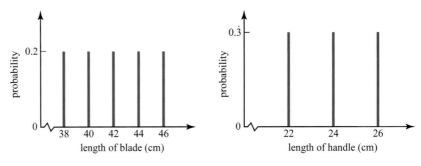

Figure 11.1

The blades and handles can be joined together to make bats of various lengths, and it may be assumed that the lengths of the two sections are independent.

(i) How many different (total) bat lengths are possible?

(ii) Work out the mean and variance of random variable X_1, the length (in cm) of the blades.

(iii) Work out the mean and variance of random variable X_2, the length (in cm) of the handles.

(iv) Work out the mean and variance of random variable $X_1 + X_2$, the total length of the bats.

(v) Verify that

$$E(X_1 + X_2) = E(X_1) + E(X_2)$$

and $\quad \mathrm{Var}(X_1 + X_2) = \mathrm{Var}(X_1) + \mathrm{Var}(X_2).$

SOLUTION

(i) The number of different bat lengths is 7. This can be seen from the sample space diagram below.

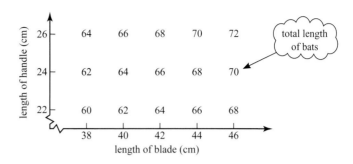

Figure 11.2

(ii)

Length of blade (cm)	38	40	42	44	46
Probability	0.2	0.2	0.2	0.2	0.2

$$E(X_1) = \mu_1 = \sum xp$$
$$= (38 \times 0.2) + (40 \times 0.2) + (42 \times 0.2) + (44 \times 0.2) + (46 \times 0.2)$$
$$= 42 \text{ cm}$$

$$\text{Var}(X_1) = E\left(X_1^2\right) - \mu_1^2$$
$$E\left(X_1^2\right) = (38^2 \times 0.2) + (40^2 \times 0.2) + (42^2 \times 0.2) + (44^2 \times 0.2) + (46^2 \times 0.2)$$
$$= 1772$$
$$\text{Var}(X_1) = 1772 - 42^2 = 8$$

(iii)

Length of handle (cm)	22	24	26
Probability	$\frac{1}{3}$	$\frac{1}{3}$	$\frac{1}{3}$

$$E(X_2) = \mu_2 = \left(22 \times \tfrac{1}{3}\right) + \left(24 \times \tfrac{1}{3}\right) + \left(26 \times \tfrac{1}{3}\right)$$
$$= 24 \text{ cm}$$

$$\text{Var}(X_2) = E\left(X_2^2\right) - \mu_2^2$$
$$E\left(X_2^2\right) = \left(22^2 \times \tfrac{1}{3}\right) + \left(24^2 \times \tfrac{1}{3}\right) + \left(26^2 \times \tfrac{1}{3}\right)$$
$$= 578.667 \text{ to 3 d.p.}$$
$$\text{Var}(X_2) = 578.667 - 24^2 = 2.667 \text{ to 3 d.p.}$$

(iv) The probability distribution of $X_1 + X_2$ can be obtained from figure 11.2.

Total length of cricket bat (cm)	60	62	64	66	68	70	72
Probability	$\frac{1}{15}$	$\frac{2}{15}$	$\frac{3}{15}$	$\frac{3}{15}$	$\frac{3}{15}$	$\frac{2}{15}$	$\frac{1}{15}$

$$E(X_1 + X_2) = \left(60 \times \tfrac{1}{15}\right) + \left(62 \times \tfrac{2}{15}\right) + \left(64 \times \tfrac{3}{15}\right) + \left(66 \times \tfrac{3}{15}\right) + \left(68 \times \tfrac{3}{15}\right)$$
$$+ \left(70 \times \tfrac{2}{15}\right) + \left(72 \times \tfrac{1}{15}\right)$$
$$= 66 \, \text{cm}$$

$$\text{Var}(X_1 + X_2) = E[(X_1 + X_2)^2] - 66^2$$

$$E[(X_1 + X_2)^2] = \left(60^2 \times \tfrac{1}{15}\right) + \left(62^2 \times \tfrac{2}{15}\right) + \left(64^2 \times \tfrac{3}{15}\right) + \left(66^2 \times \tfrac{3}{15}\right) + \left(68^2 \times \tfrac{3}{15}\right)$$
$$+ \left(70^2 \times \tfrac{2}{15}\right) + \left(72^2 \times \tfrac{1}{15}\right)$$

$$= \frac{65500}{15} = 4366.667 \text{ to 3 d.p.}$$

$$\text{Var}(X_1 + X_2) = 4366.667 - 66^2 = 10.667 \text{ to 3 d.p.}$$

(v) $E(X_1 + X_2) = 66 = 42 + 24 = E(X_1) + E(X_2)$, as required.

$\text{Var}(X_1 + X_2) = 10.667 = 8 + 2.667 = \text{Var}(X_1) + \text{Var}(X_2)$, as required.

Note

You should notice that the standard deviations of X_1 and X_2 do not add up to the standard deviation of $(X_1 + X_2)$.

$$\sqrt{8} + \sqrt{2.667} \neq \sqrt{10.667}$$

i.e. $2.828 + 1.633 \neq 3.266$

General results

Example 11.4 has illustrated the following general results for the sums and differences of random variables.

For any two random variables X_1 and X_2

- $E(X_1 + X_2) = E(X_1) + E(X_2)$

Replacing X_2 by $-X_2$ in this result gives

$$E(X_1 + (-X_2)) = E(X_1) + E(-X_2)$$

- $E(X_1 - X_2) = E(X_1) - E(X_2)$

If the variables X_1 and X_2 are independent then

- $\text{Var}(X_1 + X_2) = \text{Var}(X_1) + \text{Var}(X_2)$

Replacing X_2 by $-X_2$ gives

$$\text{Var}(X_1 + (-X_2)) = \text{Var}(X_1) + \text{Var}(-X_2)$$
$$\text{Var}(X_1 - X_2) = \text{Var}(X_1) + (-1)^2 \, \text{Var}(X_2)$$

● $\text{Var}(X_1 - X_2) = \text{Var}(X_1) + \text{Var}(X_2)$

The sums and differences of normal variables

If the variables X_1 and X_2 are normally distributed, then the distributions of $(X_1 + X_2)$ and $(X_1 - X_2)$ are also normal. The means of these distributions are $\text{E}(X_1) + \text{E}(X_2)$ and $\text{E}(X_1) - \text{E}(X_2)$.

You must, however, be careful when you come to their variances, since you may only use the result that

$$\text{Var}(X_1 \pm X_2) = \text{Var}(X_1) + \text{Var}(X_2)$$

to find the variances of these distributions if the variables X_1 and X_2 are independent.

This is the situation in the next two examples.

EXAMPLE 11.5

Robert Fisher, a keen chess player, visits his local club most days. The total time taken to drive to the club and back is modelled by a normal variable with mean 25 minutes and standard deviation 3 minutes. The time spent at the chess club is also modelled by a normal variable with mean 120 minutes and standard deviation 10 minutes. Find the probability that on a certain evening Mr Fisher is away from home for more than $2\frac{1}{2}$ hours.

SOLUTION

Let the random variable $X_1 \sim \text{N}(25, 3^2)$ represent the driving time, and the random variable $X_2 \sim \text{N}(120, 10^2)$ represent the time spent at the chess club.

Then the random variable T, where $T = X_1 + X_2 \sim \text{N}(145, (\sqrt{109})^2)$, represents his total time away.

So the probability that Mr Fisher is away for more than $2\frac{1}{2}$ hours (150 minutes) is given by

$$P(T > 150) = 1 - \Phi\left(\frac{150 - 145}{\sqrt{109}}\right)$$

$$= 1 - \Phi(0.479)$$

$$= 0.316.$$

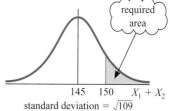

Figure 11.3

EXAMPLE 11.6

In the manufacture of a bridge made entirely from wood, circular pegs have to fit into circular holes. The diameters of the pegs are normally distributed with mean 1.60 cm and standard deviation 0.01 cm, while the diameters of the holes are normally distributed with mean 1.65 cm and standard deviation 0.02 cm. What is the probability that a randomly chosen peg will not fit into a randomly chosen hole?

SOLUTION

Let the random variable X be the diameter of a hole:

$$X \sim N(1.65, 0.02^2) = N(1.65, 0.0004).$$

Let the random variable Y be the diameter of a peg:

$$Y \sim N(1.60, 0.01^2) = N(1.6, 0.0001)$$

Let $F = X - Y$. F represents the gap remaining between the peg and the hole and so the sign of F determines whether or not a peg will fit in a hole.

$$E(F) = E(X) - E(Y) = 1.65 - 1.60 = 0.05$$

$$Var(F) = Var(X) + Var(Y) = 0.0004 + 0.0001 = 0.0005$$

$$F \sim N(0.05, 0.0005)$$

If for any combination of peg and hole the value of F is negative, then the peg will not fit into the hole.

The probability that $F < 0$ is given by

$$\Phi\left(\frac{0 - 0.05}{\sqrt{0.0005}}\right) = 1 - \Phi(-2.236)$$

$$= 1 - 0.9873$$

$$= 0.0127.$$

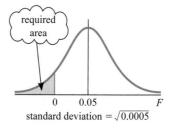

standard deviation $= \sqrt{0.0005}$

Figure 11.4

EXERCISE 11B

1 The menu at a café is shown below.

Main course		*Dessert*	
Fish and Chips	$3	Ice Cream	$1
Spaghetti	$3.50	Apple Pie	$1.50
Pizza	$4	Sponge Pudding	$2
Steak and Chips	$5.50		

The owner of the café says that all the main-course dishes sell equally well, as do all the desserts, and that customers' choice of dessert is not influenced by the main course they have just eaten.

The variable M denotes the cost of the main course, in dollars, and the variable D the cost of the dessert. The variable T denotes the total cost of a two-course meal: $T = M + D$.

(i) Find the mean and variance of M.

(ii) Find the mean and variance of D.

(iii) List all the possible two-course meals, giving the price for each one.

(iv) Use your answer to part (iii) to find the mean and variance of T.

(v) Hence verify that for these figures

$$\text{mean } (T) = \text{mean } (M) + \text{mean } (D)$$

and $\text{variance } (T) = \text{variance } (M) + \text{variance } (D).$

2   X_1 and X_2 are independent random variables with distributions N(50, 16) and N(40, 9) respectively. Write down the distributions of

(i) $X_1 + X_2$

(ii) $X_1 - X_2$

(iii) $X_2 - X_1$.

3   A play is enjoying a long run at a theatre. It is found that the play time may be modelled as a normal variable with mean 130 minutes and standard deviation 3 minutes, and that the length of the intermission in the middle of the performance may be modelled by a normal variable with mean 15 minutes and standard deviaton 5 minutes. Find the probability that the performance is completed in less than 140 minutes.

4   The time Melanie spends on her history assignments may be modelled as being normally distributed, with mean 40 minutes and standard deviation 10 minutes. The times taken on assignments may be assumed to be independent. Find

(i) the probability that a particular assignment will last longer than an hour

(ii) the time in which 95% of all assignments can be completed

(iii) the probability that two assignments will be completed in less than 75 minutes.

5   The weights of full cans of a particular brand of pet food may be taken to be normally distributed, with mean 260 g and standard deviation 10 g. The weights of the empty cans may be taken to be normally distributed, with mean 30 g and standard deviation 2 g. Find

(i) the mean and standard deviation of the weights of the contents of the cans

(ii) the probability that a full can weighs more than 270 g

(iii) the probability that two full cans together weigh more than 540 g.

6 The independent random variables X_1 and X_2 are distributed as follows:

$$X_1 \sim N(30, 9); \quad X_2 \sim N(40, 16).$$

Find the distributions of the following :

(i) $X_1 + X_2$

(ii) $X_1 - X_2$.

7 In a vending machine the capacity of cups is normally distributed, with mean 200 cm^3 and standard deviation 4 cm^3. The volume of coffee discharged per cup is normally distributed, with mean 190 cm^3 and standard deviation 5 cm^3. Find the percentage of drinks which overflow.

8 On a distant island the heights of adult men and women may both be taken to be normally distributed, with means 173 cm and 165 cm and standard deviations 10 cm and 8 cm respectively.

(i) Find the probability that a randomly chosen woman is taller than a randomly chosen man.

(ii) Do you think that this is equivalent to the probability that a married woman is taller than her husband?

9 The lifetimes of a certain brand of refrigerator are approximately normally distributed, with mean 2000 days and standard deviation 250 days. Mrs Chudasama and Mr Poole each buy one on the same date.

What is the probability that Mr Poole's refrigerator is still working one year after Mrs Chudasama's refrigerator has broken down?

10 A random sample of size 2 is chosen from a normal distribution N(100, 25). Find the probability that

(i) the sum of the sample numbers exceeds 215

(ii) the first observation is at least 19 more than the second observation.

11 A mathematics module is assessed by an examination and by coursework. The examination makes up 75% of the total assessment and the coursework makes up 25%. Examination marks, X, are distributed with mean 53.2 and standard deviation 9.3. Coursework marks, Y, are distributed with mean 78.0 and standard deviation 5.1. Examination marks and coursework marks are independent. Find the mean and standard deviation of the combined mark $0.75X + 0.25Y$.

[Cambridge International AS and A Level Mathematics 9709, Paper 7 Q2 June 2006]

12 The cost of electricity for a month in a certain town under scheme A consists of a fixed charge of 600 cents together with a charge of 5.52 cents per unit of electricity used. Stella uses scheme A. The number of units she uses in a month is normally distributed with mean 500 and variance 50.41.

(i) Find the mean and variance of the total cost of Stella's electricity in a randomly chosen month.

Under scheme *B* there is no fixed charge and the cost in cents for a month is normally distributed with mean 6600 and variance 421. Derek uses scheme *B*.

(ii) Find the probability that, in a randomly chosen month, Derek spends more than twice as much as Stella spends.

[Cambridge International AS and A Level Mathematics 9709, Paper 7 Q4 November 2007]

More than two independent random variables

The results on pages 264–265 may be generalised to give the mean and variance of the sums and differences of *n* random variables, $X_1, X_2, \ldots, X_n$.

- $E(X_1 \pm X_2 \pm \ldots \pm X_n) = E(X_1) \pm E(X_2) \pm \ldots \pm E(X_n)$

and, provided $X_1, X_2, \ldots, X_n$ are independent,

- $\mathrm{Var}(X_1 \pm X_2 \pm \ldots \pm X_n) = \mathrm{Var}(X_1) + \mathrm{Var}(X_2) + \ldots + \mathrm{Var}(X_n)$.

If $X_1, X_2, \ldots, X_n$ is a set of normally distributed variables, then the distribution of $(X_1 \pm X_2 \pm \ldots \pm X_n)$ is also normal.

EXAMPLE 11.7

The mass, *X*, of a suitcase at an airport is modelled as being normally distributed, with mean 15 kg and standard deviation 3 kg. Find the probability that a random sample of ten suitcases weighs more than 154 kg.

SOLUTION

The mass *X* of one suitcase is given by

$$X \sim N(15, 9).$$

Then the mass of each of the ten suitcases has the distribution of *X*; call them X_1, $X_2, \ldots, X_{10}$.

Let the random variable *T* be the total weight of ten suitcases.

$$T = X_1 + X_2 + \ldots + X_{10}.$$
$$E(T) = E(X_1) + E(X_2) + \ldots + E(X_{10})$$
$$= 15 + 15 + \ldots + 15$$
$$= 150$$

Similarly
$$\mathrm{Var}(T) = \mathrm{Var}(X_1) + \mathrm{Var}(X_2) + \ldots + \mathrm{Var}(X_{10})$$
$$= 9 + 9 + \ldots + 9$$
$$= 90$$

So $T \sim N(150, 90)$.

The probability that *T* exceeds 154 is given by

$$1 - \Phi\left(\frac{154 - 150}{\sqrt{90}}\right) = 1 - \Phi(0.422)$$

$$= 1 - 0.6635$$

$$= 0.3365.$$

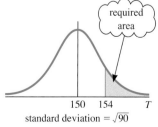

required area

150 154   *T*

standard deviation = $\sqrt{90}$

Figure 11.5

EXAMPLE 11.8

The running times of the four members of a 4×400 m relay team may all be taken to be normally distributed, as follows.

Member	Mean time (s)	Standard deviation (s)
Adil	52	1
Ben	53	1
Colin	55	1.5
Dexter	51	0.5

Assuming that no time is lost during changeovers, find the probability that the team finishes the race in less than 3 minutes 28 seconds.

SOLUTION

Let the total time be T.

$$E(T) = 52 + 53 + 55 + 51 = 211$$
$$Var(T) = 1^2 + 1^2 + 1.5^2 + 0.5^2 = 4.5$$

So $T \sim N(211, 4.5)$.

The probability of a total time of less than 3 minutes 28 seconds (208 seconds) is given by

$$\Phi\left(\frac{208 - 211}{\sqrt{4.5}}\right) = \Phi(-1.414)$$

$$= 1 - 0.9213$$

$$= 0.0787.$$

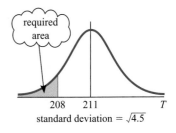

required area

standard deviation $= \sqrt{4.5}$

Figure 11.6

Linear combinations of two or more independent random variables

The results given on pages 264–265 can also be generalised to include linear combinations of random variables.

For any random variables X and Y,

- $E(aX + bY) = aE(X) + bE(Y)$,   where a and b are constants.

If X and Y are independent

- $Var(aX + bY) = a^2 \, Var(X) + b^2 \, Var(Y)$

If the distributions of X and Y are normal, then the distribution of $(aX + bY)$ is also normal.

These results may be extended to any number of random variables.

EXAMPLE 11.9

In a workshop joiners cut out rectangular sheets of laminated board, of length L cm and width W cm, to be made into work surfaces. Both L and W may be taken to be normally distributed with standard deviation 1.5 cm. The mean of L is 150 cm, that of W is 60 cm, and the lengths L and W are independent. Both of the short sides and one of the long sides have to be covered by a protective strip (the other long side is to lie against a wall and so does not need protection).

What is the probability that a protecting strip 275 cm long will be too short for a randomly selected work surface?

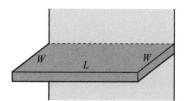

Figure 11.7

SOLUTION

Denoting the length and width by the independent random variables L and W and the total length of strip required by T:

$$T = L + 2W$$
$$\mathrm{E}(T) = \mathrm{E}(L) + 2\mathrm{E}(W)$$
$$= 150 + 2 \times 60$$
$$= 270$$

$$\mathrm{Var}(T) = \mathrm{Var}(L) + 2^2\,\mathrm{Var}(W)$$
$$= 1.5^2 + 4 \times 1.5^2$$
$$= 11.25$$

The probability of a strip 275 cm long being too short is given by

$$1 - \Phi\left(\frac{275 - 270}{\sqrt{11.25}}\right) = 1 - \Phi(1.491)$$
$$= 1 - 0.932$$
$$= 0.068.$$

Note

You have to distinguish carefully between the random variable $2W$, which means twice the size of one observation of the random variable W, and the random variable $W_1 + W_2$, which is the sum of two independent observations of the random variable W.

In the last example $\qquad$ $\mathrm{E}(2W) = 2\mathrm{E}(W) = 120$

and $\qquad$ $\mathrm{Var}(2W) = 2^2\mathrm{Var}(W) = 4 \times 2.25 = 9.$

In contrast, $\qquad$ $\mathrm{E}(W_1 + W_2) = \mathrm{E}(W_1) + \mathrm{E}(W_2) = 60 + 60 = 120$

and $\qquad$ $\mathrm{Var}(W_1 + W_2) = \mathrm{Var}(W_1) + \mathrm{Var}(W_2) = 2.25 + 2.25 = 4.5.$

EXAMPLE 11.10

A machine produces sheets of paper the thicknesses of which are normally distributed with mean 0.1 mm and standard deviation 0.006 mm.

(i) State the distribution of the total thickness of eight randomly selected sheets of paper.

(ii) Single sheets of paper are folded three times (to give eight thicknesses). State the distribution of the total thickness.

SOLUTION

Denote the thickness of one sheet (in mm) by the random variable W, and the total thickness of eight sheets by T.

(i) *Eight separate sheets*

In this situation $T = W_1 + W_2 + W_3 + W_4 + W_5 + W_6 + W_7 + W_8$

where W_1, W_2, ..., W_8 are eight independent observations of the variable W. The distribution of W is normal with mean 0.1 and variance 0.006^2. So the distribution of T is normal with

$$\text{mean} = 0.1 + 0.1 + \ldots + 0.1 = 8 \times 0.1 = 0.8$$
$$\text{variance} = 0.006^2 + 0.006^2 + \ldots + 0.006^2$$
$$= 8 \times 0.006^2$$
$$= 0.000\,288$$
$$\text{standard deviation} = \sqrt{0.000\,288} = 0.017.$$

The distribution is $N(0.8, 0.017^2)$.

(ii) *Eight thicknesses of the same sheet*

In this situation $T = W_1 + W_1 + W_1 + W_1 + W_1 + W_1 + W_1 + W_1 = 8W_1$

where W_1 is a single observation of the variable W.

So the distribution of T is normal with

$$\text{mean} = 8 \times E(W) = 0.8$$

$$\text{variance} = 8^2 \times \text{Var}(W) = 8^2 \times 0.006^2 = 0.002\,304$$

$$\text{standard deviation} = \sqrt{0.002\,304} = 0.048.$$

The distribution is $N(0.8, 0.048^2)$.

❓ Notice that in both cases the mean thickness is the same but for the folded paper the variance is greater. Why is this?

1 A garage offers motorists 'Road worthiness tests While U Wait' and claims that an average test takes only 20 minutes. Assuming that the time taken can be modelled as a normal variable with mean 20 minutes and standard deviation 2 minutes, find the distribution of the total time taken to conduct six tests in succession at this garage. State any assumptions you make.

2 A company manufactures floor tiles of mean length 20 cm with standard deviation 0.2 cm. Assuming the distribution of the lengths of the tiles is normal, find the probability that, when 12 randomly selected floor tiles are laid in a row, their total length exceeds 241 cm.

3 The masses of wedding cakes produced at a bakery are independent and may be modelled as being normally distributed with mean 4 kg and standard deviation 100 g. Find the probability that a set of eight wedding cakes has a total mass between 32.3 kg and 32.7 kg.

4 A random sample of 15 items is chosen from a normal population with mean 30 and variance 9. Find the probability that the sum of the variables in the sample is less than 440.

5 The distributions of four independent random variables X_1, X_2, X_3 and X_4 are N(7, 9), N(8, 16), N(9, 4) and N(10, 1) respectively.

Find the distributions of

(i) $X_1 + X_2 + X_3 + X_4$
(ii) $X_1 + X_2 - X_3 - X_4$
(iii) $X_1 - X_2 - X_3 + X_4$.

6 The distributions of X and Y are N(100, 25) and N(110, 36), and X and Y are independent. Find

(i) the probability that $8X + 2Y < 1000$
(ii) the probability that $8X - 2Y > 600$.

7 The distributions of the independent random variables A, B and C are N(35, 9), N(30, 8) and N(35, 9). Write down the distributions of

(i) $A + B + C$
(ii) $5A + 4B$
(iii) $A + 2B + 3C$
(iv) $4A - B - 5C$.

8 The distributions of the independent random variables X and Y are N(60, 4) and N(90, 9). Find the probability that

(i) $X - Y < -35$
(ii) $3X + 5Y > 638$
(iii) $3X > 2Y$.

9 If $X \sim N(60, 4)$ and $Y \sim N(90, 9)$ and X and Y are independent, find the probability that

(i) when one item is sampled from each population, the one from the Y population is more than 35 greater than the one from the X population.

(ii) the sum of a sample consisting of three items from population X and five items from population Y exceeds 638.

(iii) the sum of a sample of three items from population X exceeds that of two items from population Y.

(iv) Comment on your answers to questions 8 and 9.

10 The distribution of the weights of those rowing in a very large regatta may be taken to be normal with mean 80 kg and standard deviation 8 kg.

(i) What total weight would you expect 70% of randomly chosen crews of four rowers to exceed?

(ii) State what assumption you have made in answering this question and comment on whether you consider it reasonable.

11 The quantity of fuel used by a coach on a return trip of 200 km is modelled as a normal variable with mean 45 litres and standard deviation 1.5 litres.

(i) Find the probability that in nine return journeys the coach uses between 400 and 406 litres of fuel.

(ii) Find the volume of fuel which is 95% certain to be sufficient to cover the total fuel requirements for two return journeys.

12 The weekly takings at three cinemas are modelled as independent normally distributed random variables with means and standard deviations as shown in the table, in $.

	Mean	Standard deviation
Cinema A	6000	400
Cinema B	9000	800
Cinema C	5100	180

(i) Find the probability that the weekly takings at cinema A will be less than those at cinema C.

(ii) Find the probability that the weekly takings at cinema B will be at least twice those at cinema C.

(iii) The parent company receives a weekly levy consisting of 12% of the weekly takings at cinema A, 20% of those at cinema B and 8% of those at cinema C. Find the probability that this levy exceeds $3000 in any given week. Hence find the probability that in a 4-week period the weekly levy exceeds $3000 at least twice.

[MEI, *adapted*]

13 Assume that the weights of men and women may be taken to be normally distributed, men with mean 75 kg and standard deviation 4 kg, and women with mean 65 kg and standard deviation 3 kg.

At a village fair, tug-of-war teams consisting of either five men or six women are chosen at random. The competition is then run on a knock-out basis, with teams drawn out of a hat. If in the first round a women's team is drawn against a men's team, what is the probability that the women's team is the heavier? State any assumptions you have made and explain how they can be justified.

14 The four runners in a relay team have individual times, in seconds, which are normally distributed, with means 12.1, 12.2, 12.3, 12.4, and standard deviations 0.2, 0.25, 0.3, 0.35 respectively. Find the probability that, in a randomly chosen race,

(i) the total time of the four runners is less than 48 seconds

(ii) runners 1 and 2 take longer than runners 3 and 4.

What assumption have you made and how realistic is the model?

15 Jim Longlegs is an athlete whose specialist event is the triple jump. This is made up of a *hop*, a *step* and a *jump*. Over a season the lengths of the *hop*, *step* and *jump* sections, denoted by H, S and J respectively, are measured, from which the following models are proposed:

$$H \sim N(5.5, 0.5^2) \quad S \sim N(5.1, 0.6^2) \quad J \sim N(6.2, 0.8^2)$$

where all distances are in metres. Assume that H, S and J are independent.

(i) In what proportion of his triple jumps will Jim's total distance exceed 18 metres?

(ii) In six successive independent attempts, what is the probability that at least one total distance will exceed 18 m?

(iii) What total distance will Jim exceed 95% of the time?

(iv) Find the probability that, in Jim's next triple jump, his step will be greater than his hop.

[MEI]

16 The random variable X has the distribution $N(3.2, 1.2^2)$. The sum of 60 independent observations of X is denoted by S. Find $P(S > 200)$.

[Cambridge International AS and A Level Mathematics 9709, Paper 7 Q2 June 2007]

17 Weights of garden tables are normally distributed with mean 36 kg and standard deviation 1.6 kg. Weights of garden chairs are normally distributed with mean 7.3 kg and standard deviation 0.4 kg. Find the probability that the total weight of 2 randomly chosen tables is more than the total weight of 10 randomly chosen chairs.

[Cambridge International AS and A Level Mathematics 9709, Paper 7 Q3 November 2008]

18 A journey in a certain car consists of two stages with a stop for filling up with fuel after the first stage. The length of time, T minutes, taken for each stage has a normal distribution with mean 74 and standard deviation 7.3. The length of time, F minutes, it takes to fill up with fuel has a normal distribution with mean 5 and standard deviation 1.7. The length of time it takes to pay for the fuel is exactly 4 minutes. The variables T and F are independent and the times for the two stages are independent of each other.

(i) Find the probability that the total time for the journey is less than 154 minutes.

(ii) A second car has a fuel tank with exactly twice the capacity of the first car. Find the mean and variance of this car's fuel fill-up time.

(iii) This second car's time for each stage of the journey follows a normal distribution with mean 69 minutes and standard deviation 5.2 minutes. The length of time it takes to pay for the fuel for this car is also exactly 4 minutes. Find the probability that the total time for the journey taken by the first car is more than the total time taken by the second car.

[Cambridge International AS and A Level Mathematics 9709, Paper 7 Q7 November 2005]

KEY POINTS

1 For any discrete random variable X and constants a and c:

- $E(c) = c$
- $E(aX) = aE(X)$
- $E(aX + c) = aE(X) + c$
- $Var(c) = 0$
- $Var(aX) = a^2 Var(X)$
- $Var(aX + c) = a^2 Var(X)$.

2 For two random variables X and Y, whether independent or not, and constants a and b,

- $E(X \pm Y) = E(X) \pm E(Y)$
- $E(aX + bY) = aE(X) + bE(Y)$

and, if X and Y are independent,

- $Var(X \pm Y) = Var(X) + Var(Y)$
- $Var(aX \pm bY) = a^2 Var(X) + b^2 Var(Y)$.

3 For a set of n random variables, $X_1, X_2, \ldots, X_n$,

- $E(X_1 \pm X_2 \pm \ldots \pm X_n) = E(X_1) \pm E(X_2) \pm \ldots \pm E(X_n)$

and, if the variables are independent,

- $Var(X_1 \pm X_2 \pm \ldots \pm X_n) = Var(X_1) + Var(X_2) + \ldots + Var(X_n)$.

4 If random variables are normally distributed so are the sums, differences and other linear combinations of them.

12 Sampling

If you wish to learn swimming you have to go into the water.

G. Polya

PoliticsNow.com

Independent set to become member of parliament

Next week's local election looks set to produce the first independent member of parliament for many years, according to an opinion poll conducted by the PoliticsNow.com team.

When 30 potential voters were asked who they thought would make the best member of parliament, 12 opted for Independent candidate Mrs Chalashika. The other three candidates attracted between 3 and 9 votes.

Mrs Grace Chalashika is taking the polls by storm.

Assuming that the figures quoted in the article are true, does this really mean that Independent Mrs Chalashika will be elected to Parliament next week?

Only time will tell that, but meanwhile the newspaper report raises a number of questions that should make you suspicious of its conclusion.

Was the sample large enough? Thirty seems a very small number.

Were those interviewed asked the right question? They were asked who they thought would make the best member of parliament, not who they intended to vote for.

How was the sample selected? Was it representative of the whole electorate?

Before addressing these questions you will find it helpful to be familiar with the language and notation associated with sampling.

Terms and notation

PoliticsNow.com took a sample of size 30. Taking samples and interpreting them is an essential part of statistics. The populations in which you are interested are often so large that it would be quite impractical to use every item; the electorate for that area might well number 70 000.

A *sample* provides a set of data values of a random variable, drawn from all such possible values, the *parent population*. The parent population can be finite, such as all professional footballers, or infinite, such as the points where a dart can land on a dart board.

A representation of the items available to be sampled is called the *sampling frame*. This could, for example, be a list of the sheep in a flock, a map marked with a grid or an electoral register. In many situations no sampling frame exists nor is it possible to devise one, for example, for the cod in the North Atlantic. The proportion of the available items that are actually sampled is called the *sampling fraction*.

A parent population, often just called the *population*, is described in terms of its *parameters*, such as its mean, μ, and variance, σ^2. By convention Greek letters are used to denote these parameters.

A value derived from a sample is written in Roman letters: mean, $\bar{x}$, variance, s^2, etc. Such a number is the value of a *sample statistic* (or just *statistic*).When sample statistics are used to estimate the parent population parameters they are called *estimates*.

Thus if you take a random sample in which the mean is $\bar{x}$, you can use $\bar{x}$ to estimate the parent mean, μ. If in a particular sample $\bar{x} = 23.4$, then you can use 23.4 as an estimate of the population mean. The true value of μ will generally be somewhat different from your estimated value.

Upper case letters, X, Y, etc., are used to represent the random variables, and lower case letters, x, y, etc., to denote particular values of them. In the example of PoliticsNow.com's survey of voters, you could define X to be the percentage of voters, in a sample of size 30, showing support for Mrs Chalashika. The particular value from this sample, x, is $\left(\frac{12}{30}\right) \times 100 = 40\%$.

Sampling

There are essentially two reasons why you might wish to take a sample:

- to estimate the values of the parameters of the parent population
- to conduct a hypothesis test.

There are many ways you can interpret data. First you will consider how sample data are collected and the steps you can take to ensure their quality.

An estimate of a parameter derived from sample data will in general differ from its true value. The difference is called the *sampling error*. To reduce the sampling error, you want your sample to be as representative of the parent population as you can make it. This, however, may be easier said than done.

Here are a number of questions that you should ask yourself when about to take a sample.

1 Are the data relevant?

It is a common mistake to replace what you need to measure by something else for which data are more easily obtained.

You must ensure that your data are relevant, giving values of whatever it is that you really want to measure. This was clearly not the case in the example of the PoliticsNow.com survey, where the question people were asked, 'Who would make the best member of parliament?', was not the one whose answer was required. The question should have been 'Which person do you intend to vote for?'.

2 Are the data likely to be biased?

Bias is a systematic error. If, for example, you wished to estimate the mean time of young women running 100 metres and did so by timing the members of a hockey team over that distance, your result would be biased. The hockey players would be fitter and more athletic than most young women and so your estimate for the time would be too low.

You must try to avoid bias in the selection of your sample.

3 Does the method of collection distort the data?

The process of collecting data must not interfere with the data. It is, for example, very easy when designing a questionnaire to frame questions in such a way as to lead people into making certain responses. 'Are you a law-abiding citizen?' and 'Do you consider your driving to be above average?' are both questions inviting the answer 'Yes'.

In the case of collecting information on voting intentions another problem arises. Where people put the cross on their ballot papers is secret and so people are being asked to give away private information. There may well be those who find this offensive and react by deliberately giving false answers.

People often give the answer they think the questioner wants to receive.

4 Is the right person collecting the data?

Bias can be introduced by the choice of those taking the sample. For example, a school's authorities want to estimate the proportion of the students who smoke, which is against the school rules. Each class teacher is told to ask five students whether they smoke. Almost certainly some smokers will say 'No' to their teacher for fear of getting into trouble, even though they might say 'Yes' to a different person.

5 Is the sample large enough?

The sample must be sufficiently large for the results to have some meaning. In this case the intention was to look for differences of support between the four candidates and for that a sample of 30 is totally inadequate. For opinion polls, a sample size of about 1000 is common.

The sample size depends on the precision required in the results. For example, in the opinion polls for elections a much larger sample is required if you want the estimate to be reliable to within 1% than if 5% will do.

6 Is the sampling procedure appropriate in the circumstances?

The method of choosing the sample must be appropriate. Suppose, for example, that you were carrying out the survey of people's voting intentions in the forthcoming election for PoliticsNow.com. How would you select the sample of people you are going to ask?

If you stood in the town centre in the middle of one morning and asked passers-by, you would probably get an unduly high proportion of those who, for one reason or another, were not employed. It is quite possible that this group has different voting intentions from those in work.

If you selected names from the telephone directory, you would automatically exclude those who do not have telephones, those who do not have landlines and those who are ex-directory.

It is actually very difficult to come up with a plan which will yield a fair sample, one that is not biased in some direction or another. There are, however, a number of established sampling techniques and these are described in the next section of this chapter.

Each of the situations below involves a *population* and a *sample*. In each case identify both, briefly but precisely.

1 A member of parliament is interested in whether her constituents support proposed legislation to make convicted drug dealers do hard physical work every day while they are in prison. Her staff report that letters on the proposed legislation have been received from 361 constituents of whom 309 support it.

2 A flour company wants to know what proportion of households in Karachi bake some or all of their own bread. A sample of 500 residential addresses in Karachi is taken and interviewers are sent to these addresses. The interviewers are employed during regular working hours on weekdays and interview only during these hours.

3 The Chicago Police Department wants to know how black residents of Chicago feel about police service. A questionnaire with several questions about the police is prepared. A sample of 300 postal addresses in predominantly black areas of Chicago is taken and a police officer is sent to each address to administer the questionnaire to an adult living there.

Each sampling situation contains a serious source of probable bias. In each case give the reason that bias may occur and also the direction of the bias.

Sampling techniques

In considering the following techniques it is worth repeating that a key aim when taking a sample is to obtain a sample that is *representative* of the parent population being investigated. It is assumed that the sampling is done without replacement, otherwise, for example, one person could give an opinion twice, or more. The fraction of the population which is selected is called the *sampling fraction*.

- Sampling fraction $= \dfrac{\text{sample size}}{\text{population size}}$

Random sampling

In a *random sampling procedure*, every member of the population may be selected; there is a non-zero probability of this happening (and, of course, the probability is less than 1). In many random sampling procedures, for example, drawing names out of a hat, every member of the population has an equal probability of being selected.

In a *simple random sampling* procedure, every possible sample of a given size is equally likely to be selected. It follows that in such a procedure every member of the parent population is equally likely to be selected. However, the converse is not true. It is possible to devise a sampling procedure in which every member is equally likely to be selected but some samples are not permissible.

---

1 A school has 20 classes, each with 30 students. One student is chosen at random from each class, giving a sample size of 20. Why is this not a simple random sampling procedure?

2 If you write the name of each student in the school on a slip of paper, put all the slips in a box, shake it well and then take out 20, would this be a simple random sample?

Simple random sampling is fine when you can do it, but you must have a sampling frame. The selection of items within the frame is often done using tables of random numbers.

Using random numbers

Usually, each element in the frame is given a number, starting at 1. You then select elements for the sample using random number tables or the random number generator on a calculator or computer.

Suppose that you need to select a sample of 15 houses from a numbered list of 483 houses. Using random number tables, you choose a random starting position and take the digits in groups of three. If the first set of three digits is 247, you put house number 247 from the list into your sample. If the next number is 832, you ignore it because it does not correspond to a house in the list. You continue in this way until you have a sample of 15 houses. (If any number occurs more than once, you still only include it once in your sample.)

In some circumstances, you might choose to assign random numbers in a less wasteful way. For example, you could subtract 500 from any random numbers above 500, so instead of discarding 832 you would choose house (832 – 500) = 332. Whether this is worthwhile depends on the sample size and the method being used to link the numbers to the elements in the sampling frame.

When using a random number generator on a calculator, you use the same procedure. If the calculator only provides three digits and you need five, you can generate two sets of three digits and discard the last digit.

ACTIVITY 12.1 Using the random numbers below, which items would you choose from a numbered list of the 17 841 inhabitants of a town if you want a random sample of size 10? Start with the top left random number and work along each row in order.

54	66	35	88	98	91	45	92	12	47
12	16	71	83	94	22	44	57	43	43
45	32	26	37	19	89	27	02	77	14
85	98	46	56	50	71	07	65	33	63
51	63	71	95	36	36	17	77	53	40
25	95	65	04	59	80	16	59	21	43
91	55	88	14	82	48	48	94	38	34
60	87	82	35	35	45	45	08	44	37

e **Other sampling techniques**

There are many other sampling techniques. *Survey design,* the formulation of the most appropriate sampling procedure in a particular situation, is a major topic within statistics.

Stratified sampling

You have already thought about the difficulty of conducting a survey of people's voting intentions in a particular area before an election. In that situation it is possible to identify a number of different sub-groups which you might expect to have different voting patterns: low, medium and high income groups; urban, suburban and rural dwellers; young, middle-aged and elderly voters; men and women; and so on. The sub-groups are called *strata*. In *stratified sampling,* you would ensure that all strata were sampled. You would need to sample from high income, suburban, elderly women; medium income, rural young men; etc. In this example, 54 strata (3 × 3 × 3 × 2) have been identified. If the numbers sampled in the various strata are proportional to the size of their populations, the procedure is called *proportional stratified sampling.* If the sampling is not proportional, then appropriate weighting has to be used.

The selection of the items to be sampled within each stratum is usually done by simple random sampling. Stratified sampling will usually lead to more accurate results about the entire population, and will also give useful information about the individual strata.

Cluster sampling

Cluster sampling also starts with sub-groups, or strata, of the population, but in this case the items are chosen from one or several of the sub-groups. The sub-groups are now called clusters. It is important that each cluster should be reasonably representative of the entire population. If, for example, you were asked to investigate the incidence of a particular parasite in the puffin population of Northern Europe, it would be impossible to use simple random sampling. Rather you would select a number of sites and then catch some puffins at each place. This is cluster sampling. Instead of selecting from the whole population you are choosing from a limited number of clusters.

Systematic sampling

Systematic sampling is a method of choosing individuals from a sampling frame. If you were surveying telephone subscribers, you might select a number at random, say 66, and then sample the 66th name on every page of the directory. If the items in the sampling frame are numbered 1, 2, 3, ..., you might choose a random starting point like 38 and then sample numbers 38, 138, 238 and so on.

When using systematic sampling you have to beware of any cyclic patterns within the frame. For example, suppose a school list is made up class by class, each of exactly 25 children, in order of merit, so that numbers 1, 26, 51, 76, 101, ..., in the frame are those at the top of their class. If you sample every 50th child starting with number 26, you will conclude that the children in the school are very bright.

Quota sampling

Quota sampling is the method often used by companies employing people to carry out opinion surveys. An interviewer's quota is always specified in stratified terms: how many males and how many females, etc. The choice of who is sampled is then left up to the interviewer and so is definitely non-random.

EXERCISE 12A

1 Alan wishes to choose one child at random from the eleven children in his music class. The children are numbered 2, 3, 4, and so on, up to 12. Alan then throws two fair dice, each numbered from 1 to 6, and chooses the child whose number is the sum of the scores on the two dice.

(i) Explain why this is an unsatisfactory method of choosing a child.

(ii) Describe briefly a satisfactory method of choosing a child.

[Cambridge International AS and A Level Mathematics 9709, Paper 7 Q1 November 2008]

e **2** Identify the sampling procedures that would be appropriate in the following situations.

(i) A local education officer wishes to estimate the mean number of children per family on a large housing estate.

(ii) A consumer protection body wishes to estimate the proportion of trains that are running late.

(iii) A marketing consultant wishes to investigate the proportion of households in a town that have a personal computer.

(iv) A local politician wishes to carry out a survey into people's views on capital punishment within your area.

(v) A health inspector wishes to investigate what proportion of people wear spectacles.

(vi) Ministry officials wish to estimate the proportion of cars with bald tyres.

(vii) A television company wishes to estimate the proportion of householders who have not paid their television licence fee.

(viii) The police want to find out how fast cars travel in the outside lane of a motorway.

(ix) A sociologist wants to know how many girlfriends the average 18-year-old boy has had.

(x) The headteacher of a large school wishes to estimate the average number of hours of homework done per week by the students.

KEY POINTS

1 There are essentially two reasons why you might wish to take a sample:

- to estimate the values of the parameters of the parent population

- to conduct a hypothesis test.

2 When taking a sample you should ensure that:

- the data are relevant

- the data are unbiased

- the data are not distorted by the act of collection

- a suitable person is collecting the data

- the sample is of a suitable size

- a suitable sampling procedure is being followed.

3 In a random sample, every member of the population has a non-zero probability of being selected. In many random sampling procedures, every member of the population has an equal probability of being selected.

e In simple random sampling, every possible sample of a given size has an equal probability of being selected.

e Other sampling procedures include stratified sampling, cluster sampling, systematic sampling and quota sampling.

13 Hypothesis testing and confidence intervals using the normal distribution

When we spend money on testing an item, we are buying confidence in its performance.

Tony Cutler

Interpreting sample data using the normal distribution

Sydney set to become greenhouse?

from our Science Correspondent Ama Williams

On a recent visit to a college in Sydney, I was intrigued to find experiments being conducted to measure the level of carbon dioxide in the air we are all breathing. Readers will of course know that high levels of carbon dioxide are associated with the greenhouse effect.

Lecturer Ray Peng showed me round his laboratory. 'It is delicate work, measuring parts per million, but I am trying to establish what is the normal level in this area. Yesterday we took ten readings and you can see the results for yourself: 336, 334, 332, 332, 331, 331, 330, 330, 328, 326.'

When I commented that there seemed to be a lot of variation between the readings, Ray assured me that that was quite in order.

'I have taken hundreds of these measurements in the past,' he said. 'There is always a standard deviation of 2.5. That's just natural variation.'

I suggested to Ray that his students should test whether these results are significantly above the accepted value of 328 parts per million. Certainly they made me feel uneasy. Is the greenhouse effect starting here in Australia?

Ray Peng has been trying to establish the carbon dioxide level in Sydney. How do you interpret his figures? Do you think the correspondent has a point when she says she is worried that the greenhouse effect is already happening in Australia?

If suitable sampling procedures have not been used, then the resulting data may be worthless, indeed positively misleading. You may wonder if that is the case with Ray's figures, and about the accuracy of his analysis of the samples too. His data are used in subsequent working in this chapter, but you may well feel there is something of a question mark hanging over them. You should always be prepared to treat data with a healthy degree of caution.

S2

13

Hypothesis testing and confidence intervals using the normal distribution

Putting aside any concerns about the quality of the data, what conclusions can you draw from them?

Estimating the population mean, μ

Ray's data were as follows.

336, 334, 332, 332, 331, 331, 330, 330, 328, 326.

His intention in collecting them was to estimate the mean of the parent population, the population mean.

The mean of these figures, the sample mean, is given by

$$\bar{x} = \frac{336 + 334 + 332 + 332 + 331 + 331 + 330 + 330 + 328 + 326}{10}$$

$$= 331.$$

What does this tell you about the population mean, μ?

It tells you that it is about 331 but it certainly does not tell you that it is definitely and exactly 331. If Ray took another sample, its mean would probably not be 331 but you would be surprised (and suspicious) if it were very far away from it. If he took lots of samples, all of size 10, you would expect their means to be close together but certainly not all the same.

If you took 1000 such samples, each of size 10, the distribution of their means might look like figure 13.1. You will notice that this distribution looks rather like the normal distribution and so may well wonder if this is indeed the case.

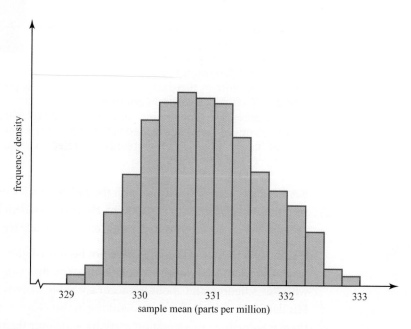

Figure 13.1

286

The distribution of sample means

In this chapter, it is assumed that the underlying population has a normal distribution with mean μ and standard deviation σ so it can be denoted by $N(\mu, \sigma^2)$. In that case the distribution of the means of samples is indeed normal; its mean is μ and its standard deviation is $\dfrac{\sigma}{\sqrt{n}}$. This is called the *sampling distribution of the means*, or often just the *sampling distribution*, and is denoted by $N\left(\mu, \dfrac{\sigma^2}{n}\right)$. This is illustrated in figure 13.2. It is a special case of the Central Limit Theorem which you will meet later in this chapter, on page 298.

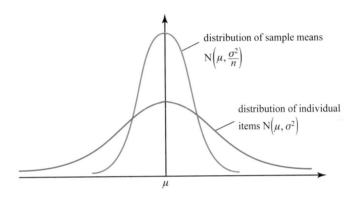

Figure 13.2

A hypothesis test for the mean using the normal distribution

If your intention in collecting sample data is to test a theory, then you should set up a hypothesis test.

Ray Peng was mainly interested in establishing data on carbon dioxide levels for Sydney. The correspondent, however, wanted to know whether levels were above normal, and so she could have set up and conducted a test.

Here is the relevant information, given in a more condensed format.

EXAMPLE 13.1

Ama Williams believes that the carbon dioxide level in Sydney has risen above the usual level of 328 parts per million. A sample of 10 specimens of Sydney air are collected and the carbon dioxide level within them is determined. The results are as follows.

336, 334, 332, 332, 331, 331, 330, 330, 328, 326.

Extensive previous research has shown that the standard deviation of the levels within such samples is 2.5, and that the distribution may be assumed to be normal.

Use these data to test, at the 0.1% significance level, Ama's belief that the level of carbon dioxide at Sydney is above normal.

SOLUTION

As usual with hypothesis tests, you use the distribution of the statistic you are measuring, in this case the normal distribution of the sample means, to decide which values of the test statistic are sufficiently extreme as to suggest that the alternative hypothesis, not the null hypothesis, is true.

Null hypothesis, H_0: $\mu = 328$ The level of carbon dioxide in Sydney is normal.

Alternative hypothesis, H_1: $\mu > 328$ The level of carbon dioxide in Sydney is above normal.

One-tail test

The significance level is 0.1%. This is the probability of a Type I error for this test.

Method 1: Using critical regions

Since the distribution of sample means is $N\left(\mu, \dfrac{\sigma^2}{n}\right)$, critical values for a test on

the sample mean are given by $\mu \pm k \times \dfrac{\sigma}{\sqrt{n}}$.

In this case, if H_0 is true, $\mu = 328$; $\sigma = 2.5$; $n = 10$.

The test is one-tail, for $\mu > 328$, so only the right-hand tail applies. This gives a value of $k = 3.090$ since normal distribution tables give $\Phi(3.090) = 0.999$ and so $1 - \Phi(3.090) = 0.001$.

The critical value is thus $328 + 3.09 \times \dfrac{2.5}{\sqrt{10}} = 330.4$, as shown in figure 13.3.

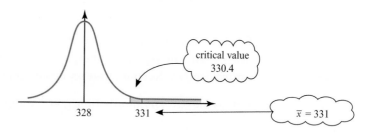

Figure 13.3

However, the sample mean $\bar{x} = 331$, and $331 > 330.4$.

Therefore the sample mean lies within the critical region, and so the null hypothesis is rejected in favour of the alternative hypothesis: that the mean carbon dioxide level is above 328, at the 0.1% significance level.

Method 2: Using probabilities

The distribution of sample means, $\bar{X}$, is $N\left(\mu, \dfrac{\sigma^2}{n}\right)$.

According to the null hypothesis, $\mu = 328$ and it is known that $\sigma = 2.5$ and $n = 10$.

So this distribution is $N\left(328, \dfrac{2.5^2}{10}\right)$; see figure 13.4.

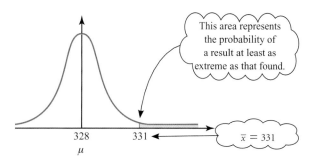

This area represents the probability of a result at least as extreme as that found.

328
μ

331 ← $\bar{x} = 331$

Figure 13.4

The probability of the mean, $\bar{X}$, of a randomly chosen sample being greater than the value found, i.e. 331, is given by

$$P(\bar{X} \geqslant 331) = 1 - \Phi\left(\frac{331 - 328}{\dfrac{2.5}{\sqrt{10}}}\right)$$

The figure 0.999 93 comes from normal distribution tables for suitable values of z.

$$= 1 - \Phi(3.79)$$

$$= 1 - 0.999\,93 = 0.000\,07$$

Since $0.000\,07 < 0.001$, the required significance level (0.1%), the null hypothesis is rejected in favour of the alternative hypothesis.

Method 3: Using critical ratios

The *critical ratio* is given by $z = \dfrac{\text{observed value} - \text{expected value}}{\text{standard deviation}}$.

In this case
$$z = \frac{331 - 328}{\dfrac{2.5}{\sqrt{10}}} = 3.79$$

This is now compared with the critical value for z given in your tables.

p	0.75	0.90	0.95	0.975	0.99	0.995	0.9975	0.999	0.9995
z	0.674	1.282	1.645	1.960	2.326	2.576	2.807	3.090	3.291

Figure 13.5 Critical values for the normal distribution

So the critical value is $z = 3.090$.

Since $3.79 > 3.09$, H_0 is rejected.

Notes

1 A hypothesis test should be formulated before the data are collected and not after. If sample data lead you to form a hypothesis, then you should plan a suitable test and collect further data on which to conduct it. It is not clear whether or not the test in the previous example was being carried out on the same data which were used to formulate the hypothesis.

2 If the data were not collected properly, any test carried out on them may be worthless.

EXAMPLE 13.2

Observations over a long period of time have shown that the mass of adult males of a type of bat is normally distributed with mean 110 g and standard deviation 10 g. A scientist has a theory that in one area these bats are becoming smaller, possibly as an adaptation to changes in their environment. He plans to trap 20 adult male bats, weigh them and then release them. He will then use the data to carry out a suitable hypothesis test at the 5% significance level.

(i) State the null and alternative hypotheses.
(ii) Find the critical value for the test.
(iii) Find the probability of a Type I error.

In fact the mean mass of the bats has reduced to 108 g but the standard deviation has remained unaltered.

(iv) Calculate the probability that the test will produce a Type II error.

The mean mass of the scientist's sample of bats is 107 g.

(v) Carry out the hypothesis test and state what type of error, if any, results.

SOLUTION

(i) The hypotheses are:

Null hypothesis H_0: $\quad\mu = 110 \quad$ The mean mass of the bats is still 110 g.

Alternative hypothesis H_1: $\quad\mu < 110 \quad$ The mean mass of the bats is less than 110 g.

(ii) This is a one-tail test at the 5% significance level so the critical value is:

$$\bar{X} = 110 - 1.645 \times \frac{10}{\sqrt{20}} = 106.3 \text{ to 1 d.p.}$$

where $\bar{X}$ is the sample mean.

The null hypothesis will be rejected if $\bar{X} < 106.3$.

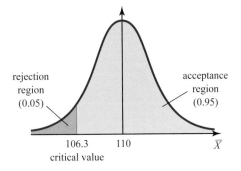

Figure 13.6

(iii) A Type I error occurs when a true null hypothesis is rejected. In this case, the probability of this happening is represented by the dark pink area in figure 13.6. It is just the same as the significance level of the test and so is 5% or 0.05.

(iv) A Type II error will occur if $\overline{X} > 106.3$ because in that case the null hypothesis, which is false, will be accepted.

In fact $\mu = 108$ and so the probability that $\overline{X} > 106.3$ is given by

$$1 - \Phi\left(\frac{106.3 - 108}{\frac{10}{\sqrt{20}}}\right) = 0.77 \text{ (to 2 s.f.)}$$

(v) Since $107 > 106.32$, the null hypothesis is accepted. The evidence does not support the scientist's theory.

However, this is the wrong result so a Type II error has occurred. The answer from part **(iv)** shows that with the test set up as it was, a Type II error is quite likely to occur.

Known and estimated standard deviation

Notice that you can only use this method of hypothesis testing if you already know the value of the standard deviation of the parent population, σ. Ray Peng had said that from taking hundreds of measurements he knew it to be 2.5.

It is more often the situation that you do not know the population standard deviation or variance and so have to estimate it from your sample data. For such estimates the estimated standard deviation, s, is worked out using slightly differently formulae from those you met in Chapter 1. In certain places $n - 1$ is used instead of n.

To calculate an unbiased estimate of the population mean and variance from a sample you should use the following formulae for these estimators:

Estimated mean, $\quad \bar{x} = \dfrac{\sum x}{n}$

Estimated variance, $\quad s^2 = \dfrac{1}{n-1}\left(\sum x^2 - \dfrac{\left(\sum x\right)^2}{n}\right)$

An alternative notation to s for the estimated standard deviation, which is sometimes used, is $\hat{\sigma}$.

EXAMPLE 13.3

An IQ test, established some years ago, was designed to have a mean score of 100. A researcher puts forward a theory that people are becoming more intelligent (as measured by this particular test). She selects a random sample of 150 people, all of whom take the test. The results of the tests, where x represents the score obtained, are $n = 150$, $\Sigma x = 15\,483$, $\Sigma x^2 = 1\,631\,680$.

Carry out a suitable hypothesis test on the researcher's theory, at the 1% significance level. You may assume that the test scores are normally distributed.

SOLUTION

H_0: The parent population mean is unchanged, i.e. $\mu = 100$.
H_1: The parent population mean has increased, i.e. $\mu > 100$.

One-tail test

The significance level is 1%. This is the probability of Type I error for this test.

From the sample, unbiased estimates for the mean and standard deviation are:

$$\bar{x} = \frac{\sum x}{n} = \frac{15483}{150} = 103.22$$

$$s^2 = \frac{1}{n-1}\left(\sum x^2 - \frac{\left(\sum x\right)^2}{n}\right) = \frac{1}{149}\left(1\,631\,680 - \frac{15483^2}{150}\right) = 224.998\ldots$$

So $\qquad s = 15.0$ (to 3 s.f.)

The standardised z value corresponding to $\bar{x} = 103.22$ is calculated using $\mu = 100$ and approximating σ by $s = 15.0$.

$$z = \frac{\bar{x} - \mu}{\dfrac{\sigma}{\sqrt{n}}} = \frac{103.22 - 100}{\dfrac{15}{\sqrt{150}}} = 2.629$$

For the 1% significance level, the critical value is $z = 2.326$.

The test statistic is compared with the critical value and since $2.629 > 2.326$ the null hypothesis is rejected.

The evidence supports the view that scores on this IQ test are now higher; see figure 13.7.

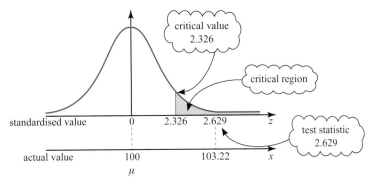

Figure 13.7

1 A magazine conducted a survey about the sleeping time of adults. A random sample of 12 adults was chosen from the adults travelling to work on a train.

(i) Give a reason why this is an unsatisfactory sample for the purposes of the survey.

(ii) State a population for which this sample would be satisfactory.

A satisfactory sample of 12 adults gave numbers of hours of sleep as shown below.

$$4.6 \quad 6.8 \quad 5.2 \quad 6.2 \quad 5.7 \quad 7.1 \quad 6.3 \quad 5.6 \quad 7.0 \quad 5.8 \quad 6.5 \quad 7.2$$

(iii) Calculate unbiased estimates of the mean and variance of the sleeping times of adults.

[Cambridge International AS and A Level Mathematics 9709, Paper 7 Q1 June 2008]

2 For each of the following, the random variable $X \sim N(\mu, \sigma^2)$, with *known* standard deviation. A random sample of size n is taken from the parent population and the sample mean, $\bar{x}$, is calculated.

Carry out hypotheses tests, given H_0 and H_1, at the significance level indicated.

	σ	n	$\bar{x}$	H_0	H_1	Sig. level
(i)	8	6	195	$\mu = 190$	$\mu > 190$	5%
(ii)	10	10	47.5	$\mu = 55$	$\mu < 55$	1%
(iii)	15	25	104.7	$\mu = 100$	$\mu \neq 100$	10%
(iv)	4.3	15	34.5	$\mu = 32$	$\mu > 32$	2%
(v)	40	12	345	$\mu = 370$	$\mu \neq 370$	5%

3 A machine is designed to make paperclips with mean mass 4.00 g and standard deviation 0.08 g. The distribution of the masses of the paperclips is normal. Find

(i) the probability that an individual paperclip, chosen at random, has mass greater than 4.04 g

(ii) the standard error of the mass for random samples of 25 paperclips

(iii) the probability that the mean mass of a random sample of 25 paperclips is greater than 4.04 g.

A quality control officer weighs a random sample of 25 paperclips and finds their total mass to be 101.2 g.

(iv) Conduct a hypothesis test at the 5% significance level of whether this provides evidence of an increase in the mean mass of the paperclips. State your null and alternative hypotheses clearly.

4 It is known that the mass of a certain type of lizard has a normal distribution with mean 72.7 g and standard deviation 4.8 g. A zoologist finds a colony of lizards in a remote place and is not sure whether they are of the same type. In order to test this, she collects a sample of 12 lizards and weighs them, with the following results.

80.4   67.2   74.9   78.8   76.5   75.5   80.2   81.9   79.3   70.0   69.2   69.1

(i) Write down, in precise form, the zoologist's null and alternative hypotheses, and state whether a one-tail or two-tail test is appropriate.

(ii) Carry out the test at the 5% significance level and write down your conclusion.

(iii) Would your conclusion have been the same at the 10% significance level?

5 Observations over a long period of time have shown that the mid-day temperature at a particular place during the month of June is normally distributed with a mean value of 23.9 °C with standard deviation 2.3 °C. An ecologist sets up an experiment to collect data for a hypothesis test of whether the climate is getting hotter. She selects at random 20 June days over a five-year period and records the mid-day temperature. Her results (in °C) are as follows.

20.1   26.2   23.3   28.9   30.4   28.4   17.3   22.7   25.1   24.2
15.4   26.3   19.3   24.0   19.9   30.3   32.1   26.7   27.6   23.1

(i) State the null and alternative hypotheses that the ecologist should use.

(ii) Carry out the test at the 10% significance level and state the conclusion.

(iii) Calculate an unbiased estimate of the population variance and comment on it.

6 The keepers of a lighthouse were required to keep records of weather conditions. Analysis of their data from many years showed the visibility at mid-day to have a mean value of 14 nautical miles with standard deviation 5.4 nautical miles. A new keeper decided he would test his theory that the air had become less clear (and so visibility reduced) by carrying out a hypothesis test on data collected for his first 36 days on duty. His figures (in nautical miles) were as follows.

35	21	12	7	2	1.5	1.5	1	0.25	0.25	15	17
18	20	16	11	8	8	9	17	35	35	4	0.25
0.25	5	11	28	35	35	16	2	1	0.5	0.5	1

(i) Write down a distributional assumption for the test to be valid.

(ii) Write down suitable null and alternative hypotheses.

(iii) Carry out the test at the 2.5% significance level and state the conclusion that the lighthouse keeper would have come to.

(iv) Criticise the sampling procedure used by the keeper and suggest a better one.

7 A chemical is packed into bags by a machine. The mean weight of the bags is controlled by the machine operator, but the standard deviation is fixed at 0.96 kg. The mean weight should be 50 kg, but it is suspected that the machine has been set to give underweight bags. If a random sample of 36 bags has a total weight of 1789.20 kg, is there evidence to support the suspicion? (You must state the null and alternative hypotheses and you may assume that the weights of the bags are normally distributed.)

[MEI]

8 Archaeologists have discovered that all skulls found in excavated sites in a certain country belong either to racial group A or to racial group B. The mean lengths of skulls from group A and group B are 190 mm and 196 mm respectively. The standard deviation for each group is 8 mm, and skull lengths are distributed normally and independently.

A new excavation produced 12 skulls of mean length $\bar{x}$ and there is reason to believe that all these skulls belong to group A. It is required to test this belief statistically with the null hypothesis (H_0) that all the skulls belong to group A and the alternative hypothesis (H_1) that all the skulls belong to group B.

(i) State the distribution of the mean length of 12 skulls when H_0 is true.

(ii) Explain why a test of H_0 versus H_1 should take the form:

'Reject H_0 if $\bar{x} > c$',

where c is some critical value.

(iii) Calculate this critical value c to the nearest 0.1 mm when the probability of rejecting H_0 when it is in fact true is chosen to be 0.05.

(iv) Perform the test, given that the lengths (in mm) of the 12 skulls are as follows.

| 204.1 | 201.1 | 187.4 | 196.4 | 202.5 | 185.0 |
| 192.6 | 181.6 | 194.5 | 183.2 | 200.3 | 202.9 |

[MEI]

9 The packaging on a type of electric light bulb states that the average lifetime of the bulbs is 1000 hours. A consumer association thinks that this is an overestimate and tests a random sample of 64 bulbs, recording the lifetime, x hours, of each bulb. You may assume that the distribution of the bulbs' lifetimes is normal.

The results are summarised as follows.

$$n = 64, \quad \Sigma x = 63\,910.4, \quad \Sigma x^2 = 63\,824\,061$$

(i) Calculate unbiased estimates for the population mean and variance.

(ii) State suitable null and alternative hypotheses to test whether the statement on the packaging is overestimating the lifetime of this type of bulb.

(iii) Carry out the test, at the 5% significance level, stating your conclusions carefully.

10 A sample of 40 observations from a normal distribution X gave $\Sigma x = 24$ and $\Sigma x^2 = 596$. Performing a two-tail test at the 5% level, test whether the mean of the distribution is zero.

11 A random sample of 75 eleven-year-olds performed a simple task and the time taken, t minutes, was noted for each. You may assume that the distribution of these times is normal.

The results are summarised as follows.

$$n = 75, \quad \Sigma t = 1215, \quad \Sigma t^2 = 21\,708$$

(i) Calculate unbiased estimates for the population mean and variance.

(ii) State suitable null and alternative hypotheses to test whether there is evidence that the mean time taken to perform this task is greater than 15 minutes.

(iii) Carry out the test, at the 1% significance level, stating your conclusions carefully.

12 Bags of sugar are supposed to contain, on average, 2 kg of sugar. A quality controller suspects that they actually contain less than this amount, and so 90 bags are taken at random and the mass, x kg, of sugar in each is measured. You may assume that the distribution of these masses is normal.

The results are summarised as follows.

$$n = 90, \quad \Sigma x = 177.9, \quad \Sigma x^2 = 353.1916$$

(i) Calculate unbiased estimates for the population mean and variance.

(ii) State suitable null and alternative hypotheses to test whether there is any evidence that the sugar is being sold 'underweight'.

(iii) Carry out the test, at the 2% significance level, stating your conclusions carefully.

13 A machine produces jars of skin cream, filled to a nominal volume of 100 ml. The machine is actually supposed to be set to 105 ml, to ensure that most jars actually contain more than the nominal volume of 100 ml. You may assume that the distribution of the volume of skin cream in a jar is normal.

To check that the machine is correctly set, 80 jars are chosen at random, and the volume, x ml, of skin cream in each is measured.

The results are summarised as follows.

$$n = 80, \qquad \Sigma x = 8376, \qquad \Sigma x^2 = 877\,687$$

(i) Calculate unbiased estimates for the population mean and standard deviation.

(ii) State suitable null and alternative hypotheses for a test to see whether the machine appears to be set correctly.

(iii) Carry out the test, at the 10% significance level, stating your conclusions carefully.

14 A study of a large sample of books by a particular author shows that the number of words per sentence can be modelled by a normal distribution with mean 21.2 and standard deviation 7.3. A researcher claims to have discovered a previously unknown book by this author. The mean length of 90 sentences chosen at random in this book is found to be 19.4 words.

(i) Assuming the population standard deviation of sentence lengths in this book is also 7.3, test at the 5% level of significance whether the mean sentence length is the same as the author's. State your null and alternative hypotheses.

(ii) State in words relating to the context of the test what is meant by a Type I error and state the probability of a Type I error in the test in part (i).

[Cambridge International AS and A Level Mathematics 9709, Paper 7 Q4 June 2005]

15 The number of cars caught speeding on a certain length of motorway is 7.2 per day, on average. Speed cameras are introduced and the results shown in the following table are those from a random selection of 40 days after this.

Number of cars caught speeding	4	5	6	7	8	9	10
Number of days	5	7	8	10	5	2	3

(i) Calculate unbiased estimates of the population mean and variance of the number of cars per day caught speeding after the speed cameras were introduced.

(ii) Taking the null hypothesis H_0 to be $\mu = 7.2$, test at the 5% level whether there is evidence that the introduction of speed cameras has resulted in a reduction in the number of cars caught speeding.

(iii) State what is meant by Type I error in words relating to the context of the test in part (ii). Without further calculation, illustrate on a suitable diagram the region representing the probability of this Type I error.

[Cambridge International AS and A Level Mathematics 9709, Paper 7 Q7 June 2006]

16 A machine has produced nails over a long period of time, where the length in millimetres was distributed as N(22.0, 0.19). It is believed that recently the mean length has changed. To test this belief a random sample of 8 nails is taken and the mean length is found to be 21.7 mm. Carry out a hypothesis test at the 5% significance level to test whether the population mean has changed, assuming that the variance remains the same.

[Cambridge International AS and A Level Mathematics 9709, Paper 7 Q3 June 2007]

17 In summer the growth rate of grass in a lawn has a normal distribution with mean 3.2 cm per week and standard deviation 1.4 cm per week. A new type of grass is introduced which the manufacturer claims has a slower growth rate. A hypothesis test of this claim at the 5% significance level was carried out using a random sample of 10 lawns that had the new grass. It may be assumed that the growth rate of the new grass has a normal distribution with standard deviation 1.4 cm per week.

(i) Find the rejection region for the test.

(ii) The probability of making a Type II error when the actual value of the mean growth rate of the new grass is m cm per week is less than 0.5. Use your answer to part **(i)** to write down an inequality for m.

[Cambridge International AS and A Level Mathematics 9709, Paper 7 Q2 November 2007]

The Central Limit Theorem

---

organicveg.com

The perfect apple grower

Fruit buyer Tom Sisulu writes:

Fruit grower, Rose Ncune, believes that, after years of trials, she has developed trees that will produce the perfect supermarket apple. 'There are two requirements' Rose told me. 'The average weight of an apple should be 100 grams and they should all be nearly the same size. I have measured hundreds of mine and the standard deviation is a mere 5 grams.'

Rose invited me to take any ten apples off the shelf and weigh them for myself. It was quite uncanny; they were all so close to the magic 100 grams: 98, 107, 105, 98, 100, 99, 104, 93, 105, 103.

Rose is calling her apple the 'Cape Pippin'.

What can you conclude from the weights of Tom's sample of ten apples?

Before going any further, it is appropriate to question whether his sample was random. Rose invited Tom to 'take any ten apples off the shelf'. That is not necessarily the same as taking any ten off the tree. The apples on the shelf could all have been specially selected to impress him. So what follows is based on the assumption that Rose has been honest and the ten apples really do constitute a random sample.

The sample mean is

$$\bar{x} = \frac{98 + 107 + 105 + 98 + 100 + 99 + 104 + 93 + 105 + 103}{10} = 101.2$$

❓ What does that tell you about the population mean, μ?

To estimate how far the value of μ is from 101.2, you need to know something about the spread of the data; the usual measure is the standard deviation, σ. In the blog for organicveg.com you are told that $\sigma = 5$.

The result that if repeated samples of size n are drawn from a population with a normal distribution with mean μ and standard deviation σ, the distribution of the sample means is also normal; its mean is μ and its standard deviation is $\frac{\sigma}{\sqrt{n}}$ is proved in Appendix 6 on the CD.

This is actually a special case of a more general result called the Central Limit Theorem. The Central Limit Theorem covers the case where samples are drawn from a population which is not necessarily normal.

● The Central Limit Theorem states that for samples of size n drawn from **any** distribution with mean μ and finite variance σ^2, the distribution of the

sample means is approximately $N\left(\mu, \frac{\sigma^2}{n}\right)$ for sufficiently large n.

This theorem is fundamental to much of statistics and so it is worth pausing to make sure you understand just what it is saying.

It deals with the distribution of sample means. This is called the *sampling distribution* (or more correctly the *sampling distribution of the means*). There are three aspects to it.

1 The mean of the sample means is μ, the population mean of the original distribution. That is not a particularly surprising result but it is extremely important.

2 The standard deviation of the sample means is $\frac{\sigma}{\sqrt{n}}$. This is often called the *standard error of the mean*.

Within a sample you would expect some values above the population mean, others below it, so that overall the deviations would tend to cancel each other out, and the larger the sample the more this would be the case. Consequently the standard deviation of the sample means is smaller than that of individual items, by a factor of $\sqrt{n}$.

3 The distribution of sample means is approximately normal.

This last point is the most surprising part of the theorem. Even if the underlying parent distribution is not normal, the distribution of the means of samples of a particular size drawn from it is approximately normal. The larger the sample size, n, the closer this distribution is to the normal. For any given value of n the sampling distribution will be closest to normal where the parent distribution is not unlike the normal.

In many cases the value of n does not need to be particularly large. For most parent distributions you can rely on the distribution of sample means being normal if n is about 20 or 25 (or more).

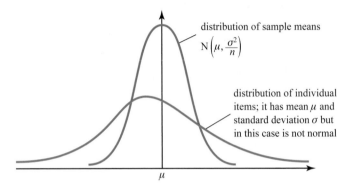

distribution of sample means

$N\left(\mu, \dfrac{\sigma^2}{n}\right)$

distribution of individual items; it has mean μ and standard deviation σ but in this case is not normal

μ

Figure 13.8

Confidence intervals

Returning to the figures on the Cape Pippin apples, you would estimate the population mean to be the same as the sample mean, namely 101.2.

You can express this by saying that you estimate μ to lie within a range of values, an interval, centred on 101.2:

$$101.2 - \text{a bit} < \mu < 101.2 + \text{a bit}.$$

Such an interval is called a *confidence interval.*

Imagine you take a large number of samples and use a formula to work out the interval for each of them. If you catch the true population mean in 90% of your intervals, the confidence interval is called a 90% confidence interval. Other percentages are also used and the confidence intervals are named accordingly. The width of the interval is clearly twice the 'bit'.

Finding a confidence interval involves a very simple calculation but the reasoning behind it is somewhat subtle and requires clear thinking. It is explained in the next section, but you may prefer to make your first reading of it a light one. You should, however, come back to it at some point; otherwise you will not really understand the meaning of confidence intervals.

The theory of confidence intervals

To understand confidence intervals you need to look not at the particular sample whose mean you have just found, but at the parent population from which it was drawn. For the data on the Cape Pippin apples this does not look very promising. All you know about it is its standard deviation σ (in this case 5). You do not know its mean, μ, which you are trying to estimate, or even its shape.

It is now that the strength of the Central Limit Theorem becomes apparent. This states that the distribution of the means of samples of size n drawn from this population is approximately normal with mean μ and standard deviation $\dfrac{\sigma}{\sqrt{n}}$.

In figure 13.9 the central 90% region has been shaded leaving the two 5% tails, corresponding to z values of ± 1.645, unshaded. So if you take a large number of samples, all of size n, and work out the sample mean $\bar{x}$ for each one, you would expect that in 90% of cases the value of $\bar{x}$ would lie in the shaded region between A and B.

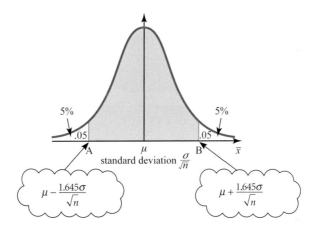

Figure 13.9

For such a value of $\bar{x}$ to be in the shaded region

it must be to the right of A: $\qquad\qquad \bar{x} > \mu - 1.645\,\dfrac{\sigma}{\sqrt{n}}$ ①

it must be to the left of B: $\qquad\qquad \bar{x} < \mu + 1.645\,\dfrac{\sigma}{\sqrt{n}}$ ②

Rearranging these two inequalities:

① $\qquad \bar{x} + 1.645\,\dfrac{\sigma}{\sqrt{n}} > \mu \quad$ or $\quad \mu < \bar{x} + 1.645\,\dfrac{\sigma}{\sqrt{n}}$

② $\qquad \bar{x} - 1.645\,\dfrac{\sigma}{\sqrt{n}} < \mu$

Putting them together gives the result that in 90% of cases

$$\bar{x} - 1.645\,\dfrac{\sigma}{\sqrt{n}} < \mu < \bar{x} + 1.645\,\dfrac{\sigma}{\sqrt{n}}$$

and this is the 90% confidence interval for μ.

The numbers corresponding to the points A and B are called the 90% *confidence limits* and 90% is the *confidence level*. If you want a different confidence level, you use a different z value from 1.645.

This number is often denoted by k; commonly used values are:

Confidence level	k
90%	1.645
95%	1.960
99%	2.576

and the confidence interval is given by

$$\bar{x} - k\frac{\sigma}{\sqrt{n}} \quad \text{to} \quad \bar{x} + k\frac{\sigma}{\sqrt{n}}.$$

Note

Notice that this is a two-sided symmetrical confidence interval for the mean, μ. Confidence intervals do not need to be symmetrical and can be one-sided. The term 'confidence interval' is a general one, applying not just to the mean but to other population parameters, like variance and skewness, as well. All these cases, however, are outside the scope of this book.

The $P\%$ confidence interval for the mean is an interval constructed from sample data in such a way that $P\%$ of such intervals will include the true population mean. Figure 13.10 shows a number of confidence intervals constructed from different samples, one of which fails to catch the population mean.

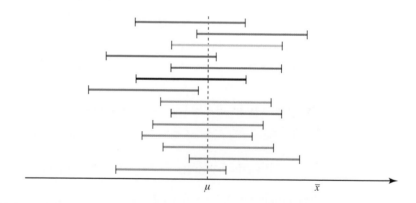

Figure 13.10

In the case of the data on the Cape Pippin apples,

$$\bar{x} = 101.2, \qquad \sigma = 5, \qquad n = 10$$

and so the 90% confidence interval is

$$101.2 - 1.645 \times \frac{5}{\sqrt{10}} \quad \text{to} \quad 101.2 + 1.645 \times \frac{5}{\sqrt{10}}$$

$$98.6 \quad \text{to} \quad 103.8.$$

Known and estimated standard deviation

Notice that you can only use this procedure if you already know the value of the standard deviation of the parent population, σ. In this example, Rose Ncune said that she knew, from hundreds of measurements of her apples, that its value is 5.

It is more often the situation that you do not know the population standard deviation or variance, and have to estimate it from your sample data. If that is the case, the procedure is different in that you use the t distribution rather than the normal provided that the parent population is normally distributed, and this results in different values of k. However, the use of the t distribution is beyond the scope of this book.

However, if the sample is large, for example over 50, confidence intervals worked out using the normal distribution will be reasonably accurate even though the standard deviation used is an estimate from the sample. So it is quite acceptable to use the normal distribution for large samples whether the standard deviation is known or not.

EXPERIMENTS

These experiments are designed to help you understand confidence intervals, rather than to teach you anything new about dice.

When a single die is thrown, the possible outcomes, 1, 2, 3, 4, 5, 6, are all equally likely with probability $\frac{1}{6}$. Consequently the expectation or mean score from throwing a die is

$$\mu = 1 \times \tfrac{1}{6} + 2 \times \tfrac{1}{6} + \ldots + 6 \times \tfrac{1}{6} = 3.5.$$

Similarly the standard deviation is

$$\sigma = \sqrt{(1^2 \times \tfrac{1}{6} + 2^2 \times \tfrac{1}{6} + \ldots + 6^2 \times \tfrac{1}{6}) - 3.5^2} = 1.708.$$

Imagine that you know σ but don't know μ and wish to construct a 90% confidence interval for it.

Converging confidence intervals

Start by throwing a die once. Suppose you get a 5. You have a sample of size 1, namely {5}, which you could use to work out a sort of 90% confidence interval (but see the warning overleaf).

This confidence interval is given by

$$5 - 1.645 \times \frac{1.708}{\sqrt{1}} \quad \text{to} \quad 5 + 1.645 \times \frac{1.708}{\sqrt{1}}$$
$$2.19 \quad \text{to} \quad 7.81.$$

So far the procedure is not valid. The sample is small and the underlying distribution is not normal. However, things will get better. The more times you throw the die, the larger the sample size and so the more justifiable the procedure.

Now throw the die again. Suppose this time you get a 3. You now have a sample of size 2, namely {5, 3}, with mean 4, and can work out another confidence interval.

The confidence interval is given by

$$4 - 1.645 \times \frac{1.708}{\sqrt{2}} \quad \text{to} \quad 4 + 1.645 \times \frac{1.708}{\sqrt{2}}$$
$$2.79 \quad \text{to} \quad 5.21.$$

Now throw the die again and find a third confidence interval, and a fourth, fifth and so on. You should find them converging on the population mean of 3.5; but it may take some time to get close, particularly if you start with, say, two 6s. This demonstrates that, the larger the sample you take, the narrower the range of values within the confidence interval.

Catching the population mean

Organise a group of friends to throw five dice (or one die five times), and do this 100 times. Each of these gives a sample of size 5 and so you can use it to work out a 90% confidence interval for μ.

You know that the real value of μ is 3.5 and it should be that this is caught within 90% of 90% confidence intervals.

? Out of your 100 confidence intervals, how many actually enclose 3.5?

How large a sample do you need?

You are now in a position to start to answer the question of how large a sample needs to be. The answer, as you will see in Example 13.4, depends on the precision you require, and the confidence level you are prepared to accept.

EXAMPLE 13.4

A trading standards officer is investigating complaints that a coal merchant is giving short measure. Each sack should contain 25 kg but some variation will inevitably occur because of the size of the lumps of coal; the officer knows from experience that the standard deviation should be 1.5 kg.

The officer plans to take, secretly, a random sample of n sacks, find the total weight of the coal inside them and thereby estimate the mean weight of the coal per sack. He wants to present this figure correct to the nearest kilogram with 95% confidence. What value of n should he choose?

SOLUTION

The 95% confidence interval for the mean is given by

$$\bar{x} - 1.96\frac{\sigma}{\sqrt{n}} \quad \text{to} \quad \bar{x} + 1.96\frac{\sigma}{\sqrt{n}}$$

and so, since $\sigma = 1.5$, the inspector's requirement is that

$$\frac{1.96 \times 1.5}{\sqrt{n}} \leqslant 0.5$$

$$\Rightarrow \qquad \frac{1.96 \times 1.5}{0.5} \leqslant \sqrt{n}$$

$$\Rightarrow \qquad n \geqslant 34.57.$$

So the inspector needs to take 35 sacks.

Large samples

Given that the width of a confidence interval decreases with sample size, why is it not standard practice to take very large samples?

The answer is that the cost and time involved have to be balanced against the quality of information produced. Because the width of a confidence interval depends on $\frac{1}{\sqrt{n}}$ and not on $\frac{1}{n}$, increasing the sample size does not produce a proportional reduction in the width of the interval. You have, for example, to increase the sample size by a factor of 4 to halve the width of the interval. In the previous example the inspector had to weigh 35 sacks of coal to achieve a class interval of $2 \times 0.5 = 1$ kg with 95% confidence. That is already quite a daunting task; does the benefit from reducing the interval to 0.5 kg justify the time, cost and trouble involved in weighing another 105 sacks?

Confidence intervals for a proportion

In this chapter you have seen how to calculate confidence intervals for the population mean. Confidence intervals can also be found for other population parameters, like the variance or, in a binomial situation, the proportion of the population with a particular characteristic.

In Example 13.5 a confidence interval for a population proportion is found. The method assumes that the sample taken is large, and so the normal approximation to the binomial distribution may be used.

In an experiment where a (large) sample of size n has been taken and m items are found to have the characteristic under investigation, the population proportion is estimated to be $p = \frac{m}{n}$.

For all samples of size n, the following estimates may then be made:

- Mean number of occurrences per sample $= np$
- Variance of number of occurrences per sample $= npq = np(1 - p)$
- Variance of estimated proportion $= \dfrac{np(1 - p)}{n^2} = \dfrac{p(1 - p)}{n}$
- Standard deviation of estimated proportion $= \sqrt{\dfrac{p(1 - p)}{n}}$

So the confidence interval for the proportion is given by

$$p - k\sqrt{\frac{p(1 - p)}{n}} < \text{population proportion} < p + k\sqrt{\frac{p(1 - p)}{n}},$$

where the values of k are taken from the normal distribution: 1.96 for a 95% (two-sided) confidence interval, 1.645 for a 90% interval, etc.

EXAMPLE 13.5

A certain type of moth is found in two colours, brown and white. In an experiment, 100 moths from a particular region are captured. 30 of them are found to be brown, the remainder white.

Calculate the 95% confidence interval for the population proportion of brown moths.

SOLUTION

Estimated population proportion of brown moths, $p = \frac{30}{100} = 0.3$.

So the 95% confidence interval is given by

$$0.3 - 1.96\sqrt{\frac{0.3(1 - 0.3)}{100}} < \text{population proportion} < 0.3 + 1.96\sqrt{\frac{0.3(1 - 0.3)}{100}}$$

giving

$$0.210 < \text{population proportion} < 0.390 \text{ (to 3 s.f.).}$$

EXERCISE 13B

1 A biologist studying a colony of beetles selects and weighs a random sample of 20 adult males. She knows that, because of natural variability, the weights of such beetles are normally distributed with standard deviation 0.2 g. Their weights, in grams, are as follows.

5.2	5.4	4.9	5.0	4.8		5.7	5.2	5.2	5.4	5.1
5.6	5.0	5.2	5.1	5.3		5.2	5.1	5.3	5.2	5.2

(i) Find the mean weight of the beetles in this sample.

(ii) Find 95% confidence limits for the mean weight of such beetles.

2 An aptitude test for deep-sea divers has been designed to produce scores which are approximately normally distributed on a scale from 0 to 100 with standard deviation 25. The scores from a random sample of people taking the test were as follows.

$$23 \quad 35 \quad 89 \quad 35 \quad 12 \qquad 45 \quad 60 \quad 78 \quad 34 \quad 66$$

(i) Find the mean score of the people in this sample.

(ii) Construct a 90% confidence interval for the mean score of people taking the test.

(iii) Construct a 99% confidence interval for the mean score of people taking the test. Compare this confidence interval with the 90% confidence interval.

3 In a large city the distribution of incomes per family has a standard deviation of $5200.

(i) For a random sample of 400 families, what is the probability that the sample mean income per family is within $500 of the actual mean income per family?

(ii) Given that the sample mean income was, in fact, $8300, calculate a 95% confidence interval for the actual mean income per family.

[**MEI**, *adapted*]

4 A manufacturer of women's clothing wants to know the mean height of the women in a town (in order to plan what proportion of garments should be of each size). She knows that the standard deviation of their heights is 5 cm. She selects a random sample of 50 women from the town and finds their mean height to be 165.2 cm.

(i) Use the available information to estimate the proportion of women in the town who were

(a) over 170 cm tall

(b) less than 155 cm tall.

(ii) Construct a 95% confidence interval for the mean height of women in the town.

(iii) Another manufacturer in the same town wants to know the mean height of women in the town to within 0.5 cm with 95% confidence. What is the minimum sample size that would ensure this?

5 An examination question, marked out of 10, is answered by a very large number of candidates. A random sample of 400 scripts are taken and the marks on this question are recorded.

Mark	0	1	2	3	4	5	6	7	8	9	10
Frequency	12	35	11	12	3	20	57	87	20	14	129

(i) Calculate the sample mean and the sample standard deviation.

(ii) Assuming that the population standard deviation has the same value as the sample standard deviation, find 90% confidence limits for the population mean.

6 An archaeologist discovers a short manuscript in an ancient language which he recognises but cannot read. There are 30 words in the manuscript and they contain a total of 198 letters. There are two written versions of the language. In the *early* form of the language the mean word length is 6.2 letters with standard deviation 2.5; in the *late* form words were given prefixes, raising the mean length to 7.6 letters but leaving the standard deviation unaltered. The archaeologist hopes the manuscript will help him to date the site.

(i) Construct a 95% confidence interval for the mean word length of the language.

(ii) What advice would you give the archaeologist?

7 A football boot manufacturer did extensive testing on the wear of the front studs of its Supa range. It found that, after 30 hours' use, the wear (i.e. the amount by which the length was reduced) was normally distributed with standard deviation 1.3 mm. However, the mean wear on the studs of the boot on the dominant foot of the player was 4 mm more than on the studs of the other boot.

(i) Using the manufacturer's figure, find the standard deviation of the differences in wear between a pair of boots after 30 hours' use.

The coach of a football team accepted the claim for the standard deviation but was suspicious of the claim about the mean difference. He chose ten of his squad at random. He fitted them with new boots and measured the wear after 30 hours of use with the following results.

Player	1	2	3	4	5	6	7	8	9	10
Dominant foot	6.5	8.3	4.5	6.7	9.2	5.3	7.6	8.1	9.0	8.4
Other foot	4.2	4.6	2.3	3.8	7.0	4.7	1.4	3.8	8.4	5.7

(ii) Using the value found in part (i) for the population standard deviation of the differences, calculate 95% confidence limits for the mean difference in wear based on the sample data.

(iii) Use these limits to explain whether or not you consider the coach's suspicions were justified.

8 A school decided to introduce a new P.E. programme for its new students to try to improve the fitness of the students. In order to see whether the programme was effective, several tests were done. For one of these, the students were timed on a run of 1 kilometre in their first week in the school and again ten weeks later. A random sample of 100 of the students did both runs. The differences of their mean times, subtracting the time of the second run from that of the first, were calculated. The mean and standard deviation were found to be 0.75 minutes and 1.62 minutes respectively.

Calculate a 90% confidence interval for the population mean difference. You may assume that the differences are distributed normally. What assumption have you made in finding this confidence interval?

The organiser of the programme considers that it should lead to an improvement of at least half a minute in the average times. Explain whether or not this aim has been achieved.

9 In an experiment to see if reaction times were affected by whether or not individuals are hungry, 2000 randomly chosen soldiers were tested before and after they had eaten a substantial lunch. The test used was to drop a metre rule, which was held vertically so that its lower end was level with the thumb and first finger of each person, and to measure how far the rule fell before it was caught. For each person, the difference, d, of the distance measured after lunch minus the distance measured before lunch was found. From these it was calculated that $\Sigma d = 1626$ and $\Sigma d^2 = 258\,632$.

Use these data to provide a 98% confidence interval for the population mean difference, stating any assumptions you have made.

What does your confidence interval suggest about reaction times before and after a meal?

10 The weights in grams of oranges grown in a certain area are normally distributed with mean μ and standard deviation σ. A random sample of 50 of these oranges was taken, and a 97% confidence interval for μ based on this sample was (222.1, 232.1).

(i) Calculate unbiased estimates of μ and σ^2.

(ii) Estimate the sample size that would be required in order for a 97% confidence interval for μ to have width 8.

[Cambridge International AS and A Level Mathematics 9709, Paper 7 Q2 June 2009]

11 (i) Give a reason why, in carrying out out a statistical investigation, a sample rather than a complete population may be used.

(ii) Rose wishes to investigate whether men in her town have a different life-span from the national average of 71.2 years. She looks at government records for her town and takes a random sample of the ages of 110 men who have died recently. Their mean age in years was 69.3 and the unbiased estimate of the population variance was 65.61.

(a) Calculate a 90% confidence interval for the population mean and explain what you understand by this confidence interval.

(b) State with a reason what conclusion about the life-span of men in her town Rose could draw from this confidence interval.

[Cambridge International AS and A Level Mathematics 9709, Paper 7 Q4 November 2005]

12 Diameters of golf balls are known to be normally distributed with mean μ cm and standard deviation σ cm. A random sample of 130 golf balls was taken and the diameters, x cm, were measured. The results are summarised by $\Sigma x = 555.1$ and $\Sigma x^2 = 2371.30$.

(i) Calculate unbiased estimates of μ and σ^2.

(ii) Calculate a 97% confidence interval for μ.

(iii) 300 random samples of 130 golf balls are taken and a 97% confidence interval is calculated for each sample. How many of these intervals would you expect **not** to contain μ?

[Cambridge International AS and A Level Mathematics 9709, Paper 7 Q4 November 2008]

13 A random sample of n people were questioned about their internet use. 87 of them had a high-speed internet connection. A confidence interval for the population proportion having a high-speed internet connection is $0.1129 < p < 0.1771$.

(i) Write down the mid-point of this confidence interval and hence find the value of n.

(ii) This interval is an α% confidence interval. Find α.

[Cambridge International AS and A Level Mathematics 9709, Paper 71 Q2 June 2010]

14 (i) Explain what is meant by the term 'random sample'.

In a random sample of 350 food shops it was found that 130 of them had Special Offers.

(ii) Calculate an approximate 95% confidence interval for the proportion of all food shops with Special Offers.

(iii) Estimate the size of a random sample required for an approximate 95% confidence interval for this proportion to have a width of 0.04.

[Cambridge International AS and A Level Mathematics 9709, Paper 7 Q3 November 2007]

15 A survey of a random sample of n people found that 61 of them read *The Reporter* newspaper. A symmetric confidence interval for the true population proportion, p, who read *The Reporter* is $0.1993 < p < 0.2887$.

(i) Find the mid-point of this confidence interval and use this to find the value of n.

(ii) Find the confidence level of this confidence interval.

[Cambridge International AS and A Level Mathematics 9709, Paper 7 Q3 June 2005]

1 **Distribution of sample means**

- For samples of size n drawn from a normal distribution with mean μ and finite variance σ^2, the distribution of sample means is normal with mean μ and variance $\dfrac{\sigma^2}{n}$, i.e. $\bar{x} \sim N\left(\mu, \dfrac{\sigma^2}{n}\right)$.

- The standard error of the mean (i.e. the standard deviation of the sample means) is given by $\dfrac{\sigma}{\sqrt{n}}$.

2 **Hypothesis testing**

- Sample data may be used to carry out a hypothesis test on the null hypothesis that the population mean has some particular value, μ_0, i.e. $H_0: \mu = \mu_0$.

- The test statistic is $z = \dfrac{\bar{x} - \mu_0}{\dfrac{\sigma}{\sqrt{n}}}$ and the normal distribution is used.

For situations where the population mean, μ, is unknown but the population variance, σ^2 (or standard deviation, σ), is known:

3 **The Central Limit Theorem**

For samples of size n drawn from any distribution with mean μ and finite variance σ^2, the distribution of the sample means is approximately

$N\left(\mu, \dfrac{\sigma^2}{n}\right)$ for sufficiently large n.

4 **The standard error of the mean**

The standard error of the mean (i.e. the standard deviation of the sample means) is given by $\dfrac{\sigma}{\sqrt{n}}$.

5 **Confidence intervals**

- Two-sided confidence intervals for μ are given by

$$\bar{x} - k\frac{\sigma}{\sqrt{n}} \quad \text{to} \quad \bar{x} + k\frac{\sigma}{\sqrt{n}}.$$

- The value of k for any confidence level can be found using normal distribution tables.

Confidence level	k
90%	1.645
95%	1.960
99%	2.576

Answers

Neither University of Cambridge International Examinations nor OCR bear any responsibility for the example answers to questions taken from their past question papers which are contained in this publication.

Chapter 1

❷ (Page 3)

The editor has explained clearly why the investigation is worth doing: there is growing concern about cycling accidents involving children.

Good quality data is data that best represents the research topic: in this case it is to establish whether or not the number of accidents is significant.

❷ (Page 4)

The reporter is focusing on two aspects of the investigation: he is looking at cycling accidents in the area over a period of time and he is considering the distribution of ages of accident victims. Both of these sources are relevant to the investigation.

Another thing he might consider is to investigate accidents in a similar community in order to be able to make comparisons.

❷ (Page 7)

Not all the branches have leaves. However, all the branches must be shown in order to show correctly the shape of the distribution.

❷ (Page 9)

If the basic stem-and-leaf diagram has too many lines, you may *squeeze* it as shown below. In doing this you lose some of the information but you should get a better idea of the shape of the distribution.

Unsqueezed

```
30 | 2  6              30 | 2 represents 3.02
31 | 4
32 | 0  5
33 | 3
34 | 3  6  7
35 | 0  3  4  4  8
36 | 0  0  4  4  4
37 | 0  1  1  3  3  4  8
38 | 3  3  3  5
39 | 0  0  4
40 | 2
41 | 0  0  1  1  4  4
42 |
43 | 0  2  4
```

Squeezed

The data is rounded to one decimal place, so 3.02 becomes 3.0 etc.

3* | 0 represents 3.0

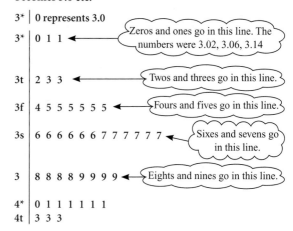

```
3* | 0  1  1
3t | 2  3  3
3f | 4  5  5  5  5  5  5
3s | 6  6  6  6  6  6  7  7  7  7  7  7
3  | 8  8  8  8  9  9  9  9
4* | 0  1  1  1  1  1  1
4t | 3  3  3
```

❷ (Page 9)

Positive and negative data can be represented on a stem-and-leaf diagram in the following way.

Data set:

−36 −32 −28 −25 −24 −20 −18 −15
−12 −6   5   8   12   13   18   26

$n = 16$

−3 | 2 represents −32

```
−3 | 6  2
−2 | 8  5  4  0
−1 | 8  5  2
−0 | 6
 0 | 5  8
 1 | 2  3  8
 2 | 6
```

Exercise 1A (page 10)

1 3.27, 3.32, 3.36, 3.43, 3.45, 3.49, 3.50, 3.52, 3.56, 3.56, 3.58, 3.61, 3.61, 3.64, 3.72

2 0.083, 0.086, 0.087, 0.090, 0.091, 0.094, 0.098, 0.102, 0.103, 0.105, 0.108, 0.109, 0.109, 0.110, 0.111, 0.114, 0.123, 0.125, 0.131

3 $n = 13$

21 | 2 represents 0.212

```
21 | 2
22 | 3 6
23 | 0 3 7
24 | 1 2 8
25 | 3 3 9
26 | 2
```

4 $n = 10$

780 | 1 represents 78.01

```
780 | 1
790 | 4 6
800 | 4 8
810 | 3 7 9
820 | 0 5
```

5 0.013, 0.089, 1.79, 3.43, 3.51, 3.57, 3.59, 3.60, 3.64, 3.66, 3.68, 3.71, 3.71, 3.73, 3.78, 3.79, 3.80, 3.85, 3.94, 7.45, 10.87

6 (i) $n = 40$

2 | 8 represents 28 years of age

```
0 | 5
1 | 9
2 | 2 6 6 8 8 9 9
3 | 2 3 3 4 5 5 5 6 6 7 7 7 8 8 8 9 9
4 | 1 4 5 5 6
5 | 2 5 9
6 | 0 1 2 3 6
7 |
8 | 1
```

(ii) The distribution has positive skew.

7 (i) 83 years

(ii)
```
1 | 6 8 9 9
2 | 0 1 1 1 2 3 4 5 6 6 7 8 8 9
3 | 0 0 0 1 2 2 3 5 9
4 | 3 3 4 5 5 6 6 7 8 9
5 | 1 2 2 7
6 |
7 |
8 | 3
```

(iii)
```
1* |
1  | 6 8 9 9
2* | 0 1 1 1 2 3 4
2  | 5 6 6 7 8 8 9
3* | 0 0 0 1 2 2 3
3  | 5 9
4* | 3 3 4
4  | 5 5 6 6 7 8 9
5* | 1 2 2
5  | 7
6* |
6  |
7* |
7  |
8* | 3
```

(iv) The stem-and-leaf diagram with steps of 10 suggests a slight positive skew.

The stretched stem-and-leaf diagram shows a clear bimodal spread to the distribution. The first peak (20s) may indicate first marriages and the second peak (40s) may indicate second marriages.

8 (i) $n = 30$

2 | 1 represents 21 °C

```
−1 | 5 4 1
−0 | 9 7 4 2
 0 | 1 2 3 3 4 7 8 8
 1 | 0 1 4 4 5 8 9 9
 2 | 1 3 6 7 9
 3 | 2 5
```

(ii) The distribution is approximately symmetrical and unimodal.

9 $n = 87$

1 | 8 represents 18 marks

```
 1 | 7 8
 2 | 2 5 6 6 9
 3 | 0 0 2 4 4 5 6 7 7 7 9 9
 4 | 0 0 3 4 4 4 5 5 6 8 9 9
 5 | 0 1 1 1 2 2 3 4 4 4 5 6 7 9
 6 | 0 1 2 4 5 6 6 6 6 7 8 8 9 9
 7 | 0 0 1 3 4 4 5 5 6 6 7
 8 | 0 2 7 7
 9 | 0 0 1 2 4 5 5 6 7 7 8
10 | 0 0
```

The distribution is symmetrical apart from a peak in the 90s. There is a large concentration of marks between 30 and 80.

10 (i) $n = 40$

1 | 9 represents 19 years of age

```
1 | 7 9 9 9
2 | 0 1 1 2 2 3 3 3 4 5 6 6 6 6 8 8 8 9
3 | 0 0 1 4 5 7
4 | 0 5
5 | 7 8 8
6 | 5 5 5 6 7 9
7 | 2
```

(ii) The distribution is bimodal. This is possibly because those who hang-glide are the reasonably young and active (average age about 25 years) and those who are retired and have taken it up as a hobby (average age about 60).

11 $n = 50$

```
        7 | 5 | means 57 kg (untreated)

     Untreated                    Treated
              8 8 5 5 | 0 |
7 6 4 4 4 4 2 2 2 1 0 0 | 1 | 8 8 9
        9 9 5 2 2 2 0 0 | 2 | 0 1 3 3 3 4 4 5 5 5 6 7
              3 2 1 0 0 | 3 | 0 0 1 1 2 3 3 3 3 5 5 5 8 8 8
        8 8 5 3 2 1 0 0 | 4 | 1 1 2 2 4 4 4 7 9
        8 6 5 3 2 1 1 0 | 5 | 0 2 3 3 4 4 9
              3 2 1 1 1 | 6 | 1 1 2 3
```

GRO seems to have improved the yield of lime trees, though there are a significant number of untreated trees that are matching the yield of the treated trees.

12 (i) $n = 25$

11 | 4 represents 1.14 metres

```
11 | 4  5  8
12 | 1  4  6  6  8  9  9
13 | 0  0  0  0  0  2  2  3  3
14 | 0  1  2  6
15 | 4
16 | 5
```

(ii) 1.46, 1.18

(iii) 1.30

(iv) The median 1.30 is close to the mean value of this range (1.32) so the median seems a reasonable estimate of the length.

? (Page 18)

The median as it is not affected by the extreme values.

Exercise 1B (page 18)

1 (i) mode = 45, mean = 39.6, median = 41

(ii) bimodal, 116 and 132, mean = 122.5, median = 122

(iii) mode = 6, mean = 5.3, median = 6

2 (i) (a) mode = 14 years 8 months, mean = 14 years 5.5 months, median = 14 years 6 months

(b) Small data set so mode is inappropriate. You would expect all the students in one class to be uniformly spread between 14 years 0 months and 15 years, so any of the other measures would be acceptable.

(ii) (a) mode = 0, mean = 52.8, median = 58

(b) The median. Small sample makes the mode unreliable and the mean is influenced by extreme values.

(iii) (a) mode = 0 and 21 (bimodal), mean = 29.4, median = 20

(b) Small sample so the mode is inappropriate; the mean is affected by outliers, so the median is the best choice.

(iv) (a) no unique mode, mean = 3.45, median = 3.5

(b) Anything but the mode will do. The distribution, uniform in theory, means that mean = median. This sample reflects that well.

3 (i)

```
              7 | 13 | 2 means 13.7 minutes
                |    |        and 13.2 minutes
        16-year-olds        9-year-olds
          7  4 | 11 |
          9  8 | 12 |
          7  0 | 13 | 0  2  7
             8 | 14 | 2  4
               | 15 | 0  1  9
             5 | 16 | 0  1  4  7
```

(ii) 15.6 minutes

Exercise 1C (Page 22)

1 (i) mode = 2

(ii) median = 3

(iii) mean = 3.24

2 (i) mode = 39

(ii) median = 40

(iii) mean = 40.3

(iv) The sample has a slight positive skew. Any of the measures would do; however, the mean allows one to calculate the total number of matches.

3 (i) mode = 19

(ii) median = 18

(iii) mean = 17.9

(iv) The outliers affect the mean. As the distribution is, apart from the extremes, reasonably symmetrical, the median or mode are acceptable. The median is the safest for a relatively small data set.

4 (i) mode = 1, mean = 1.4, median = 1

(ii) the median

5 (i) mode = 1, mean = 2.1, median = 2

(ii) the median

(Page 25)

The upper boundaries are not stated. 0– could mean 0–9 or it could mean at least 0.

(Page 27)

The mode can be estimated as in this example for a unimodal histogram.

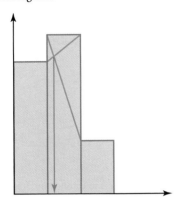

The median can be estimated by interpolation of the interval containing the median or by use of a cumulative frequency curve.

The mean of the original data is 39.73. The estimate is reasonably close at 39.855.

(Page 28)

The median, as it is least affected by extreme values.

(Page 29)

The fairest answer is there is not enough information. Ignoring the journalistic prose, '. . . our town council rate somewhere between savages and barbarians . . .', the facts given are correct. However, to say whether or not the council is negligent one would need to compare accident statistics with other *similar* communities. Also, one would need to ask who is responsible for a cyclist's risk of having or not having an accident? Perhaps parents should ensure there is adequate training given to their children, and so on.

(Page 30)

Robert needs to increase his estimate by 0.5 cm (162.32 cm becomes 162.82 cm). The mean of the raw data is 162.86 cm. The estimated value is very close.

Exercise 1D (page 31)

1 Mid-class values: 114.5, 124.5, 134.5, 144.5, 154.5, 164.5, 174.5, 184.5

Mean = 161.5 cm

2 (i) Mid-class values: 24.5, 34.5, 44.5, 54.5, 64.5, 79.5, 104.5

Mean = 48.5 minutes

(ii) The second value seems significantly higher. To make the comparison valid the method of data collection would have to be similar, as would the target children sampled.

3 (i) Mid-interval values: 4.5, 14.5, 24.5, 34.5, 44.5, 54.5, 64.5, 74.5, 84.5

Mean (stated age) = 29.7

(ii) Add 0.5; mean age = 30.2 years

(iii) The estimated mean age once adjusted compares well with the actual mean of 30.4 years.

4 Mean = 43.1 cm

5 (i) Mid-class values: 25, 75, 125, 175, 250, 400, 750, 3000

Mean = 950.8 m

(ii) The way in which this data is grouped seems to have a marked effect on the mean. This is probably because the distribution is so skewed.

6 (i) $59.5 \leqslant x < 99.5$

(ii) 138.5 g

(Page 35)

With the item $90 removed the mean is $15.79, compared to $19.50. The extreme value 'dragged' the value of the mean towards it.

(Page 35)

Each deviation is by definition the data value – the mean. As the mean is *central* to the data, some deviations will be negative (below the mean) and some will be positive (above the mean). The total deviation above the mean cancels out the total deviation below the mean.

(Page 40)

Using 656 instead of the accurate value of 655.71… results in

$$\text{variance} = 430\,041.14\ldots - 430\,336$$
$$= -294.85\ldots$$

which, being negative, is impossible.

? **(Page 41)**

With the value 96 omitted mean = 54.2, standard deviation = 7.9. The value 96 is more than five standard deviations above the new mean value.

Exercise 1E (page 41)

1 (i) Mean = 2.36

(ii) Standard deviation = 1.49

2 Mean = 6.04, standard deviation = 1.48

(i) Mahmood: mean = 1.03, standard deviation = 1.05
Raheem: mean = 1.03, standard deviation = 0.55

(ii) On average they scored the same number of goals but Raheem was more consistent.

4 Mean = 1.1, standard deviation = 1.24

5 Mean = 0.4, standard deviation = 0.4

6 (i) A: mean = 25 °C, standard deviation = 1.41 °C
B: mean = 25 °C, standard deviation = 2.19 °C

(ii) Thermostat A is better. The smaller standard deviation shows it is more consistent in its settings.

(iii) Mean = 24.8 °C, standard deviation = 1.05 °C

7 (i) Town route: mean time = 20 minutes, standard deviation = 4.60 minutes
Country route: mean time = 20 minutes, standard deviaiton = 1.41 minutes

(ii) Both routes have the same mean time but the country route is less variable or more consistent.

8 (i) Yes. The value is more than two standard deviations above the mean rainfall.

(ii) No. The value is less than one standard deviation below the mean rainfall.

(iii) Overall mean rainfall = 1.62 cm, overall standard deviation = 0.135 cm

(iv) 84.4 cm

9 (i) No. The harvest was less than two standard deviations above the expected value.

(ii) The higher yield was probably the result of the underlying variability but that is likely to be connected to different weather patterns.

10 (i) Sample mean = 2.075 mm, standard deviation = 0.185 mm

(ii) The desired mean is less than 0.5 standard deviations from the observed mean so the machine setting seems acceptable.

11 (i) Standard deviation = 2.54 cm

(ii) The value 166 cm is less than two standard deviations above 162.82 (Robert's data) and is less than two standard deviations below 170.4 (Asha's data). Consequently it is impossible to say, without further information, which data set it belongs to.

The value 171 is more than three standard deviations above 162.82 and less than one standard deviation above 170.4 so it seems likely that this value is from Asha's data set.

12 (i) Total weight = 3147.72 g

(ii) $\sum x^2 = 84\,509.9868$

(iii) $n = 200$, $\sum x = 5164.84$, $\sum x^2 = 136\,549.913$

(iv) Mean = 25.8 g, standard deviation = 3.98 g

13 (i) Mode = 1

(ii) The distribution is unimodal and has positive skew.

(iii) Mean = 2, standard deviation = 1.70; the value 8 may be regarded as an outlier as it is more than two standard deviations above the mean.

(iv) (a) Exclude it since a difference of 8 is impossible.

(b) Check the validity and include if valid.

(v) Mean = 1.88, standard deviation = 1.48

14 (i) 44.1 years

(ii) 14.0 years

15 (i) Since the standard deviation is $0, all Fei's rides must cost the same. Since the mean is $2.50, it follows that both the roller coaster and the water slide cost $2.50.

(ii) $1.03

Exercise 1F (page 49)

1 Mean = 252.34 g, standard deviation = 5.14 g

2 (i) $\bar{x} = -1.7$, standard deviation = 3.43

(ii) Mean = 94.83 mm, standard deviation = 0.343 mm

(iii) −18 is more than four standard deviations below the mean value.

(iv) New mean = 94.863 mm,
new standard deviation = 0.255 mm

3 (i) Mean = 6.19, standard deviation = 0.484

(ii) 6.68

4 (i) No unique mode (5 & 6), mean = 5, median = 5

(ii) 50 & 60, 50, 50

(iii) 15 & 16, 15, 15

(iv) 10 & 12, 10, 10

5 (i) $\bar{x} = -4.3\,\text{cm}$, standard deviation = 13.98 cm

(ii) −47 is many more than two standard deviations from the mean.

(iii) −2.05, 10.24

6 (i) $n = 14$

4 | 7 represents 47

4 | 7 9
5 | 9
6 | 2 6 7 8 8
7 | 0 2 3 4
8 | 0 4

Some negative skew, but otherwise a fairly normal shape.

(ii) Mean = 67.07; standard deviation = 9.97

7 Mean = 6, standard deviation = 3

8 Mean = 4, standard deviation = 6.39

9 $a = 5$, standard deviation = 3.93

10 $a = 7$, standard deviation = 2.51

11 Mean = 33.75 minutes, standard deviation = 2.3 minutes

12 (i) $a = 12$

(ii) Standard deviation = 8.88

Chapter 2

❓ (Page 52)

170 friends; 143 friends (to 3 s.f.)

❓ (Page 54)

The modal class is that with the largest frequency density and so it has the highest bar on a histogram.

❓ (Page 58)

The first interval has width 9.5, the last 10.5. All the others are 10. The reason for this is that the data can neither be negative nor exceed 70. So even if part marks were given, and so a mark such as 22.6 was possible, a student still could not obtain less than 0 or more than the maximum of 70.

Exercise 2A (page 59)

1 (i) $0.5 \leqslant d < 10.5$, $10.5 \leqslant d < 15.5$, $15.5 \leqslant d < 20.5$, $20.5 \leqslant d < 30.5$, $30.5 \leqslant d < 50.5$

(ii)

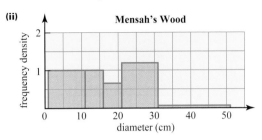

(iii) Mensah's Wood: 21–30; Ashanti Forest: 16–20

(iv) For Mensah's Wood there is a reasonably even spread of trees with diameter from 0.5 cm to 30.5 cm. For Ashanti Forest the distribution is centred about trees with diameter in the 16–20 cm interval. Neither wood has many trees with diameter greater than 30 cm.

2 (i)

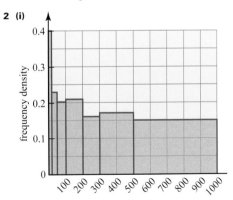

(ii) The distribution has strong positive skew.

3 (i)

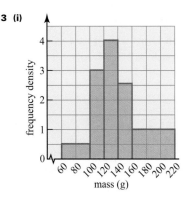

(ii) 138.4 g

4 (i)

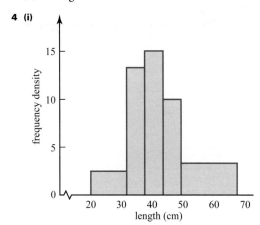

(ii) 42.1 cm

5 (i)

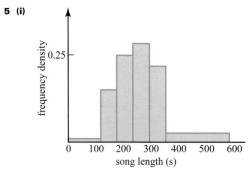

(ii) 264 seconds

6 6.0 volts, 0.067 volts

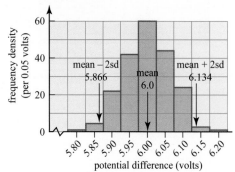

7 (i) The data are discrete. 'Number of pages' can only take integer values.

(ii) The data are positively skewed. Even though the data are discrete (suggesting a stem-and-leaf diagram or vertical line graph) the data are very spread out with most of the data values less than 200. A histogram will show the distribution properties best.

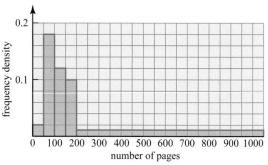

8 (i)

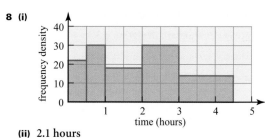

(ii) 2.1 hours

Activity 2.1 (Page 63)

For a list of n items of data, an Excel spreadsheet uses the 'method of hinges'. It places the median, Q_2, at position $\frac{n+1}{2}$, the lower quartile, Q_1, at position

$$\frac{1}{2}\left(1 + \frac{n+1}{2}\right) = \frac{1}{2} + \frac{n+1}{4}$$ and the upper quartile, Q_3, at

position $\frac{1}{2}\left(\frac{n+1}{2} + n\right) = \frac{3(n+1)}{4} - \frac{1}{2}$.

Whilst the quartiles Q_1 and Q_3 differ from those obtained with a graphical calculator, either method is acceptable.

❓ (Page 63)

The data are a sample from a parent population. The true values for the quartiles are those of the parent population, but these are unknown.

1 (i) (a) 7   **(b)** 6

  (c) 4.5, 7.5   **(d)** 3

  (e) none

(ii) (a) 15   **(b)** 11

  (c) 8, 14   **(d)** 6

  (e) none

(iii) (a) 23   **(b)** 26

  (c) 23, 28   **(d)** 5

  (e) 14, 37

(iv) (a) 36   **(b)** 118

  (c) 115, 125   **(d)** 10

  (e) 141

2 (i) 5, 5

  (ii) 35, 5

  (iii) 50, 50

  (iv) 80, 50

3 (i) 74

  (ii) 73, 76

  (iii) 3

  (iv)

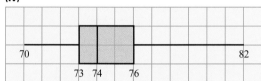

  (v) On average the golfers played better in the second round; their average score (median) was four shots better. However, the wider spread of data (the IQR for the second round was twice that for the first) suggests some golfers played very much better but a few played less well.

4 (i)

  (ii) The vertical line graph as it retains more data for this small sample.

5 (i)

$y \leqslant$	Cumulative frequency
50	1
60	6
70	13
80	17
90	19
100	20

(ii)

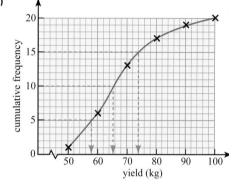

(iii) 65 kg, 16 kg

(iv)

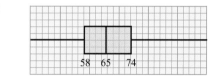

(v) 66 kg, 18.5 kg; the estimated values are quite close to these figures.

(vi) Grouping allows one to get an overview of the distribution but in so doing you lose detail.

6 (i)

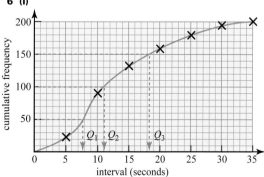

(ii) (a) 11 s   **(b)** 10.5 s

(iii) 13.1 s

7

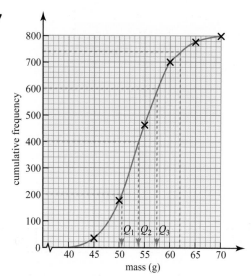

mass (g)

(i) 7.5%

(ii) 54 g

(iii) 7 g

8 (i) 12.2 s, 6.11 s

(ii)

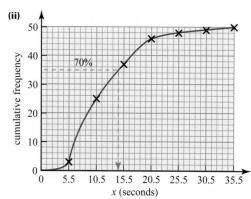

x (seconds)

14.5 seconds

9 (i) $a = 494$, $b = 46$

(ii)

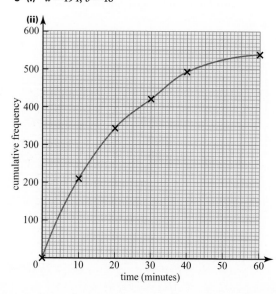

time (minutes)

(iii) 13.5 to 14.6 minutes

(iv) $m = 18.2$ minutes, $s = 14.2$ minutes

(v) 155 to 170 people

10 (i) 1 | 2 represents 12 people

```
0 | 2 5 6 8 8
1 | 2 4 6 7 7 9
2 | 1 2 3 3 3 5 6 7
3 | 1 5
```

(ii) Median = 19, $Q_1 = 10$, $Q_3 = 24$, IQR = 14

(iii) The median is preferable. The mode (23) is not near the centre of the data.

Chapter 3

Exercise 3A (page 86)

1 $\frac{66}{534}$, assuming each faulty torch has only one fault.

2 (i) $\frac{1}{6}$ **(ii)** $\frac{3}{6} = \frac{1}{2}$ **(iii)** $\frac{3}{6} = \frac{1}{2}$ **(iv)** $\frac{3}{6} = \frac{1}{2}$

3 (i) $\frac{12}{98} = \frac{6}{49}$ **(ii)** $\frac{53}{98}$ **(iii)** $\frac{45}{98}$ **(iv)** $\frac{42}{98} = \frac{3}{7}$

(v) $\frac{56}{98} = \frac{4}{7}$ **(vi)** $\frac{5}{98}$

4 (i) 0.35

(ii) They might draw.

(iii) 0.45

(iv) 0.45

5 (i)
```
18 E  12        13  3  O    15  𝒞
   2          S
  10        4       1     5
  6            16    9
  20   14      8    11      19
                            17
```

(ii) (a) $\frac{10}{20} = \frac{1}{2}$ **(b)** $\frac{4}{20} = \frac{1}{5}$ **(c)** $\frac{10}{20} = \frac{1}{2}$ **(d)** $\frac{2}{20} = \frac{1}{10}$

(e) $\frac{12}{20} = \frac{3}{5}$ **(f)** 0 **(g)** 1

(h) $P(E \cup S) = P(E) + P(S) - P(E \cap S)$

(i) $P(E \cup O) = P(E) + P(O) - P(E \cap O)$

Exercise 3B (page 90)

1

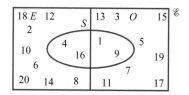

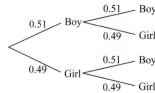

(i) 0.2401

(ii) 0.5002

(iii) 0.4998

2

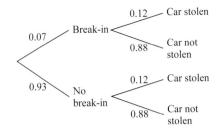

Break-in tree diagram:
- 0.07 Break-in
  - 0.12 Car stolen
  - 0.88 Car not stolen
- 0.93 No break-in
  - 0.12 Car stolen
  - 0.88 Car not stolen

(i)   0.0084

(ii) 0.1732

(iii) 0.1816

3

Tree diagram:
- $\frac{1}{12}$ Correct
  - $\frac{1}{12}$ Correct
    - $\frac{1}{12}$ Correct
    - $\frac{11}{12}$ Wrong
  - $\frac{11}{12}$ Wrong
    - $\frac{1}{12}$ Correct
    - $\frac{11}{12}$ Wrong
- $\frac{11}{12}$ Wrong
  - $\frac{1}{12}$ Correct
    - $\frac{1}{12}$ Correct
    - $\frac{11}{12}$ Wrong
  - $\frac{11}{12}$ Wrong
    - $\frac{1}{12}$ Correct
    - $\frac{11}{12}$ Wrong

(i)   (a) 0.000 58

    (b) 0.77

    (c) 0.020

(ii) (a) 0.0052

    (b) 0.52

    (c) 0.094

4 0.93

5

Tree diagram:
- 0.008 Colour-blind
  - 0.2 Left-handed
  - 0.8 Not left-handed
- 0.992 Not colour-blind
  - 0.2 Left-handed
  - 0.8 Not left-handed

(i)   0.0016

(ii) 0.0064

(iii) 0.2064

(iv) 0.7936

6 (i) $\frac{2}{27}$ or 0.0741

(ii) $\frac{125}{216}$ or 0.5787

(iii) $\frac{5}{9}$ or 0.5556

7 For a sequence of events you multiply the probabilities. However, $\frac{1}{6} \times \frac{1}{6} \times \frac{1}{6} \times \frac{1}{6} \times \frac{1}{6} \times \frac{1}{6}$ gives the probability of six 6s in six throws. To find the probability of at least one 6 you need $1 - \text{P(no 6s)}$ and that is $1 - \frac{5}{6} \times \frac{5}{6} \times \frac{5}{6} \times \frac{5}{6} \times \frac{5}{6} \times \frac{5}{6} = 0.665$.

8 (i)

		First die				
	1	**2**	**3**	**4**	**5**	**6**
1	2	3	4	5	6	7
2	3	4	5	6	7	8
3	4	5	6	7	8	9
4	5	6	7	8	9	10
5	6	7	8	9	10	11
6	7	8	9	10	11	12

(Second die labels the rows)

(ii) $\frac{3}{36} = \frac{1}{12}$

(iii) 7

(iv) The different outcomes are not all equally probable.

9 0.31

10 (i) $\frac{11}{12}$

(iii) 0.382

(iv) 0.618

11 (i) $\frac{1}{4}$

(ii) $\frac{81}{256}$

(iii) $\frac{81}{1024}$

(iv) $\frac{1}{16}$

(v) $\frac{3}{4}$

(vi) $\frac{3}{32}$

? **(Page 98)**

$P(T \mid S) = \frac{109}{169} = 0.645$

$P(T \mid S') = \frac{43}{87} = 0.494$

So $P(T \mid S) \neq P(T \mid S')$

? **(Page 98)**

T represents those who had training; T' those with no training: S those who stayed in the company; $\mathcal{E}$ all employees. S' is inside the $\mathcal{E}$ box but not in the S region.

For example, in part **(i)**, the answer is $\frac{152}{256}$. 152 is in T (but not in T'), 256 is everyone.

? **(Page 100)**

The first result was used in answering part **(i)** and the second result in answering part **(iii)**.

Exercise 3C (page 100)

1 (i) 0.6   **(ii)** 0.556

   (iii) 0.625   **(iv)** 0.047

   (v) 0.321   **(vi)** 0.075

   (vii) 0.028   **(viii)** 0.0021

   (ix) 0.000 95   **(x)** 0.48

2 (i) $\frac{35}{100} = \frac{7}{20}$ **(ii)** $\frac{42}{100} = \frac{21}{50}$ **(iii)** $\frac{15}{65} = \frac{3}{13}$

3 (i) $\frac{1}{6}$ **(ii)** $\frac{5}{12}$ **(iii)** $\frac{2}{5}$

4 (i) $\frac{7}{15}$ **(ii)** $\frac{11}{21}$

   (iii) $\frac{5}{21}$ **(iv)** $\frac{5}{11}$

5 (i) 0.5 and 0.875

   (ii) $P(B\,|\,A) \neq P(B)$ and $P(A\,|\,B) \neq P(A)$ so the events A and B are not independent.

6 (i)

	Hunter dies	Hunter lives	Total
Quark dies	$\frac{1}{12}$	$\frac{5}{12}$	$\frac{1}{2}$
Quark lives	$\frac{2}{12}$	$\frac{1}{3}$	$\frac{1}{2}$
Totals	$\frac{1}{4}$	$\frac{3}{4}$	1

   (ii) $\frac{1}{12}$ **(iii)** $\frac{5}{12}$ **(iv)** $\frac{5}{6}$

7 (i)

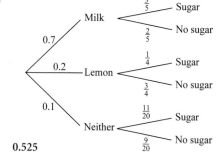

      0.525

   (ii) 0.805

   (iii) 0.42; 0.8

8 (i)

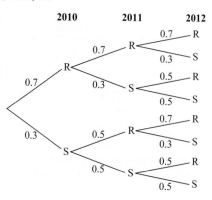

(ii) 0.372

(iii) 0.395

(iv) 8

9 (i)

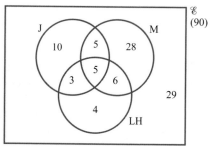

Key: J = Juniors
     M = Males
     LH = Left-handed players

(ii) (a) $\frac{1}{4}$ **(b)** $\frac{1}{6}$ **(c)** $\frac{28}{45}$

      (d) $\frac{4}{5}$ **(e)** $\frac{19}{24}$ **(f)** $\frac{10}{39}$

10 (i) $\frac{618}{1281} = \frac{206}{427}$

   (ii) $\frac{412}{1281}$

   (iii) $P(E) = \frac{717}{1281} = \frac{239}{427}$

      If M and E are independent events then $P(M \text{ and } E) = P(M) \times P(E)$.

      However, $\frac{412}{1281} \neq \frac{618}{1281} \times \frac{717}{1281}$ and so M and E are not independent events.

   (iv) $\frac{358}{564} = \frac{179}{282}$

11 (i) 0.4375

   (ii) 0.3

12 (i) 0.252

   (ii) 0.440

13 (i)

1st set of lights	2nd set of lights	3rd set of lights

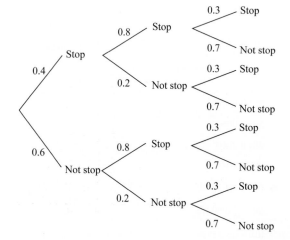

(ii) 0.224

(iii) 0.392

(iv) 0.633

Chapter 4

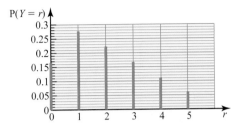

❓ **(Page 105)**

You could conduct a traffic survey at peak times, over fixed periods of time, for example, 1 hour in the morning and 1 hour in the evening, over a period of a working week. You could count both the number of vehicles and the number of people travelling in each vehicle.

❓ **(Page 105)**

A discrete frequency distribution is best illustrated by a vertical line chart.

Using such a diagram you can see that the frequency distribution is positively skewed, see figure 4.1.

Exercise 4A (Page 111)

1 (i)

r	$P(X = r)$
2	$\frac{1}{36}$
3	$\frac{2}{36}$
4	$\frac{3}{36}$
5	$\frac{4}{36}$
6	$\frac{5}{36}$
7	$\frac{6}{36}$
8	$\frac{5}{36}$
9	$\frac{4}{36}$
10	$\frac{3}{36}$
11	$\frac{2}{36}$
12	$\frac{1}{36}$

(ii) The distribution is symmetrical.

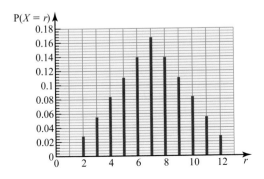

(iii) (a) $\frac{5}{18}$ **(b)** $\frac{1}{2}$ **(c)** $\frac{2}{3}$

2 (i)

r	0	1	2	3	4	5
$P(Y = r)$	$\frac{3}{18}$	$\frac{5}{18}$	$\frac{4}{18}$	$\frac{3}{18}$	$\frac{2}{18}$	$\frac{1}{18}$

(ii) The distribution has positive skew.

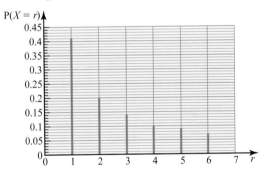

(iii) (a) $\frac{2}{3}$ **(b)** $\frac{1}{2}$

3 (i) $k = 0.4$

r	2	4	6	8
$P(X = r)$	0.1	0.2	0.3	0.4

(ii) (a) 0.3   **(b)** 0.35

4 (i) $k = \frac{20}{49}$

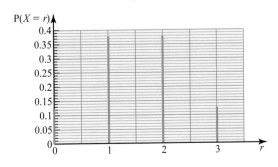

(ii) 0.248 (to 3 s.f.)

5 (i)

r	0	1	2	3
$P(X = r)$	$\frac{1}{8}$	$\frac{3}{8}$	$\frac{3}{8}$	$\frac{1}{8}$

(ii) The distribution is symmetrical.

(iii) 0.5

(iv) No, an equal number of heads and tails is possible, so probability < 0.5.

6 (i)

r	$P(X = r)$
1	$\frac{1}{16}$
2	$\frac{2}{16}$
3	$\frac{2}{16}$
4	$\frac{3}{16}$
6	$\frac{2}{16}$
8	$\frac{2}{16}$
9	$\frac{1}{16}$
12	$\frac{2}{16}$
16	$\frac{1}{16}$

(ii) $\frac{1}{4}$

7 (i) $k = 0.08$

r	0	1	2	3	4
$P(X = r)$	0.2	0.24	0.32	0.24	0

(ii) Let Y represent the number of chicks.

r	0	1	2	3
$P(Y = r)$	0.351 04	0.449 28	0.184 32	0.015 36

8 (i) $a = 0.42$

(ii) $k = \frac{1}{35}$

(iii) Since the probability distributions look quite different, the model is not a good one.

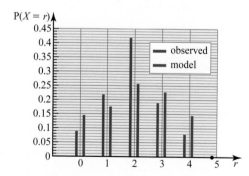

9 (i) $P(X = 1) = \frac{1}{216}$

(ii) $P(X \leqslant 2) = \frac{8}{216} = \frac{1}{27}$

(iii) $P(X \leqslant 3) = \frac{27}{216}$, $P(X = 3) = \frac{19}{216}$;

$P(X \leqslant 4) = \frac{64}{216}$, $P(X = 4) = \frac{37}{216}$;

$P(X \leqslant 5) = \frac{125}{216}$, $P(X = 5) = \frac{61}{216}$;

$P(X \leqslant 6) = 1$, $P(X = 6) = \frac{91}{216}$

(iv) The distribution has negative skew.

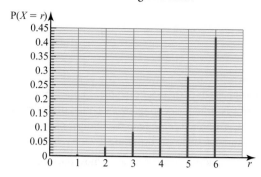

10 (i)

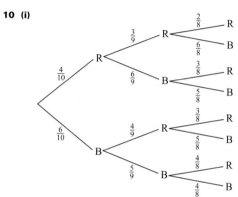

(ii)

r	0	1	2	3
$P(X = r)$	$\frac{1}{6}$	$\frac{1}{2}$	$\frac{3}{10}$	$\frac{1}{30}$

11 (i) $\frac{3}{11}$

(iii)

r	0	1	2	3
$P(X = r)$	$\frac{14}{55}$	$\frac{28}{55}$	$\frac{12}{55}$	$\frac{1}{55}$

❓ (Page 114)

Carshare.com could have based their claim on the results of traffic surveys. These could be used to calculate summary statistics such as the mean and standard deviation of the number of people per vehicle, as well as the number of vehicles per hour.

❓ (Page 114)

By comparing measures of central tendency and spread, it is possible to infer whether or not there is a significant difference between their values. There are many different tests of statistical inference; the ideas involved are introduced in Chapter 8 if you go on to study *Statistics 2*. It is also possible to compare statistically the proportion of vehicles with a single occupant.

Activity 4.1 (Page 114)

Mean = 2
Variance = 0.86

Activity 4.2 (Page 116)

Mean = 1.7
Variance = 0.87

The increase in average occupancy, together with a significant reduction in the proportion of vehicles with a single occupant, could be used to infer that the scheme has been successful.

The two measures of spread are almost the same.

 (Page 117)

If the expectation, $E(X)$, is not exact in decimal form, then calculations by hand using the definition of $Var(X)$ may be tedious and/or prone to arithmetic errors by premature approximation of $E(X)$. The alternative formulation of $Var(X)$ may be more appropriate in such cases.

Exercise 4B (Page 118)

1 $E(X) = 3$

2 (i) $E(X) = 3.125$

(ii) $P(X < 3.125) = 0.5625$

3 (i) $p = 0.8$

r	4	5
P(X = r)	0.8	0.2

(ii)

r	50	100
P(Y = r)	0.4	0.6

4 (i) $E(X) = 7$

(ii) $Var(X) = 5.833$

(iii) (a) $\frac{5}{12}$ **(b)** $\frac{1}{6}$ **(c)** $\frac{17}{18}$

5 (i) $E(X) = 1.944$; $Var(X) = 2.052$

(ii) (a) $\frac{5}{9}$ **(b)** $\frac{1}{18}$

6 (i) $E(X) = 1.5$

(ii) $Var(X) = 0.75$

(iii) $E(Y) = 5$, $Var(Y) = 2.5$

7 (i) $k = 0.1$

(ii) 1.25

(iii) 0.942 (to 3 s.f.)

8 (ii)

r	0	1	2	3	4	6
P(X = r)	$\frac{1}{4}$	$\frac{1}{3}$	$\frac{1}{9}$	$\frac{1}{6}$	$\frac{1}{9}$	$\frac{1}{36}$

(iii) $E(X) = \frac{5}{3}$, $Var(X) = \frac{41}{18}$

9 (i)

r	0	80	120	160
P(X = r)	$\frac{5}{28}$	$\frac{20}{28}$	$\frac{2}{28}$	$\frac{1}{28}$

(ii) $E(X) = \$71.43$, $Var(X) = 1412.245$ (to 3 s.f.)

(iii) $E(W) = \$500$, $Var(X) = 3600$ *or* $13\,200$

10 (i) $P(X = r)$

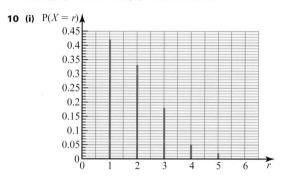

(ii) Mean = 1.92, standard deviation = 0.987 (to 3 s.f.)

(iii) 0.25

(iv) 0.431

11 $a = 0.2$, $b = 0.25$

12 (i)

Attempt 1   Attempt 2   Attempt 3   Attempt 4

0.5 — Answers
0.5 — Does not answer
  0.5 — Answers
  0.5 — Does not answer
    0.5 — Answers
    0.5 — Does not answer
      0.5 — Answers
      0.5 — Does not answer

(ii)

x	0	1	2	3	4
P(X = x)	$\frac{1}{2}$	$\frac{1}{4}$	$\frac{1}{8}$	$\frac{1}{16}$	$\frac{1}{16}$

(iii) $\frac{15}{16}$

13 (ii) $E(X) = 3.75$, $\mathrm{Var}(X) = 2.1875$

14 (i) $2q - p = 0.39$, $p + q = 0.42$; $p = 0.15$, $q = 0.27$

(ii) 2.5875

15 (i) $\frac{1}{6}$

(ii) $E(X) = \frac{4}{3}$, $\mathrm{Var}(X) = 7\frac{5}{9}$

16 (i) 0.1951

(ii)

r	2	3	4	5	6	7
$P(X = r)$	$\frac{1}{36}$	0	$\frac{1}{18}$	0	$\frac{5}{36}$	$\frac{1}{9}$

r	8	9	10	11	12
$P(X = r)$	$\frac{1}{9}$	$\frac{1}{9}$	$\frac{1}{9}$	$\frac{2}{9}$	$\frac{1}{9}$

(iii) $8\frac{2}{3}$

(iv) $\frac{5}{9}$

Chapter 5

❓ (Page 124)

Oscar could have put the bricks in order by chance.
A probability of $\frac{1}{120}$ is small but not very small. What would really be convincing is if he could repeat the task whenever he was given the bricks.

Exercise 5A (Page 127)

1 (i) 40 320

(ii) 56

(iii) $\frac{5}{7}$

2 (i) $\frac{1}{n}$

(ii) $n - 1$

3 (i) $(n + 3)(n + 2)$

(ii) $n(n - 1)$

4 (i) $\frac{8! \times 2!}{5! \times 5!}$

(ii) $\frac{16!}{14! \times 4!}$

(iii) $\frac{(n + 1)!}{(n - 2)! \times 4!}$

5 (i) $9 \times 7!$

(ii) $n!(n + 2)$

6 24

7 40 320

8 720

9 (i) 120

(ii) $\frac{1}{120}$

10 (i) 14!

(ii) $\frac{1}{14!}$

11 (i) $\frac{1}{10!}$

(ii) 1.38 (i.e. 1 or 2 people)

12 $\frac{6}{24} = \frac{1}{4}$ (OPTS, POST, POTS, SPOT, STOP, TOPS)

13 (i) 24

(ii) 120

(iii) 362 880

(iv) 12

(v) 420

(vi) 50 400

14 (i) 2520

(ii) 360

(iii) 720

(iv) 1800

Investigations (Page 129)

1 $n > 6$, $n > 7$, $n > 8$

2 Examples are $\frac{7!}{5!}$, $3! + 3! + 3! + 3! + 3! + 3! + 3!$, $4! + 4! - 3!$, etc.

3 (i) 4^4

(ii) (a) 12

(b) 4

❓ (Page 130)

No, it does not matter.

❓ (Page 131)

Multiply top and bottom by 43!

$$\frac{49 \times 48 \times 47 \times 46 \times 45 \times 44}{6!} \times \frac{43!}{43!} = \frac{49!}{6 \times 43!}$$

❓ (Page 131)

$${}^{49}C_6 = \binom{49}{6} = 13\,983\,816 \approx 14\ \text{million}$$

❓ (Page 131)

By following the same argument as for the UK National Lottery example but with n for 49 and r for 6.

(Page 132)

$${}^nC_0 = \binom{n}{0} = \frac{n!}{0! \times n!} = 1 \qquad \text{if } 0! = 1$$

$${}^nC_n = \binom{n}{n} = \frac{n!}{n!(n-n)!} = 1 \qquad \text{again if } 0! = 1$$

(Page 135)

1 The probability is $\frac{1}{24}$, assuming the selection is done at random, so RChowdhry is not justified in saying 'less than one in a hundred'.

2 As a product of probabilities $\frac{1}{3} \times \frac{1}{2} \times \frac{1}{4} = \frac{1}{24}$

Exercise 5B (Page 137)

1 (i) (a) 30   (b) 1680   (c) 5040

   (ii) (a) 15   (b) 70   (c) 210

2 $\frac{1}{2730}$

3 $\frac{1}{593\,775}$

4 715

5 280

6 (i) 31824

   (ii) 3000

7 (i) 210

   (ii) (a) $\frac{1}{14}$ (b) $\frac{3}{7}$

8 (i) 126

   (ii) (a) $\frac{1}{126}$ (b) $\frac{45}{126}$

9 (i) $\frac{1}{120}$

   (ii) $\frac{1}{7893600}$

10 (i) (a) 15   (b) 75

    (ii) (a) 90720   (b) 120

11 (i) 4.94×10^{11}

    (ii) 79833600

    (iii) 21

12 (i) 2177280

    (ii) 90

13 (i) 33033000

    (ii) 86400

    (iii) 288

14 (i) 259459200

    (ii) 3628800

    (iii) 0.986

15 (i) 831600

    (ii) 900

    (iii) 126

16 (i) (a) 60   (b) 216

    (ii) (a) 1316   (b) 517

Chapter 6

(Page 142)

She should really try to improve her production process so as to reduce the probability of a bulb being substandard.

Exercise 6A (Page 145)

1 $\frac{15}{64}$

2 0.271

3 0.214

4 0.294

5 (i) 0.146

   (ii) Poor visibility might depend on the time of day, or might vary with the time of year. If so, this simple binomial model would not be applicable.

6 (i) $\frac{1}{8}$

   (ii) $\frac{3}{8}$

   (iii) $\frac{3}{8}$

   (iv) $\frac{1}{8}$

7 (i) 0.246

   (ii) Exactly 7 heads

8 (i) (a) 0.058   (b) 0.198

       (c) 0.296   (d) 0.448

   (ii) 2

9 (i) (a) 0.264   (b) 0.368

       (c) 0.239   (d) 0.129

   (ii) Assumed the probability of being born in January $= \frac{31}{365}$. This ignores the possibility of leap years and seasonal variations in the pattern of births throughout the year.

10 The three possible outcomes are not equally likely: 'one head and one tail' can arise in two ways (HT or TH) and is therefore twice as probable as 'two heads' (or 'two tails').

Activity 6.1 (Page 147)

Expectation of $X = \sum_{r=0}^{n} r \times P(X = r)$

Since the term with $r = 0$ is zero

Expectation of $X = \sum_{r=1}^{n} r \times P(X = r)$

$$= \sum_{r=1}^{n} r \times {}^nC_r p^r q^{n-r}.$$

The typical term of this sum is

$$r \times \frac{n!}{r!(n-r)!} p^r q^{n-r} = np \times \frac{(n-1)!}{(r-1)!(n-r)!} p^{r-1} q^{n-r}$$

$$= np \times \frac{(n-1)!}{(r-1)!((n-1)-(r-1))!}$$

$$\times p^{r-1} q^{(n-1)-(r-1)}$$

Using $(n-1) - (r-1) = n - r$

$$= np \times {}^{n-1}C_{r-1} p^{r-1} q^{(n-1)-(r-1)}$$

$$= np \times {}^{n-1}C_s p^s q^{(n-1)-s}$$

where $s = r - 1$

In the summation, np is a common factor and s runs from 0 to $n - 1$ as r runs from 1 to n. Therefore

Expectation of $X = np \times \sum_{s=0}^{n-1} {}^{n-1}C_s p^s q^{(n-1)-s}$

$$= np(q + p)^{n-1}$$

$$= np \qquad \text{since } q + p = 1.$$

Exercise 6B (Page 150)

1 (i) (a) 0.000 129   (b) 0.0322   (c) 0.402

   (ii) 0 and 1 equally likely

2 (i) 2

   (ii) 0.388

   (iii) 0.323

3 (i) 0.240

   (ii) 0.412

   (iii) 0.265

   (iv) 0.512

   (v) 0.384

   (vi) 0.096

   (vii) 0.317

Assumption: the men and women in the office are randomly chosen from the population (as far as their weights are concerned).

4 (i) (a) $\frac{1}{81}$ (b) $\frac{8}{81}$ (c) $\frac{24}{81}$ (d) $\frac{32}{81}$

   (ii) 2 min 40 s

5 (i) 0.0735

   (ii) 2.7

   (iii) 0.267

6 (i) 0.002 69

   (ii) 0.121

   (iii) 0.167

   (iv) 0.723

7 (i) (a) 0.195   (b) 0.299

   (ii) 3 correct answers most likely; 0.260

8 (i) 0.003 22

   (ii) 0.0193

   (iii) 0.0386

9 (i) $\frac{1}{64}$

   (ii) $\frac{15}{64}$

   (iii) $\frac{45}{512}$

   (iv) $\frac{45}{2048}$

   (v) $\frac{405}{8192}$

10 (i) 0.99; 0.93

   (ii) 0.356; expected number of boxes with no broken eggs = $100 \times 0.356 = 35.6$, which agrees well with the observed number, 35.

   (iii) 0.0237

11 (i) 0.132

   (ii) 0.0729

   (iii) 0.0100

   (iv) Mean $= \frac{5}{3}$, variance $= \frac{10}{9}$

12 0.212

Chapter 7

Exercise 7A (Page 166)

1 (i) 0.841

   (ii) 0.159

   (iii) 0.5

   (iv) 0.341

2 (i) 0.726

(ii) 0.274

(iii) 0.0548

(iv) 0.219

3 (i) 0.159

(ii) 0.841

(iii) 0.841

(iv) 0.683

4 (i) 0.8413

(ii) 0.0228

(iii) 0.1359

5 (i) 0.0668

(ii) 0.6915

(iii) 0.2417

6 (i) 0.0668

(ii) 0.1587

(iii) 0.7745

7 (i) 31, 1.98

(ii) 2.1, 13.3, 34.5, 34.5, 13.4, 2.1

(iii) More data would need to be collected to say reliably that the weights are normally distributed.

8 (i) 5.48%

(ii) (a) 25 425 km

(b) 1843 km

9 (i) 78.65%

(ii) 5.254 cm, 0.054 cm

10 (i) 0.0765

(ii) 0.2216

(iii) 0.4315

11 (i) 0.077

(ii) 0.847

(iii) 0.674

(iv) 1.313 m

12 20.05, 0.024 77, 0.7794, 22.6%

13 0.0312

(i) 0.93

(ii) 0.080

14 11.09%, 0.0123, 0.0243

15 (i) 0.29

(ii) 4340

(iii) Because the probability of scoring between 0 and 10 is about 0.99.

(iv) 0.0258

(v) 113 or more

16 (i)

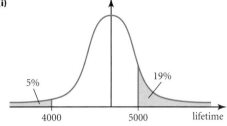

(ii) $\mu = 4650$

(iii) 0.44 (2 s.f.)

(iv) 3700 hours

(v) 0.76 (2 s.f.)

17 (i) 0.004 29

(ii) 1.71 bars, 2.09 bars

18 (i) 7.29

(ii) 0.136

(iii) 0.370

19 (i) 7.24

(ii) 546

20 (i) 8.75

(ii) 0.546

21 (i) 0.595

(ii) 0.573

22 (i) 0.0276

(ii) 7.72

23 (i) 0.484

(ii) 96.9 minutes, 103.1 minutes

❓ (Page 175)

One possibility is that some people, knowing their votes should be secret, resented being asked who they had supported and so deliberately gave wrong answers. Another is that the exit poll was taken at a time of day when those voting were unrepresentative of the electorate as a whole.

Exercise 7B (Page 175)

1 (i) 106

(ii) 75 and 125

(iii) 39

2 (i) 0.282

(ii) 0.526

(iii) (a) 25

(b) 4.33

(iv) 0.102

3 0.246, 0.0796, 0.0179

The normal distribution is used for continuous data; the binomial distribution is used for discrete data. If a normal approximation to the binomial distribution is used then a continuity correction must be made. Without this the result would not be accurate.

4 (i) (a) 0.315

(b) 0.307; assuming the answer to part (i) (a) is correct, there is a 2.5% error; worse

(ii) 0.5245

5 $\frac{1}{3}$; 6.667; 4.444; 13

6 $2000C_N\left(\frac{1}{30}\right)^N\left(\frac{29}{30}\right)^{2000-N}$

86; more (96)

7 0.677

8 (i) 0.126

(ii) 0.281

9 (i) 0.748

(ii) 0.887

10 (i) 0.298

(ii) 0.118

(iii) 13

11 (i) 0.311

(ii) Not appropriate because $np < 5$.

(iii) 0.181

Chapter 8

❓ (Page 182)

Assuming both types of parents have the same fertility, boys born would outnumber girls in the ratio 3:1. In a generation's time there would be a marked shortage of women of child-bearing age.

❓ (Page 186)

Yes. The test was set up before the data were known, the data are random and independent and it is indeed testing the claim.

Exercise 8A (Page 187)

1 0.057   Accept H_0

2 0.0547 > 5%   Accept H_0

3 H_0: probability that toast lands butter-side down = 0.5
H_1: probability that toast lands butter-side down > 0.5
0.015   Accept H_0

4 0.047   Reject H_0
There is evidence that the complaints are justified at the 5% significance level, though Mr McTaggart might object that the candidates were not randomly chosen.

5 0.104   Accept H_0
Insufficient evidence at the 5% significance level that the machine needs servicing.

6 (i) 2; 1.183

(ii) P(2 defectives in 10) = 0.302
In 50 samples of 10, the expected number of samples with two defectives is 15.1, which agrees well with the observed 15.

(iii) H_0: P(mug defective) = 0.2
H_1: P(mug defective) < 0.2
$n = 20$. P(0 or 1 defective mug) = 0.0692
Accept H_0 since 0.0692 > 5%
It is not reasonable to assume that the proportion of defective mugs has been reduced.

(iv) Opposite conclusion since 0.0692 < 10%

7 (i) 0.590

(ii) 0.044

(iii) 0.000 071 2

(iv) 0.0292

(v) H_0: P(long question right) = 0.5
H_1: P(long question right) > 0.5

(vi) No

8 H_0: P(car is red) = 0.3
H_1: P(car is red) < 0.3
Accept H_0 (Isaac's claim) since 0.060 > 5%

9 H_0: P(support for Citizens Party) = $\frac{1}{3}$
H_1: P(support for Citizens Party) < $\frac{1}{3}$
Accept H_0 since 0.0604 > 2.5%.
There is insufficient evidence to suggest that support has decreased.

(Page 191)

Rejection region at 10% significance level is $X \leqslant 4$.

Exercise 8B (Page 192)

1 (i) 0.430

(ii) 0.9619

(iii) 0.0046

(iv) $H_0: p = 0.9$, $H_1: p < 0.9$

(v) $n = 17$; $P(X \leqslant 13) = 0.0826 > 5\%$;
not sufficient evidence to reject H_0.

(vi) Critical region is $X \leqslant 12$, since
$P(X \leqslant 12) = 0.0221$.

2 (i) (a) 0.0278

(b) 0.0384

(ii) Let $p = P(\text{blackbird is male})$
$H_0: p = 0.5$, $H_1: p > 0.5$

(iii) Result is significant at the 5% significance level.
Critical region is $X \geqslant 12$.

(iv) You would be more reluctant to accept H_1.
Although H_0 is still $p = 0.5$, the sampling method
is likely to give a non-random sample.

3 (i) (a) 0.0991

(b) 0.1391

(ii) Let $p = P(\text{seed germinates})$
$H_0: p = 0.8$, $H_1: p > 0.8$, since a higher
germination rate is suspected.

(iii) Critical region is $X \geqslant 17$, since
$P(X \geqslant 17) = 0.0991 < 10\%$ but
$P(X \geqslant 16) = 0.2713 > 10\%$.

(iv) (a) When $p = 0.8$, he reaches the wrong
conclusion if he rejects H_0, i.e. if $X \geqslant 17$, with
probability 0.0991.

(b) When $p = 0.82$, he reaches the wrong
conclusion if he fails to reject H_0, i.e. if
$X \leqslant 16$, with probability $1 - 0.1391 = 0.8609$.

Exercise 8C (Page 195)

1 $P(X \leqslant 3) = 0.073 > 5\%$ Accept H_0

2 $P(X \geqslant 13) = 0.0106 < 2\frac{1}{2}\%$ Reject H_0

3 $P(X \geqslant 9) = 0.0730 > 2\frac{1}{2}\%$ Accept H_0

4 0 correct or > 6 correct

5 Critical region is $\leqslant 3$ or $\geqslant 13$ letter Zs

6 (i) 5

(ii) 0.196

(iii) Complaint justified at the 10% significance level

7 (i) 0.0417

(ii) 0.0592

(iii) 0.0833

(iv) 0.1184

(v) Let $p = P(\text{man selected})$
$H_0: p = 0.5$, $H_1: p \neq 0.5$
$P(X \leqslant 4 \text{ or } X \geqslant 11) = 0.1184 > 5\%$
There is not sufficient evidence to reject H_0, so
it is reasonable to suppose that the process is
satisfactory.

(vi) $4 \leqslant w \leqslant 11$

Exercise 8D (Page 200)

1 (i) 0.0480

(ii) 0.0480

(iii) 0.601

2 (i) If H_0 is wrongly rejected because there were only
0 or 1 red chocolate beans in the sample although
20% of the population were actually red.

(ii) 0.167

3 (i) $H_0: P(\text{pass on 1st attempt}) = 0.36$
$H_1: P(\text{pass on 1st attempt}) > 0.36$
Reject H_0 (accept the driving instructor's claim)
since $0.013 < 5\%$

(ii) Type I error; 0.0293

4 (i) $H_0: P(\text{six}) = \frac{1}{6}$
$H_1: P(\text{six}) > \frac{1}{6}$
Accept H_0 since $0.225 > 10\%$
There is no evidence that the die is biased.

(ii) $P(\text{4 or more sixes}) = 0.0697$

(iii) Concluding that the die is fair when it is biased.

Chapter 9

Exercise 9A (Page 207)

1 (i) 0.266

  (ii) 0.826

2 (i) 0.224

  (ii) 0.185

  (iii) 0.815

3 (i) 0.058

  (ii) 0.099

4 (i) 25

  (ii) 75

  (iii) 112

  (iv) 288
     Assume that mistakes occur randomly, singly,
     independently and at a constant mean rate.

5 (i) 0.111, 0.244, 0.268, 0.377

  (ii) 3

6 (i) 3

  (ii) 27.5

  (iii) 460 or 461

7 (i) The mean is much greater than the variance
     therefore X does not have a Poisson distribution.

  (ii) Yes because now the values of the mean and
     variance are similar.

  (iii) 0.012

8 Some bottles will contain two or more hard particles.
   This will decrease the percentage of bottles that have
   to be discarded.
   13.9%
   Assume the hard particles occur singly,
   independently and randomly.

9 (i) 0.144

  (ii) 0.819

  (iii) 2.88

10 (i) 0.209

   (ii) 0.219

   (iii) 6

11 (i) 0.184

   (ii) 0.125

12 (i) 0.738

   (ii) 0.478, 0.353, 0.130, 0.032, 0.006, 0.0009

   (iii) 239.0, 176.4, 65.1, 16.0, 3.0, 0.4

   (iv) Yes, there seems to be reasonable agreement
      between the actual data and the Poisson
      predictions.

❓ (Page 213)

1 It is not necessarily the case that a car or lorry
   passing along the road is a random event. Regular
   users will change both Poisson parameters which in
   turn will affect the solution to the problem.

2 With so few vehicles they probably are independent.

3 They are more likely in the day than the night. This
   raises serious doubts about the test associated with
   this model.

4 It could be that their numbers are negligible or it
   might be assumed they do not damage the cattle grid.

Exercise 9B (Page 213)

1 (i) (a) 0.175

     (b) 0.973

     (c) 0.031

  (ii) 0.125; 0.249

2 (i) (a) 0.180

     (b) 0.264

     (c) 0.916

  (ii) 0.296

  (iii) 0.549

3 (i) (a) 0.007

     (b) 0.034

     (c) 0.084

  (ii) $T \sim Po(5.0)$

4 (i) (a) 0.134

     (b) 0.848

  (ii) 0.086

  (iii) 0.673

5 (i) (a) 0.257

     (b) 0.223

     (c) 0.168

  (ii) 0.340

6 (i) 0.531

  (ii) 0.065

  (iii) 0.159

7 (i) (a) 0.270 (3 s.f.)

   (b) 0.001 44

   (c) 0.962

  (ii) $\lambda = -\ln(0.2) = 1.6094 \approx 1.61$

  (iii) 0.1896

  (iv) 0.369

8 (i) (a) 0.485 (3 s.f.)

   (b) 0.116 (3 s.f.)

   (c) 0.087 (2 s.f.)

  (ii) The Poisson parameter is unlikely to be the same for each team and there is a lack of independence.

9 (i) Mean = 1.84, variance = 1.75 (3 s.f.)

  (ii) Independence of arrival and random distribution through time or uniform average rate of occurrence or mean and variance approximately equal or n is large and p is small.

  (iii) 26.9 days

  (iv) 0.410 (3 s.f.)

  (v) 0.0424

Exercise 9C (Page 221)

1 (i) 0.135 768, 0.140 374, 3.4%

  (ii) 0.140 078, 0.140 374, 0.2%

  (iii) 0.140 346, 0.140 374, 0.02%

The agreement between the values improves as n increases and p decreases.

2 (i) 0.224

  (ii) 0.616

3 (i) 0.104

  (ii) 0.560

  (iii) 0.762

4 (i) 0.0378

  (ii) 0.0671

5 (i) 0.362

  (ii) 0.544

  (iii) 0.214

  (iv) 0.558

6 (i) 0.082

  (ii) 0.891

  (iii) 0.287

7 (i) 0.161

  (ii) 0.554

  (iii) 8

  (iv) 0.016

  (v) 0.119

8 (i) $X \sim B(150, \frac{1}{80})$; $X \sim Po(1.875)$; the Poisson distribution is a suitable approximating distribution because n is large and p is small.

  (ii) 0.559

9 (i) $X \sim B(108, 0.05)$; it must be assumed that whether or not each person turns up is independent of whether or not any other person turns up.

  (ii) (a) 0.12 (2 s.f.)

   (b) 0.37 (2 s.f.)

   (c) 0.29 (2 s.f.)

10 (i) $X \sim B(500, 0.01)$

  (ii) 0.7419

  (iii) 0.049 (to 2 s.f.)

Exercise 9D (Page 227)

1 0.180; 60, 7.75, 0.9124

2 (i) 2.5; assume that service calls occur singly, independently and randomly.

  (ii) 0.918, 0.358

  (iii) 0.158

3 (i) 0.4928

  (ii) 0.0733

  (iii) 0.6865

4 (i) 0.7620

  (ii) 0.0329

  (iii) 0.3536

5 (i) 0.188

  (ii) 0.9906

  (iii) (a) 0.9629

   (b) 1.0000

Four lots of 50 is only one of many ways to make 200, so you would expect the probability in part **(b)** to be higher than that in part **(a)**.

6 (i) (a) 0.6144

(b) 0.8342

(ii) You must assume that the same number of emails will be received, on average, in the future.

(iii) For longer time periods, there are more and more different ways in which the total can be reached, so the probability increases.

7 (i) (a) 0.617

(b) 0.835

(ii) 0.0593

8 (i) $H_0: \mu = 5.6$ where μ is the mean number of shooting stars
$H_1: \mu < 5.6$

(ii) $X \leqslant 2$ where X is the number of shooting stars

(iii) 0.0824

(iv) The null hypothesis is not rejected. The evidence does not support the astronomer's theory.

9 (i) 0.122

(ii) 0.532

(iii) 0.0135

(iv) 0.229

10 (i) People can be expected to call randomly, independently and at an average uniform rate.

(ii) 0.113

(iii) 0.0211

11 (i) 0.143

(ii) 0.118

(iii) 0.0316

12 (ii) 0 or 1

(iii) 0.0916

(iv) 1 is in the rejection region so there is evidence that the new guitar string lasts longer.

13 (i) 0.0202

(ii) 0.972

(iii) 0.0311

14 (i) There is enough evidence to accept at the 10% significance level that ploughing has increased the number of pieces of metal found.

(ii) There is not enough evidence to accept at the 5% significance level that ploughing has increased the number of pieces of metal found.

(iii) 0.395

15 (i) A Type I error is made if you find that the number of white blood cells has decreased when, in fact, the number of white blood cells has not decreased; 0.0342

(ii) Accept H_0, there is insufficient evidence to say that the number of white blood cells has decreased.

(iii) 0.915

Chapter 10

❓ (Page 235)

It is reasonable to regard the height of a wave as random. No two waves are exactly the same and in a storm some are much bigger than others.

Exercise 10A (Page 240)

1 (i) $k = \frac{2}{35}$

(ii)

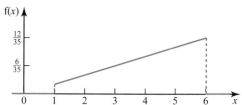

(iii) $\frac{11}{35}$

(iv) $\frac{1}{7}$

2 (i) $k = \frac{1}{12}$

(ii)

(iii) 0.207

3 (i) $a = \frac{4}{81}$

(ii)

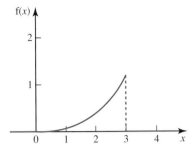

(iii) $\frac{16}{81}$

4 (i) $c = \frac{1}{8}$

(ii)

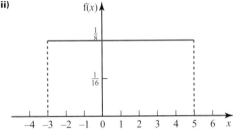

(iii) $\frac{1}{4}$

(iv) $\frac{3}{8}$

5 (i) $k = 0.048$

(ii)

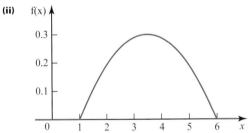

(iii) 0.248

6 (i) $k = \frac{2}{9}$

(ii) 0.067

7 (i) $k = \frac{1}{100}$

(ii)

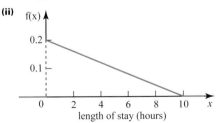

(iii) 19, 17, 28, 36

(iv) Yes

(v) Further information needed about the group 4–10 hours. It is possible that many of these stay all day and so are part of a different distribution.

8 (i)

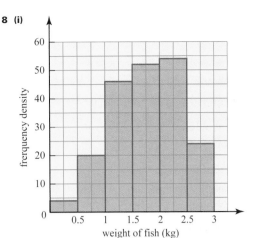

Negative skew

(ii)

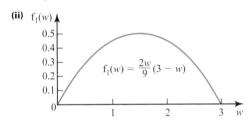

$$f_1(w) = \frac{2w}{9}(3 - w)$$

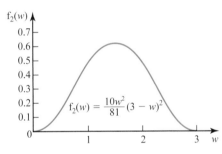

$$f_2(w) = \frac{10w^2}{81}(3 - w)^2$$

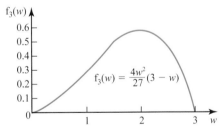

$$f_3(w) = \frac{4w^2}{27}(3 - w)$$

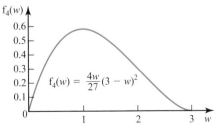

$$f_4(w) = \frac{4w}{27}(3 - w)^2$$

f_3 matches the data most closely.

(iii) 1.62, 9.49, 20.14, 28.01, 27.55, 13.19, 0

(iv) Model seems good.

9 (i) 0.803

(ii) 0.456

10 (i) 0, 0.1, 0.21, 0.12, 0.05, 0.02, 0

(ii) (a) 0.1   (b) 0.33   (c) 0.33

(d) 0.16   (e) 0.07   (f) 0.02

(iii) $k = \frac{1}{1728}$

(iv) (a) 0.132   (b) 0.275   (c) 0.280

(d) 0.201   (e) 0.095   (f) 0.016

(v) Model quite good. Both positively skewed.

11 (i) $k = \frac{1}{4}$

(ii)

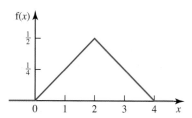

(iii) $\frac{27}{32}$

12 (i) $a = \frac{5}{12}$

(ii)

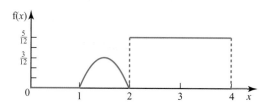

(iii) 0.292

(iv) $\frac{7}{12}$

? (Page 247)

Distributions (b) and (d)

? (Page 250)

68%. The normal distribution has a greater proportion of values near the mean, as can be seen from its shape.

Exercise 10B (Page 252)

1 (i) 2.67

(ii) 0.89

(iii) 2.828

2 (i) 2   (ii) 2   (iii) 1.76

3 (i) 0.6

(ii) 0.04

4 (i)

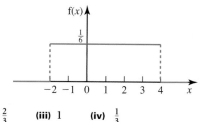

(ii) $\frac{2}{3}$ (iii) 1   (iv) $\frac{1}{3}$

5 (i) 1.5

(ii) 0.45

(iii) 1.5

(iv) 1.5

(v)

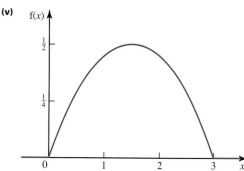

The graph is symmetrical and peaks when $x = 1.5$ thus E(X) = mode of X = median value of $X = 1.5$.

6 (ii) 1.083, 0.326

(iii) 0.5625

7 (i) $f(x) = \frac{1}{3}$ for $4 \leqslant x \leqslant 7$

(ii) 5.5

(iii) $\frac{3}{4}$

(iv) 0.233

8 (i) $f(x) = \frac{1}{10}$ for $10 \leqslant x \leqslant 20$

(ii) 15, 8.33

(iii) (a) 57.7%

(b) 100%

9 (i) $a = 1.443$

(ii)

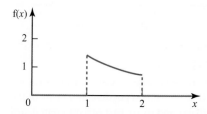

(iii) 1.443, 0.083

(iv) 41.5%

(v) 1.414

10 (ii) 104 or 105

(iii) 5.14

11 (ii) $\text{Var}(X) = 0.0267$

(iii) 0.931

(iv) 0.223

12 (ii) 0.139

(iii) 1.24 minutes

13 (ii) 4.125 minutes

(iii) 0.148

(iv) Less than 5 minutes, since $0.148 < 0.25$

14 (ii) 2.66 hours

(iii) 2.73 hours

(iv) 0.0241

15 (ii)

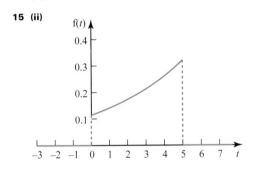

(iii) 1.48 seconds

Chapter 11

? (Page 258)

It is the variance of X.

Exercise 11A (Page 260)

1 (i) (a) $\text{E}(X) = 3.1$

(b) $\text{Var}(X) = 1.29$

2 (i) (a) $\text{E}(X) = 0.7$

(b) $\text{Var}(X) = 0.61$

4 (i) $\text{E}(2X) = 6$

(ii) $\text{Var}(3X) = 6.75$

5 (i) 10.9, 3.09

(ii) 18.4, 111.24

6 (i) 2   **(ii)** 1   **(iii)** 9

7 (i) (a) 2.79

(b) 8.97

(c) 20.94

8

$\overline{N}$	2	3	4	5	6	7	8
Probability	$\frac{1}{16}$	$\frac{2}{16}$	$\frac{3}{16}$	$\frac{4}{16}$	$\frac{3}{16}$	$\frac{2}{16}$	$\frac{1}{16}$

5, 2.5

Exercise 11B (Page 266)

1 (i) 4, 0.875

(ii) 1.5, 0.167

(iii)

Main course	Dessert	Price
Fish and chips	Ice cream	$4
Fish and chips	Apple pie	$4.50
Fish and chips	Sponge pudding	$5
Spaghetti	Ice cream	$4.50
Spaghetti	Apple pie	$5
Spaghetti	Sponge pudding	$5.50
Pizza	Ice cream	$5
Pizza	Apple pie	$5.50
Pizza	Sponge pudding	$6
Steak and chips	Ice cream	$6.50
Steak and chips	Apple pie	$7
Steak and chips	Sponge pudding	$7.50

(iv) Mean of $T = 5.5$, variance $= 1.042$

2 (i) $\text{N}(90, 25)$

(ii) $\text{N}(10, 25)$

(iii) $\text{N}(-10, 25)$

3 0.196

4 (i) 0.0228

(ii) 56.45 minutes

(iii) 0.362

5 (i) 230 g, 10.2 g

(ii) 0.1587

(iii) 0.0787

6 (i) $\text{N}(70, 25)$

(ii) $\text{N}(-10, 25)$

7 5.92%

8 (i) 0.266

(ii) No, people do not choose their spouses at random: the heights of a husband and wife may not be independent.

9 0.151

10 (i) 0.0170

(ii) 0.0037

11 Mean = 59.4, standard deviation = 7.09

12 (i) Mean = 3360, variance = 1540 (to 3 s.f.)

(ii) 0.0693

❓ (Page 272)

With folded paper it is not possible for pieces of paper that are thicker to be offset by others that are thinner, and vice versa.

Exercise 11C (Page 273)

1 N(120, 24)

Assume times are independent and no time is spent on changeovers between vehicles.

2 0.0745

3 0.1377

4 0.1946

5 (i) N(34, 20)

(ii) N(−4, 20)

(iii) N(0, 20)

6 (i) 0.316

(ii) 0.316

7 (i) N(100, 26)

(ii) N(295, 353)

(iii) N(200, 122)

(iv) N(−65, 377)

8 (i) 0.0827

(ii) 0.3103

(iii) 0.5

9 (i) 0.0827

(ii) 0.1446

(iii) 0.5

(iv) The situations in **8(i)** and **9(i)** are the same.
8(ii) considers $3X + 5Y$ whereas **9(ii)** considers $X_1 + X_2 + X_3 + Y_1 + \ldots + Y_5$, so the probabilities are different.
In both **8(iii)** and **9(iii)** the mean is zero, so the probability is 0.5, independent of the variance.

10 (i) 311.6 kg

(ii) Assume that the composition of each crew is selected randomly so that the weights of each of the four individual rowers are independent of each other. This assumption may not be reasonable since there may be some light-weight and some heavy-weight crews; also men's and women's crews. If this is so it will cast doubt on the answer to part **(i)**.

11 (i) 0.4546

(ii) 93.49 litres

12 (i) 0.0202

(ii) 0.0856

(iii) 0.3338, 0.4082

13 0.9026

Assume weights of participants are independent since told teams were chosen at random.

14 (i) 0.037

(ii) 0.238

Assume that no time is lost during baton changeovers and that the runners' times are independent, i.e. that no runners are influenced by the performance of their team mates or competitors. The model does not seem entirely realistic in this.

15 (i) 14%

(ii) 0.6

(iii) 15 m

(iv) 0.3043

16 0.195

17 0.350

18 (i) 0.387

(ii) Mean = 10, variance = 11.56

(iii) 0.647

Chapter 12

❓ (Page 280)

1 The population is made up of the member of parliament's constituents. The sample is a part of that population of constituents. Without information relating to how the constituents' views were elicited, the views obtained seem to be biased towards those constituents who bother to write to their member of parliament.

2 The population is made up of households in Karachi. We are not told how the sample is chosen. Even if a random sample of households were chosen the views obtained are still likely to be biased as the interview timing excludes the possibility of obtaining views of most of those residents in employment.

3 The population is made up of black residents in Chicago. The sample is made up of black people (and possibly some white people as the areas are 'predominantly black') from a number of areas in Chicago.

The survey may be biased in two ways:

(i) the areas may not be representative of all residential areas and therefore of all black people living in Chicago and

(ii) given that police officers are carrying out the survey they are unlikely to obtain negative views.

❓ **(Page 281)**

1 Each student is equally likely to be chosen but samples including two or more students from the same class are not permissible so not all samples are equally likely.

2 Yes

Activity 12.1 (Page 282)

There is no single answer since there are several ways you could use the given random numbers to generate the sample. This is one possible answer.

14 592	12 471	16 718	2771	7107
16 371	17 775	2595	4598	16 592

Exercise 12A (Page 283)

1 (i) Not all the totals have the same probability.

(ii) Possible method: writing each child's name on a piece of paper, folding them, putting them in a hat and then drawing out one at random.

2 (i) Cluster sampling. Choose representative streets or areas and sample from these streets or areas.

(ii) Stratified sample. Identify routes of interest and randomly sample trains from each route.

(iii) Stratified sample. Choose representative areas in the town and randomly sample from each area as appropriate.

(iv) Stratified sample as in part (iii).

(v) Depends on method of data collection. If survey is, say, via a postal enquiry, then a random sample may be selected from a register of addresses.

(vi) Cluster sampling. Routes and times are chosen and a traffic sampling station is established to randomly stop vehicles to test tyres.

(vii) Cluster sampling. Areas are chosen and households are then randomly chosen.

(viii) Cluster sampling. A period (or periods) is chosen to sample and speeds are surveyed.

(ix) Cluster sampling. Meeting places for 18-year-olds are identified and samples of 18-year-olds are surveyed, probably via a method to maintain privacy. This might be a questionnaire to ascertain required information.

(x) Random sampling. The school student list is used as a sampling frame to establish a random sample within the school.

Chapter 13

Exercise 13A (Page 293)

1 (i) Commuters are not representative of the whole population.

(ii) Adults who travel to work on that train

(iii) Mean = 6.17 hours, variance = 0.657 hours

2 (i) $z = 1.53$, not significant

(ii) $z = -2.37$, significant

(iii) $z = 1.57$, not significant

(iv) $z = 2.25$, significant

(v) $z = -2.17$, significant

3 (i) 0.3085

(ii) 0.016

(iii) 0.0062

(iv) $H_0: \mu = 4.00$ g, $H_1: \mu > 4.00$ g

$z = 3$, significant

4 (i) $H_0: \mu = 72.7$ g, $H_1: \mu \neq 72.7$ g; two-tail test.

(ii) $z = 1.84$, not significant

(iii) No, significant

5 **(i)** $H_0: \mu = 23.9°$, $H_1: \mu > 23.9°$

(ii) $z = 1.29$, significant

(iii) 20.6; the standard deviation 4.54 is much greater than 2.3 so the ecologist should be asking whether the temperature has become more variable.

6 **(i)** You must assume that the visibilities are normally distributed.

(ii) $H_0: \mu = 14$ nautical miles,

$H_1: \mu < 14$ nautical miles

(iii) $z = -2.284$, significant

(iv) Choosing 36 consecutive days to collect data is not a good idea because weather patterns will ensure that the data are not independent. A better sampling procedure would be to choose every tenth day. In this way the effects of weather patterns over the year would be eliminated.

7 $H_0: \mu = 50$ kg, $H_1: \mu < 50$ kg;

Yes: $z = -1.875$, significant at the 5% level

8 **(i)** $N(190, 5.\dot{3})$

(ii) The skulls in group B have greater mean lengths and so a one-tail test is required.

(iii) 193.8

(iv) $\bar{x} = 194.3$, significant $(194.3 > 193.8)$

9 **(i)** 998.6, 49.77

(ii) $H_0: \mu = 1000$, $H_1: \mu < 1000$

(iii) $z = -1.59$, not significant

10 $H_0: \mu = 0$, $H_1: \mu \neq 0$; $z = 0.98$, not significant

11 **(i)** 16.2, 27.36

(ii) $H_0: \mu = 15$, $H_1: \mu > 15$

(iii) $z = 1.986$, not significant

12 **(i)** 1.977, 0.017 33

(ii) $H_0: \mu = 2$, $H_1: \mu < 2$

(iii) $z = -1.68$, not significant

13 **(i)** 104.7, 3.019

(ii) $H_0: \mu = 105$, $H_1: \mu \neq 105$

(iii) $z = -0.89$, not significant

14 **(i)** $H_0: \mu = 21.2$, $H_1: \mu \neq 21.2$;
rejection region is $z < 19.7$ or $z > 22.7$;
$z = 19.4$, significant $(19.4 < 19.7)$

There is significant evidence to suggest that the sentence length is not the same (or the book is not by the same author).

(ii) A Type I error would have occurred if you say that the sentence length is not the same (or the book is not by the same author) when it is.

Probability = 5%

15 **(i)** Mean = 6.525, variance = 2.871

(ii) $H_0: \mu = 7.2$, $H_1: \mu < 7.2$;
rejection region is $z < 6.76$;
$z = 6.525$, significant $(6.525 < 6.76)$

The evidence supports the hypothesis that there has been a reduction in the number of cars caught speeding.

(iii) A Type I error would have occurred if you say that there had been a reduction in the number of cars caught speeding when such a reduction had not occurred.

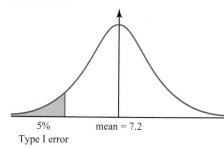

5%   mean = 7.2
Type I error

16 $H_0: \mu = 22.0$, $H_1: \mu \neq 22.0$;
rejection region is $z < 21.698$;
$z = 21.7$, not significant (just, $21.7 > 21.698$)

There is not enough evidence to say that the mean length has changed.

17 $H_0: \mu = 3.2$, $H_1: \mu < 3.2$, where μ is the growth rate of the new grass in cm per week

(i) $z < 2.47$

(ii) $m < 2.47$

? **(Page 299)**

It tells you that μ is about 101.2 but it does not tell you what 'about' means, how close to 101.2 it is reasonable to expect μ to be.

? **(Page 304)**

You would expect about 90 out of the 100 to enclose 3.5.

Exercise 13B (Page 307)

1 (i) 5.205 g

　(ii) 5.117 g, 5.293 g

2 (i) 47.7

　(ii) 34.7 to 60.7

　(iii) 27.3 to 68.1

3 (i) 0.9456

　(ii) \$7790–\$8810

4 (i) (a) 0.1685

　　(b) 0.0207

　(ii) 163.8–166.6 cm

　(iii) 385

5 (i) 6.83, 3.05

　(ii) 6.58, 7.08

6 (i) 5.71 to 7.49

　(ii) It is more likely that the short manuscript was written in the early form of the language.

7 (i) 1.838 mm

　(ii) 1.63 to 3.91

　(iii) The coach's suspicions seem to be confirmed as 4 mm is not in the confidence interval.

8 0.484 to 1.016

Assume that the sample standard deviation is an acceptable approximation for σ.

The aim has not been achieved as the interval contains values below 0.5.

9 0.223 to 1.403

Assumptions: the Central Limit Theorem applies and s^2 is a good approximation for σ^2.

The confidence interval suggests that reaction times are slower after a meal.

10 (i) $\mu = 227.1, \sigma^2 = 265$

　(ii) 78

11 (i) Possible answers: cheaper, less time-consuming, not all population destroyed if sampling is destructive

　(ii) (a) 68.0 to 70.6

　　　90% of random samples give rise to confidence intervals which contain the population mean.

　　(b) 71.2 is not in the confidence interval so there is a significant difference in the life-span from the national average.

12 (i) $\mu = 4.27, \sigma^2 = 0.00793$

　(ii) 4.253 to 4.287

　(iii) 9

13 (i) mid-point $= 0.145, n = 600$

　(ii) 97.4

14 (i) A random sample is one in which every item in the population has an equal probability of being selected.

　(ii) 0.321 to 0.422

　(iii) 2240

15 (i) 0.244, 250

　(ii) 90%

Index

Page numbers in black are in *Statistics 1*. Page numbers in blue are in *Statistics 2*.